221

GW00320477

Young**Writers**

a pocketful of

RHYME

Imagination for a new generation

West Country

Edited by Young Writers

ACC. No.

Class No.

Editorial Team:
Lynsey Hawkins
Allison Dowse
Claire Tupholme
Donna Samworth
Annabel Cook
Aimée Vanstone
Gemma Hearn
Angela Fairbrace

 Young**Writers**

First published in Great Britain in 2006 by:
Young Writers
Remus House
Coltsfoot Drive
Peterborough
PE2 9JX
Telephone: 01733 890066
Email: youngwriters@forwardpress.co.uk
Website: www.youngwriters.co.uk

All Rights Reserved

© Copyright Contributors 2006

HB ISBN 1 84602 421 8

Cover design by Tim Christian
Design by Mark Rainey

FOREWORD

Young Writers was established in 1991 and has been passionately devoted to the promotion of reading and writing in children and young adults ever since. The quest continues today. *Young Writers* remains as committed to the nurturing of poetic and literary talent as ever.

This year's *Young Writers* competition has proven as vibrant and dynamic as ever and we are delighted to present a showcase of the best poetry from across the UK and in some cases overseas. Each poem has been selected from a wealth of *A Pocketful of Rhyme* entries before ultimately being published in this, our fourteenth primary school poetry series.

Once again, we have been supremely impressed by the overall quality of the entries we have received. The imagination, energy and creativity which has gone into each young writer's entry made choosing the poems a challenging and often difficult but ultimately hugely rewarding task - the general high standard of the work submitted ensured this opportunity to bring their poetry to a larger appreciative audience.

We sincerely hope you are pleased with this final collection and that you will enjoy *A Pocketful of Rhyme - West Country* for many years to come.

A-Z OF SCHOOLS

Ashleigh CE (VC) Primary School,
Barnstaple 23

Becket Primary School,
Weston-super-Mare 31

Black Torrington CE Primary School,
Beaworthy 35

Blisland CP School, Bodmin 38

Bolham Primary School, Tiverton 41

Bowhill Primary School, Exeter 42

Combe St Nicholas CE Primary School,
Chard 57

Coxley Primary School, Wells 60

East Coker Primary School, Yeovil 65

Eggbuckland Vale Primary School,
Plymouth 72

Goosewell Primary School, Plymouth 83

Grass Royal Junior School, Yeovil 154

Hatherleigh Primary School,
Hatherleigh 161

Hazeldown Primary School,
Teignmouth 174

Holway Park Primary School, Taunton 177

Horsington CE Primary School,
Templecombe 182

Hugh Sexey Middle School, Wedmore 189

Indian Queens Primary School,
St Columb 203

Keyham Barton Catholic Primary
School, Plymouth 206

Launceston CP School, Launceston 213

Lydford Primary School, Okehampton 223

Martock Primary School, Martock 230

Menheniot Primary School, Liskeard 237

Milton Abbot Primary School,
Tavistock 240

Modbury CP School, Ivybridge 244

Mount Street Primary School,
Plymouth 247

Musbury Primary School, Axminster 249

Neroche Primary School, Ilminster 249

Nether Stowey CE (VC) Primary
School, Bridgwater 254

Newport Community School,
Barnstaple 257

Newton Ferrers CE Primary School,
Newton Ferrers 270

Okehampton Primary School,
Okehampton 273

Parkfield Primary School, Taunton 279

Polruan Community Primary School,
Fowey 287

Portishead Primary School, Bristol 293

St Mary's (VC) Primary School,
Bridgwater 309

St Peter's School, Exmouth 312

Sandford Primary School, Sandford 315

Sandy Hill Primary School, St Austell 318

Stoke St Gregory CE Primary School,
Taunton 320

Taunton Preparatory School, Taunton 323

Temple Guiting CE Primary School,
Cheltenham 358

The Park School, Yeovil 360

The Tynings School, Staple Hill 371

Tintagel Primary School, Tintagel 378

Trinity CE Primary School,
Acton Turville 387

Troon Primary School, Troon 388

Uffculme Primary School, Uffculme 392

West Coker CE (VC) Primary School,
Yeovil 410

Winkleigh Primary School, Winkleigh 413

Woolavington Village Primary School,
Bridgwater 423

A-Z OF AUTHORS

Aaron Bevan (9)	208	Alice Bowden (9)	78
Aaron Dearing (8)	274	Alice Field (9)	263
Aaron Graham (8)	150	Alice Griffin (7)	387
Aaron Mannion (10)	115	Alice Horn (10)	254
Aaron Moon (9)	392	Alice Leaman (9)	269
Abbey Boobyer (10)	321	Alice Smith (10)	115
Abbie Frankum (9)	48	Alicia Mileham (9)	354
Abbie Scarlett (10)	421	Alison Jeans (7)	182
Abbie Squire (9)	293	Alistair Dewfall (9)	71
Abbie Webb (8)	104	Alysha Antat (10)	44
Abby Bounsall (10)	219	Amala Williams (9)	246
Abby Milnes (7)	302	Amaya Salisbury (9)	315
Abi McHardy (9)	329	Amber Clark (9)	144
Abi Purchase (10)	123	Amber Clarke (8)	309
Abigail Hayward (10)	160	Amber Swan (8)	134
Abigail Horne (8)	127	Amelia Chaston (8)	131
Abigail Newton (9)	291	Amelia Laxton (11)	175
Abigail Piper (8)	170	Amelia Mason (8)	313
Adam Crocker (8)	396	Amelia Walker (8)	362
Adam Griffin (8)	34	Amy Ashford (9)	91
Adam Jones (9)	316	Amy Francis (8)	304
Adam Parnell (10)	221	Amy Greig (10)	391
Adam Smale (9)	42	Amy Howes (10)	286
Adam Thomas (8)	73	Amy Marks (11)	223
Adam Thompson (9)	210	Amy Reddaway (11)	410
Ailsa Gibb (9)	279	Amy Robinson (9)	92
Aimee Dellow (10)	251	Anastasia Cope (10)	175
Aimee Driscoll (10)	203	Andree de La Fontaine (8)	277
Aimee Kenshole (10)	46	Andrew Figgins (11)	392
Aimèe Schools (8)	307	Andrew Foster (10)	266
Alex Dupreez (9)	212	Andrew Lambert (9)	32
Alex Gilbert-Smith (10)	139	Anna Barnett (7)	271
Alex Gilborson (9)	304	Anna Brett (10)	102
Alex Hill (9)	330	Anna Fox (9)	145
Alex Hulbert (9)	84	Anna Gullis (11)	160
Alex Moore (9)	238	Anna Neale (9)	277
Alex Scott (8)	104	Annabelle Rashley (11)	67
Alex Yates (7)	119	Annie Callaghan (10)	383
Alexander Hall (10)	335	Anthony Cleave (10)	203
Alexander Maggs (9)	361	April Burgoyne (10)	420
Alexander Miles (11)	397	April Stevens (10)	224
Alexander Raikes (8)	346	Aron Blight (7)	30
Alexandra Stapleton (10)	281	Aron Finnimore (10)	213
Alice Bate (7)	292	Ashlea Easton (10)	121
Alice Bettison (9)	237	Ashleigh Hemmins (7)	95

Ashleigh Lowman (9)	403	Brandon Smith (8)	52
Ashleigh Sandford (8)	278	Cade Rendle (8)	96
Ashley Brill (10)	191	Caitlin Bawdon (7)	428
Ashley Gaylor (10)	311	Caitlin Horsnett-Bowley (10)	190
Ashley Scott (11)	108	Caitlin Neighbour (8)	88
Aston Walker (7)	119	Caitlin Williams (9)	333
Austin Guest (9)	168	Caitlyn Anderson (10)	144
Beau Donovan (9)	277	Caleb Stevens (8)	229
Ben Anstey (7)	171	Caleb Stride (8)	305
Ben Chapman (7)	107	Callum Cooper (9)	65
Ben Martin (10)	49	Callum Deakin (11)	348
Ben Palmer (9)	290	Callum Fiske (10)	337
Ben Polson (11)	141	Callum Griffin (9)	54
Ben Russell-Gray (10)	385	Callum McCarthy (9)	290
Ben Sutlieff (10)	201	Callum McKenzie (11)	197
Benjamin Bowen-Jones (7)	360	Cameron Box (7)	100
Benjamin Hunter (9)	87	Cameron Brett (9)	90
Benjamin Johnson (10)	60	Cameron Jones (10)	394
Benjamin Keen (9)	296	Cameron Lippiatt (9)	376
Benjamin King (9)	273	Cameron Murrell (8)	399
Benjamin Williams (8)	165	Cameron Tarrant (9)	295
Benson Pocock (11)	341	Cara Leahy (8)	276
Bert Rodgers (8)	241	Carly Brown (9)	331
Beth Chapman (9)	221	Caroline Craig (11)	361
Beth Cookson (8)	399	Carsten Herbert (10)	377
Beth Luscombe (9)	133	Carter Davies (8)	228
Beth Standing (11)	416	Catherine Fairbanks (9)	93
Beth Wasiewicz (10)	156	Catherine Slope (7)	153
Bethan Berry (7)	294	Catherine Turner (9)	417
Bethaney-Jade Revert (9)	23	Celyn French (10)	77
Bethany Elliott (9)	134	Chantal Williams (9)	152
Bethany Kendall (7)	95	Charles Crutchley (10)	262
Bethany Moore (7)	161	Charles Solanki (10)	339
Bethany Neil (8)	132	Charley Vaughan (7)	119
Bethany Sluman (9)	47	Charlie Gamble (9)	72
Bethany Swallow (7)	360	Charlie Lloyd-O'Keeffe (10)	47
Bethany Westcott (10)	269	Charlie Martin (9)	187
Bethany White (9)	267	Charlie Upton (9)	334
Bethany-May Hammond (8)	56	Charlotte Allman (8)	77
Betony Brock (11)	415	Charlotte Brend (11)	265
Billy Gibson (10)	137	Charlotte Butcher (8)	387
Billy Massingham (10)	179	Charlotte Duff (9)	214
Bradley Chant (7)	182	Charlotte Houghton (9)	47
Bradley Harris (8)	159	Charlotte Hubbard (7)	305
Bradley Pearce (8)	291	Charlotte Johnson (8)	162
Bran Pick (9)	410	Charlotte Martin (8)	206
Brandon Francis (9)	276	Charlotte Oliver (10)	233

Charlotte Orr (9)	76	Connor Mellody (10)	118
Charlotte Reilly (10)	158	Connor Rollings (10)	122
Charlotte Rushton (10)	263	Connor Rose (9)	411
Charlotte Thomson (9)	89	Connor Smith (9)	268
Charlotte Wardley (11)	390	Connor Twohig (9)	245
Chelsea Galloway (8)	423	Connor Williams (9)	303
Chelsea Mitchell (10)	198	Conor Bradshaw (9)	374
Chelsea Newton (11)	289	Conor Joyce (8)	395
Chloe Addison (11)	59	Conor Moy (8)	128
Chloe Britton (9)	105	Coral Bell (8)	119
Chloe Coleman (11)	358	Corrine Trivett (8)	88
Chloe Down (10)	26	Cory Clench (8)	395
Chloe Godden (9)	255	Courtney Chick (9)	126
Chloe Gratton (10)	257	Courtney Webber (7)	425
Chloe Griffiths (11)	285	Courtney-Jean Lee (7)	101
Chloe Hannigan (8)	183	Crystal Neville (10)	410
Chloe Nicholas (9)	309	Curtis Drew (9)	373
Chloe Partridge (10)	412	Curtis Kelley (11)	112
Chloe Spence (8)	94	Curtis Wherry (9)	391
Chloe Swan (8)	88	Curtis-Lee Moore (10)	235
Chris James (11)	333	Daisy Andrews (10)	63
Chris Meardon (9)	164	Daisy Copland (11)	410
Chris Spittal (11)	193	Daisy Liddle (7)	183
Christian White (7)	98	Daisy Merrifield (9)	376
Christopher Bell (11)	312	Daisy Newth (7)	306
Christopher Biddle (9)	87	Daisy Saunders (10)	46
Christopher Dixon (10)	231	Dalya Erdogan (9)	52
Christopher Roast (9)	49	Dan Friend (8)	172
Christopher Strydom (10)	123	Dani McCaughey (11)	25
Ciarain Crook (10)	118	Daniel Bond (11)	194
Ciaran McLeod (8)	95	Daniel Bradshaw (10)	220
Claire Downing (10)	218	Daniel Broom (8)	85
Claire Johnson (10)	252	Daniel Ensor (9)	48
Claire Munn (8)	170	Daniel Iggulden (8)	38
Clare Kieft (11)	200	Daniel Langman (9)	132
Clare Oliver (10)	230	Daniel Redding (8)	97
Clarissa Minns (10)	319	Daniel Rigler	23
Class 9	30	Daniel Roberts (10)	123
Claudia Wallis (7)	387	Daniel Rodgers (11)	349
Colin Stockman (10)	401	Daniel Rooney (7)	165
Connie Carter (10)	179	Daniel Stevens (8)	402
Connie McGregor (9)	128	Daniel Unsworth (8)	74
Connie-May Rawlings (8)	297	Danielle Callow (11)	191
Connor Clarke (10)	147	Danielle Glover (9)	80
Connor Coventry (9)	330	Danielle Stead (9)	255
Connor Gearty (11)	251	Danni Rundle (9)	120
Connor Gee (10)	379	David Ford (9)	121

Name	Number	Name	Number
David Sims (10)	311	Eloise Redman (10)	138
Dayna Whittingham (10)	157	Elysia Upton (11)	343
Deanna Pengelly (10)	40	Emily Cocking (9)	318
Declan Coyle (8)	278	Emily Franco (8)	274
Declan O'Connell (9)	212	Emily Friend (10)	225
Demelza Mitchell (8)	203	Emily Harris (10)	237
Demetria Middleton-Johnson (9)	23	Emily Hart (8)	31
Devina Walker (9)	62	Emily Jayne Speed (10)	174
Dion Calway (9)	160	Emily King (8)	92
Dominic Blackmore (10)	252	Emily Pearce (8)	243
Dominic Stephens (9)	366	Emily Thorowgood (11)	192
Dominic Thorne (9)	315	Emily Vickery (8)	352
Dominic Turner (10)	249	Emily Vyain (9)	270
Dominik May (9)	232	Emily White (10)	72
Drew Boorman (11)	330	Emily-Jayne Preen (10)	224
Dylan Wheeler (9)	147	Emma Bell (10)	114
Ebony Davey (10)	53	Emma Craig (10)	234
Eden Phillips (10)	39	Emma Davey (8)	327
Edward Brain (8)	229	Emma King (10)	42
Edward McBride (11)	337	Emma Read (9)	351
Edward Pratt (10)	363	Emma Stacey (8)	353
Eleanor Borthwick (9)	207	Emma Swain (9)	73
Eleanor Newton (9)	323	Erica Chambers (11)	68
Elena Hoskin (10)	389	Erika Mason (8)	303
Elisha Davies (10)	157	Erin Morris (10)	234
Elizabeth Bradley (11)	195	Esther Feaver (9)	169
Elizabeth Callaghan (8)	308	Ethan Street 10)	141
Elizabeth Dawson (9)	106	Evangeline Caroll (9)	338
Elizabeth Merson (8)	350	Fenella Chedham (9)	321
Elizabeth Wright (10)	382	Fergus Carruthers (7)	273
Ellen Cheetham (10)	407	Fergus Shaw (11)	272
Ellen Prisk (10)	238	Finn Bowdrey (11)	283
Ellice Stock (10)	122	Finn Cracknell (9)	42
Ellie Dunning (11)	68	Fiona Lee (9)	248
Ellie Fruhauf (10)	239	Fiona Norman (10)	289
Ellie Parsons (7)	41	Fiona Riches (10)	176
Ellie Passmore (8)	50	Francesca Graziano (9)	411
Ellie-Jane Desousa (11)	385	Frankie-Jo Perrott (9)	94
Ellie-Mae Hayman (7)	168	Fraser Crawford (11)	340
Ellie-Maye Taylor (10)	377	Freya Gant (10)	45
Elliot Smith (8)	95	Freya Milton (7)	396
Elliott Simpson (10)	177	Gabriel Airey (8)	364
Elliott Trivett (11)	140	Gabriella Ball (7)	360
Ellsie Hutt (8)	279	Gabrielle Jones (9)	403
Elly Chandler (11)	344	Gemma Baker (10)	233
Eloise Henson (7)	359	Gemma Clay (8)	388
Eloise Poole (7)	250	Gemma Wells (10)	264

Name	Number	Name	Number
Gemma White (9)	270	Harry Webber (10)	393
Gemma Williams (11)	134	Harvey Selwood (10)	136
George Nuttall (7)	97	Hayley Dix (9)	398
George Salisbury (11)	139	Heather Davey (9)	217
George Whitburn (8)	345	Heather Poulter (11)	338
George Willcocks-King (9)	143	Heather Wroe (11)	29
Georgia Blackwell (9)	326	Heidi Oliver (11)	176
Georgia Humphreys (9)	294	Helen Springett (10)	105
Georgia Weatherstone (10)	381	Henri Cooney (9)	351
Georgia White (8)	408	Henry Giles (10)	284
Georgia Worth (9)	24	Henry Havercroft (11)	323
Georgie Thorne (8)	185	Hollie Eyers (10)	372
Georgina Mason (10)	202	Holly Alldridge (8)	91
Grace Martinson (9)	301	Holly Conquer (9)	350
Grace Spence (10)	376	Holly Crone (10)	382
Hamish Inglis (9)	423	Holly Hindley (8)	205
Hannah Cook (10)	180	Holly Low (10)	244
Hannah Down (10)	45	Holly Nicholson (8)	358
Hannah Dunston (10)	69	Holly Vincent (8)	107
Hannah Jolley (9)	353	Holly Webb (8)	74
Hannah Ludwell (11)	137	Holly Wilson (9)	322
Hannah Meek (9)	408	Holly Yelland (9)	275
Hannah Miles (11)	380	Hope Clarkson (9)	243
Hannah Rees (9)	367	Hugh Johnson (8)	185
Hannah Rowse (8)	149	Ian King (11)	414
Hannah Sutton (10)	260	Imogen Allen (9)	331
Hannah Taylor (9)	146	Imogen Clench (10)	138
Hannah Tucker (9)	400	Imogen Gray (10)	336
Hannah Walters (9)	245	Imogen Henry (9)	328
Harri Lai (8)	314	Imogen Tarran (8)	270
Harriet Armstrong (10)	339	Imran Azlisham (8)	101
Harriet Brain (10)	223	Isaac Heather (8)	316
Harriet Cope (7)	102	Isabel Samuelson (11)	25
Harriet Kelly (10)	284	Isabelle Bean (11)	288
Harriet Turner (9)	353	Isabelle Zanelli (10)	366
Harriet van Houben (8)	169	Isobel Sheppard (9)	378
Harriet Walsh (10)	279	Issie Hartley (10)	272
Harriet Wiltshire (10)	285	Jack Bedford (8)	287
Harris Fisher (10)	390	Jack Chynoweth (10)	121
Harry Cody (10)	46	Jack Elliott (10)	57
Harry Driscoll (10)	175	Jack Lipman (8)	100
Harry Gill (9)	297	Jack Overy (11)	158
Harry Grinter (10)	371	Jack Palmer (10)	159
Harry Jee (8)	395	Jack Penwill (8)	103
Harry Michelmore (8)	312	Jack Richards (11)	266
Harry Pile (7)	119	Jack Stephens (9)	377
Harry Stannett (11)	178	Jack Wellman (8)	393

Jack Wilkins (9)	373	Jasmine Shaw (8)	402
Jack Wingate (9)	189	Jason Turner (10)	386
Jack Withers (9)	373	Jason Webster (8)	426
Jack Wotton (10)	117	Jedd Evans (10)	140
Jacob Bell (8)	317	Jemima Hosking (9)	145
Jacob Hill (7)	426	Jemma Gane (8)	365
Jacob Pearson (9)	256	Jemma Murphy (11)	399
Jacob Rail (11)	389	Jennifer Okoro (9)	44
Jacqueline White (11)	231	Jennifer Taylor (9)	412
Jade Broadhurst (8)	313	Jenny Kerr (11)	251
Jade Elliott (10)	320	Jenny Willis (9)	271
Jade Foster (11)	25	Jess Keatley (7)	204
Jade Galliford (11)	25	Jessaimée Richardson (9)	235
Jade Harris (10)	268	Jessica Bennett (10)	282
Jade Norsworthy (7)	152	Jessica Bettridge (10)	319
Jade Pring (10)	124	Jessica Commins (8)	52
Jade Shoulder (11)	405	Jessica Cottrell (10)	405
Jaimie Mills (11)	26	Jessica Flitter (9)	422
Jake Clarke (9)	407	Jessica Horne (7)	103
Jake Firstbrook (10)	66	Jessica Kelly (8)	151
Jake Ley (10)	136	Jessica Lawrence (10)	250
Jake Tozer (9)	222	Jessica Lethbridge (10)	116
Jamaul O'Connor (8)	33	Jessica Little (8)	404
James Boardman (8)	302	Jessica Loder (9)	264
James Bowell (7)	297	Jessica Owen (8)	79
James Bradley (11)	406	Jessica Parker (11)	29
James Chinnock (11)	203	Jessica Peel (10)	272
James Cowling (8)	326	Jessica Pointon (8)	304
James Dancey (8)	354	Jessica Rowden (10)	249
James Millorit (10)	394	Jessica Smith (10)	261
James Nash (8)	310	Jessica Weeks (10)	337
James Oldham (7)	151	Jessica Whittick (9)	370
James Poole (10)	357	Jodie Rudd (9)	377
James Spackman (9)	355	Joe Hastie (7)	30
James Wassell (9)	391	Joe Moore (11)	109
James Willis (8)	271	Joe Wakeham (9)	291
Jamie Craig (9)	230	Joelle Henstridge (10)	63
Jamie Griffiths (7)	103	John Polson (8)	104
Jamie Howes (10)	116	Jonathan Bishop (7)	97
Jamie Mitchell (9)	112	Jonathan Goldsworthy (11)	409
Jamie Ranger (10)	135	Jonathan Holland (8)	129
Jamie Trueman (8)	103	Jonty Colman (8)	38
Jared Duff (8)	37	Jordan Airzee (10)	113
Jarrod Howes (8)	90	Jordan Dunbar (11)	341
Jasmine Broom (10)	283	Jordan Hayman (9)	43
Jasmine Fenn (10)	154	Jordan Louise Watts (8)	79
Jasmine Moran (10)	260	Jordan Matthews (9)	51

Jordan Smith (10)	69	Keiran Palfrey (10)	392
Jordan Southey (10)	194	Keiran Patton (9)	77
Jordan Wozencroft (9)	131	Kelli McArthur (10)	247
Jordon Pryke (10)	137	Kelly Parry (10)	247
Joseph Allen (7)	98	Kelly Pert (10)	259
Joseph Coombes (10)	180	Kelsey Dalley (10)	178
Joseph Vickers (11)	161	Kennedy Neal (7)	388
Josh Collins (10)	413	Kerenza Catterall (10)	389
Josh Cox (9)	394	Keri Oaten (10)	252
Josh Ferme (10)	124	Kerry Hayes (9)	146
Josh James (9)	411	Keziah Parnell (10)	216
Josh Kelly (11)	342	Kieran Jones (10)	141
Josh McLeod (10)	112	Kieran Lukehurst (9)	125
Josh Taylor (10)	257	Kieran Reeves (10)	111
Josh Thake (10)	27	Kieran Smith (8)	423
Josh Trescowthick (10)	389	Kieron Kelly (10)	206
Josh Whalley (11)	28	Kim Carcas (8)	292
Josh Whitehead (8)	398	Kimberley Howes (10)	380
Joshua Baker (8)	301	Kirby Mullis (10)	365
Joshua Chaney (8)	167	Kirsty Densley (9)	61
Joshua Colgate (9)	404	Kirsty Evans (9)	130
Joshua McCarthy (9)	373	Kirsty Lloyd	23
Joshua Page (10)	198	Kirsty Syms (8)	205
Julian Stephens (9)	307	Kitley Lane (10)	418
Justin Southam (11)	266	Kris Jordan (10)	422
Justine Taylor (9)	233	Kristal Braund (8)	36
Kalehsha Murphy (11)	158	Kyle Anderson (8)	59
Kane Williams (8)	96	Kyle Bishop (7)	369
Karla Turner (10)	155	Kyle Fajht-Taylor (8)	293
Kate Bailey (9)	274	Kyle Murray (11)	378
Kate Drew (8)	351	Kyle Poole (9)	374
Kate Marks (9)	227	Kyra Cutler (7)	104
Kathryn Croom (7)	163	Lana Willis (9)	32
Katie Davies (9)	31	Lara Rodgers (11)	327
Katie Holdsworth (8)	387	Laura Baker (10)	192
Katie Mackenzie (10)	255	Laura Champ (9)	217
Katie Martin (9)	82	Laura Hardman (10)	43
Katie Richards (10)	196	Laura Nitti (10)	66
Katie Sealey (10)	232	Laura Walton (9)	43
Katie Stephens (8)	243	Laura Williams (8)	83
Katie Walker (11)	189	Laura Wynn (10)	24
Katie Watts (6)	250	Lauren Armson (8)	184
Katie Wells (8)	204	Lauren Bawden (10)	269
Katrina Pettitt (10)	244	Lauren Burke (11)	400
Kayleigh Bickle (9)	216	Lauren Crawford (9)	80
Kayleigh Page (9)	121	Lauren Dawe (9)	242
Kayleigh Todd (10)	124	Lauren Parr (10)	312

Lauren Porter (7)	99	Luke Easton (8)	126
Lauren Raw (9)	53	Luke Reardon (9)	149
Lauren Reason (10)	199	Luke Townsend (8)	354
Lauren Smith (9)	123	Luke Western (9)	419
Lauren Stevens (10)	397	Lulu Friend (9)	228
Lauren Street (8)	76	Lydia Gannon (11)	140
Lauren Wass (8)	204	Lynsey Ridd (11)	26
Leah Burridge (9)	403	Macauley Bridgman (9)	129
Leah Mufford (9)	388	Macauley Godfrey (9)	428
Leah Tunney (8)	153	Macauley Waites (9)	125
Leia Senington (10)	318	Maddy Stubbs (7)	308
Lewis Carrera (9)	48	Madeleine Chaston (8)	91
Lewis Slinger (9)	113	Madeline Cullen (9)	242
Lewis Stutt (9)	55	Maia White (9)	71
Liam Sloan (9)	218	Maisie Perry (9)	248
Liam Stone (10)	391	Maisie Weller (9)	45
Liam Taylor (10)	157	Marcus Worrall (9)	356
Liam Wardle (9)	50	Maria Norman (7)	293
Liana-Maria Brett (10)	132	Marina Carrick (9)	271
Lilly May (8)	54	Marnie Dimmick (8)	81
Lilly Stephenson (8)	387	Marnie List (11)	109
Lily Andrews (9)	401	Mason Bartlett (9)	44
Lily Byron-Helyar (10)	156	Mathew Morgan (8)	347
Lily Edwards (9)	240	Matt Haines (11)	336
Lily Hawkins (11)	142	Matt Millard (9)	397
Lily Kidner (11)	62	Matt Pearce (9)	328
Lily Madsen (11)	196	Matthew Green (7)	229
Lily Wildgoose (8)	300	Matthew Griffiths (9)	381
Linden Ough (9)	35	Matthew Lingard (9)	364
Lizzie King (8)	188	Matthew Pearson (11)	265
Lottie Hunt (9)	149	Matthew Spensley (8)	302
Louis Gough (10)	288	Max Jeffs (11)	325
Louise Hall (9)	256	Max Popham (8)	352
Louise Ross (9)	122	Max Savage (9)	314
Luciana Metherall (8)	350	Maxine Welch (9)	56
Lucy Burgess (10)	198	Maya Bruce (11)	57
Lucy Cheetham (8)	393	Meave Daly (10)	111
Lucy Dean (8)	278	Meg Lawrence (11)	58
Lucy Duffy (7)	120	Meg Owen (8)	301
Lucy Gammon (7)	394	Megan Dalrymple-Hay (6)	314
Lucy Griffin (9)	53	Megan Dear (11)	427
Lucy Harris (7)	98	Megan Haward (8)	313
Lucy McHale (10)	27	Megan Hobson (8)	171
Lucy Minall (7)	295	Megan Jackson (9)	219
Lucy Woodman (10)	193	Megan Lang (8)	144
Luke Carns (9)	93	Megan Overall (8)	133
Luke Dryland (10)	238	Megan Sharman (11)	383

Melisa Tucker-Cantez (8)	120	Nicholas Chapman (7)	119
Melissa Noble (10)	199	Nicholas Freemantle (8)	300
Melissa Ross (10)	290	Nicholas Liggins (7)	250
Merrily Kirton (10)	50	Nicolas Orbell (9)	173
Mey Haines (8)	332	Nicole Rae (8)	75
Michael Bramley (10)	375	Niki Thiella (10)	412
Michael Cook (9)	117	Nikita Rogers (10)	415
Michael Cooney (11)	398	Nisha Jones (10)	28
Michael Crow (10)	272	Oliver Brotherhood (10)	40
Michael Donohue (11)	110	Oliver Green (9)	133
Michael Guy (10)	135	Oliver Heptinstall (10)	404
Michael Marsh (8)	227	Oliver Hubbard (9)	298
Michael Styles (8)	325	Oliver Jones (9)	331
Michael Thornton (8)	396	Oliver Large (11)	345
Michelle Knight (11)	249	Oliver May (8)	89
Miles Kingsley (10)	267	Oliver Millner (8)	388
Millie Cloak (8)	27	Oliver O'Hare (7)	303
Millie Powell-Thomas (7)	183	Oliver Pile (8)	86
Milly Butters (8)	356	Oliver Roberts (9)	209
Miranda Jewell (8)	275	Oliver Rogers-Hargreaves (9)	33
Mitchell James Woolley (7)	307	Oliver Swift (9)	211
Moeko Takane (11)	73	Olivia Clark (11)	254
Mollie Staff (9)	372	Olivia Down (10)	24
Mollie Stallard (8)	352	Olivia Evans (10)	200
Molly Driscoll (10)	47	Olivia Gregory (7)	368
Molly Efford (11)	195	Olympia Martin-Pope (9)	356
Molly Gibson (7)	101	Oscar Milton (9)	267
Molly Meikle (10)	320	Owen Ricketts (8)	63
Molly Morris (9)	411	Pagan Ferguson (10)	181
Molly Murnan (7)	388	Paige Bradley (7)	151
Morgan Basford (9)	220	Paige De Roeper (10)	155
Morwenna Harnett (9)	334	Paige Emerson (10)	142
Myah Field (10)	262	Paige Hext (11)	69
Nancy Williams (7)	306	Paige Langdon (11)	310
Naomi Chaney (7)	166	Paul Manuel (8)	81
Naomi Slade (11)	232	Paul Sieradzki (10)	226
Naomi Sweeny (9)	273	Pete Andrews (8)	358
Naomi Taylor (10)	202	Peter Braund (11)	38
Natalie Boulton (9)	355	Peter Hansford (10)	253
Natalie Brakes (10)	424	Philip Bridge (9)	371
Natalie Brown (8)	325	Phoebe Horton (8)	308
Natalie Hill (10)	64	Phoebe Smith (7)	184
Natalie Stevenson (9)	215	Polly Morfett (8)	107
Natasha Stables (11)	75	Poppy Bridgwater (7)	359
Nathan Garlick (9)	130	Rachael Randall (8)	309
Nathan Wilson (10)	287	Rachel Best (8)	64
Niambi Ross (10)	51	Rachel Boyland (9)	166

Rachel Churches (10)	61	Rosie Johnson (10)	235
Rachel Compton (10)	239	Ross Giles (10)	154
Rachel Howard (9)	305	Ross Holland (7)	359
Rachel Nuttall (11)	335	Ross McGall (11)	318
Rachel Roberts (9)	296	Ross Slinger (10)	110
Rachel Wilson (10)	197	Rowan Jeffrey (9)	406
Rebecca Browne (10)	258	Roxanne Hall (8)	172
Rebecca Bugler (7)	424	Ruby Mitchell (9)	292
Rebecca Fletcher (8)	299	Rumbidzai Dozwa (11)	181
Rebecca Jane (10)	108	Ruth Taylor (11)	135
Rebecca Jones (11)	134	Ryan Ball (11)	118
Rebecca Kinnear (11)	342	Ryan Becker (10)	372
Rebecca Nicholson (10)	138	Ryan Bell (10)	114
Rebecca Norman (11)	419	Ryan Cornelius (9)	319
Rebecca Pratt (10)	46	Ryan Davey (10)	413
Rebecca Ward (10)	111	Ryan Deag (11)	253
Rebecca Wilson (8)	298	Ryan Fishlock (7)	153
Rebekah Rich (11)	312	Ryan Fulford (8)	162
Rebekah Stead (9)	35	Ryan Hardy (9)	143
Reece Kirkham (8)	99	Ryan Hough (9)	23
Rhiannon Groves (10)	379	Ryan Marsden (11)	281
Rhiannon Sladen (8)	228	Ryan Moth (11)	384
Richard Flower (10)	378	Ryan Turner (9)	113
Richard Lang (11)	139	Sadie Mufford (11)	390
Robbie Risdon (10)	420	Sally Eccles (11)	190
Robert Andrews (10)	251	Sally Moss (8)	86
Robert Fletcher (9)	317	Sam Dowling (10)	272
Robert Heard (7)	230	Sam Halsted-Cann (9)	173
Robert Hill (10)	418	Sam Hanlon (11)	202
Robert Lanham (8)	127	Sam Holland (8)	148
Robert Mayger (10)	374	Sam James (8)	427
Robert Nicholls (10)	395	Sam Leece (9)	35
Robert Paterson (7)	368	Sam Lipman (8)	106
Robert Trickey (11)	65	Sam Pincombe (10)	259
Robert Tunley (10)	142	Sam Underwood (10)	286
Robin Batchelor (9)	188	Samantha Platt (8)	426
Robin Evans (11)	347	Samantha Stevens (11)	110
Robyn Land (10)	213	Sammy Skinner (10)	414
Rory Harrison (11)	324	Samuel Buckley (9)	78
Rory Lethbridge (8)	106	Samuel Clarke (10)	265
Rory Montague (9)	257	Samuel Evans (9)	412
Rosemary Pryce (9)	124	Samuel Hawkins (9)	371
Roshan Kumar Chopra (10)	409	Samuel Knight (9)	148
Rosie Dunkley (11)	282	Samuel Newton (11)	340
Rosie Emma Say (9)	376	Samuel Popham (10)	343
Rosie Gibbs (9)	311	Samuel Smith (9)	70
Rosie Hadfield (10)	236	Sarah Bale (10)	191

Sarah Hamilton (11)	28	Stephanie Dobson (11)	288
Sarah Parfitt (11)	332	Stephanie Nolan (8)	241
Sarah Quirk (8)	82	Stephanie Symns (7)	41
Sarah Theobald (11)	346	Stephen Bush (9)	60
Sarah Tunley (9)	83	Steve Mears (10)	240
Sasha Lerch (9)	275	Steven Jones (9)	244
Scott Bending (9)	278	Susannah Slack (10)	280
Scott Hickery (9)	374	Tabitha Patey (8)	99
Scott Lawton (7)	152	Tamara Browning (11)	390
Scott Stevens (10)	402	Tamara Collin (10)	289
Scout Wheeler (7)	104	Tamsin Haywood (7)	37
Sean Lethbridge (9)	86	Tamsyn Stone (8)	425
Sebastian Filer-Gale (9)	37	Tania Jeffrey (10)	174
Sebastian Kempf (11)	236	Tanya Pearson (8)	272
Sebastian Ralph (10)	329	Tara Penter (9)	417
Selina Targett (8)	187	Tara Wells-McCulloch (9)	77
Shae Moore (7)	105	Tegan Williams (11)	70
Shana Clarke (8)	404	Terry Fletcher (8)	105
Shane Prater (11)	261	Tess Bryant (10)	48
Shannon Briffett (8)	310	Theo Fuge (8)	107
Shannon Brown (8)	72	Theo Howarth (8)	300
Shannon Leahy (8)	167	Thomas Barclay (9)	243
Shannon Murtagh (9)	131	Thomas Crabb (8)	186
Shannon Netherway (9)	164	Thomas Davison (10)	222
Shannon Smith (9)	236	Thomas Day (11)	194
Shannon Tinworth (8)	401	Thomas Dimmick (10)	108
Shelbie Brown (10)	375	Thomas Hayes (10)	349
Shelby Norris (10)	231	Thomas Johnson (11)	26
Shivon Burridge (9)	258	Thomas King (10)	246
Sian Rufus (10)	362	Thomas Merritt (10)	322
Sophia Mullen (10)	23	Thomas Ribbons (7)	100
Sophie Bannan (11)	109	Thomas Roode (11)	268
Sophie Bolt (10)	143	Thomas Rylands (10)	225
Sophie Cameron (9)	215	Thomas Scott (9)	247
Sophie Chappell (10)	67	Tiffany Wheeler (8)	174
Sophie Compton (9)	276	Toby Butters (11)	339
Sophie Cook (9)	254	Toby Finch-Hatton (7)	363
Sophie Evans (10)	240	Toby Knights (9)	222
Sophie Extance (11)	66	Toby Mitchell (11)	192
Sophie Knutt (11)	280	Toby Ogden (8)	106
Sophie Maries (9)	85	Tom Aston (6)	249
Sophie Olver (7)	299	Tom Chandler (10)	338
Sophie Roberts (10)	416	Tom Clogg (10)	214
Sophie Swain (8)	34	Tom Day (8)	85
Stacey Kelley (8)	102	Tom Gorst (10)	413
Stan Clarke (9)	49	Tom Green (10)	68
Stephanie Bourner (7)	119	Tom Green (10)	226

Tom Joseph Hanson (8)	407	William Jolley (10)	357
Tom Odgers (11)	348	William Mileham (11)	324
Tom Robinson (8)	55	William Patten (9)	65
Tom Strawbridge (7)	172	William Pearse (11)	384
Tommy Dyer (8)	90	William Richardson (10)	197
Toni Lawrence (10)	75	Xavier Craine (10)	386
Troy Clench (10)	392	Yasmin Andrews-Urvoy (10)	367
Tudor Filer-Gale (9)	36	Yasmin Egonu (9)	248
Tyler Clarke (11)	408	Yasmin Tucker Cantez (8)	150
Tyler Gowan (11)	386	Yola Gonzalez (10)	58
Tyler Mace (8)	76	Ysabel Thomas (10)	264
Tyrone White (8)	396	Yuiko Takane (8)	74
Vivien Keech (11)	344	Zachary Coates (10)	31
Whitney Williams (11)	137	Zoe Ashdown (9)	428
William Armstrong (8)	273	Zoe Barter (8)	51
William Baldwin (10)	357	Zoe Durnan-Steer (11)	67
William Bedford (8)	163	Zoe Hamilton (11)	142
William Cook (11)	136	Zoe Oliver (10)	234
William Haughton (8)	355	Zoë Walters (9)	244
William Jackson (8)	186		

THE POEMS

Tiger

He stands there waiting for his prey
His eyes twinkle in the stars
His teeth as sharp as a spike
Hungry for food he stands waiting
A footstep
He looks around
A deer
He jumps
He kills.

Kirsty Lloyd & Daniel Rigler
Ashleigh CE (VC) Primary School, Barnstaple

Sharks Are . . .

S is for super
H is for hunter
A is for attacker
R is for reef, the shark's hunting ground
K is for kings of the ocean.

Ryan Hough (9)
Ashleigh CE (VC) Primary School, Barnstaple

Sharks

S ly with food
H ate every fish
A lways in a mood
R ip legs and arms
K ill for a dish
S tay really calm.

Sophia Mullen (10)
Ashleigh CE (VC) Primary School, Barnstaple

Cat

Lying on the end of the bed, sleeping peacefully,
Her eyes are like black, shining armour,
Her lovely brown fur covering her shiny, claw-like crystals,
She creeps around with her bell ringing loudly.
She hides under the bed when the doorbell rings,
She shivers when the door slams shut!

Bethaney-Jade Revert & Demetria Middleton-Johnson (9)
Ashleigh CE (VC) Primary School, Barnstaple

Dear Mum

Dear Mum
While you were out . . .
A stick whacked Vincent round the face.
Vincent slammed a plate on Rebecca's head
And Rebecca whacked him round the face.
The ice fell down Rebecca's back,
It was the dog.
The jam mysteriously splatted over my jumper, somehow.
The flour poured over Rebecca's shortbread
And she blamed it on innocent me.
A giant hippo attacked the bedrooms, just after you cleaned them.
Vincent screamed because the dog stepped on his foot
And he blamed it, once again, on innocent me.
I swear Rebecca nibbled the chocolate cake.
Vincent fell down the stairs.
I moved down to Grandma's, so goodbye for now.

Laura Wynn (10)
Ashleigh CE (VC) Primary School, Barnstaple

Sharks

Sharks are dangerous,
Sharks are cool,
Sharks don't live in a swimming pool.

You can go and swim in the sea,
Maybe have a shark's cup of tea.

Then you can go back home
And leave poor shark all alone.

Olivia Down (10)
Ashleigh CE (VC) Primary School, Barnstaple

Sharks

Sharks are dangerous creatures and they really do bite,
No one knows how many sharks there are, or if they have good sight.
They may have underwater parties, but the sharks will eat all the fish up,
But they may also have water in leftover plastic cups.
There are many species of shark in the world
And some are under reefs huddled up and curled.

Georgia Worth (9)
Ashleigh CE (VC) Primary School, Barnstaple

Dear Izzy (Mum) And Ben (Dad)

While you were out:
I don't know how the toilet overflowed,
I never knew a Chelsea shirt was wasted,
Sorry to say you might have to redecorate,
The spring came out of your brand new sofa,
Whilst we went on the computer,
We came downstairs and the cat was in the oven,
The hamster turned pink,
The fish was in the toilet,
Your brand new lipstick was all over the dog,
I don't know how there are the insides from a frog all over the place,
There are messages on the mirror in your best red lipstick,
Your best budgie has been plucked,
I was being good (honest),
We know you're going to have a fit,
Me and Jade have gone camping,
To lie low for a bit.

From Jade and Dani.

Dani McCaughey & Jade Foster (11)
Ashleigh CE (VC) Primary School, Barnstaple

The Sea

A shining diamond ring
A comfortable, soft bed
Clean, fresh clothes blowing in the wind
A new, gleaming car
Waves of angels flying towards you blowing their trumpets
Salted chips tingling on your tongue
A crystal blue palace in the sun.

Jade Galliford (11)
Ashleigh CE (VC) Primary School, Barnstaple

The Rain

A pip from an apple,
Pebbles falling to the ground,
A fresh pear that has just been picked,
A wet, soggy bath mat,
Clean pyjamas that have just been washed,
A bowl of lemons and limes,
Sparkling clean windows.

Isabel Samuelson (11)
Ashleigh CE (VC) Primary School, Barnstaple

A Smoothie

A cloud of delicious fruits,
A blanket of creamy freshness,
A bowl of zesty, exotic flavours,
A cup of cool, refreshing snow,
An ice cream on a warm, sunny day,
A snowman made with extreme care,
A soft, angelic rainbow always glimmering
And the smoothness of a newborn baby's skin.

Lynsey Ridd (11)
Ashleigh CE (VC) Primary School, Barnstaple

A Motorbike

A big, fast cheetah running through the wild
A group of people humming in your ear
Soft and smooth baby skin seats
A petrol station on wheels
A roaring lion in the wilderness
A dangerous shark.

Chloe Down (10)
Ashleigh CE (VC) Primary School, Barnstaple

Clothes

Clothes smoother than a polar bear's coat,
Freshly washed clothes with the scent of apples on a tree,
Clothes more colourful than the rainbow,
Clothes tearing quicker than a lion ripping its prey,
Clothes in rapturous applause whilst drying on the line.

Thomas Johnson (11)
Ashleigh CE (VC) Primary School, Barnstaple

Tic Tacs

Tic Tacs whiter than flying snow
Compact and solid Roman turtle
Hotter than chilli burning in your mouth
Fresher than sparkling water on a hot summer's day
Smoother than a polished marble table.

Jaimie Mills (11)
Ashleigh CE (VC) Primary School, Barnstaple

Excuses, Excuses

Dear Mum,
While you were out:
The budgie started a race with next-door's canary
And got stuck in the chimney.
A gust of wind ran through the house
And took my report card from my hands
And landed it in the shredder.
I *tried* to bring in the washing
But the cat jumped and took the pegs
So it fell in the mud.
The double chocolate chip ice cream
Mysteriously disappeared from the freezer
And landed round my mouth.
My new pair of socks decreased
When the washing machine ate one
(I was being good, honest),
So knowing you're going to have a fit,
I've gone to Gran's to lie low for a bit.

Lucy McHale (10)
Ashleigh CE (VC) Primary School, Barnstaple

A Football

A round, tough zebra made from leather.
The back of an armadillo.
A black and white moon in the sky.
Two armies battling against each other.
A large, round pebble.
The smell of a new leather jacket or a horse's saddle.
Tougher than an angry rhino.
But, more enjoyable than a big bar of Galaxy chocolate.

Josh Thake (10)
Ashleigh CE (VC) Primary School, Barnstaple

My Rabbit, Sniffy

Sniffy is my bunny
She is very funny
Her fur is snowy white
She never ever bites
She likes carrots for her dinner
She is my winner.

Millie Cloak (8)
Ashleigh CE (VC) Primary School, Barnstaple

Dear Mum

While you were out:

My drink sort of knocked over.
It wasn't me,
It was the force of the dog's tail.

There is a big sort of scratch in the laminate floor
Where the guinea pig slid across it.

You left your wedding ring on the side,
Will threw it and it landed in your Coke
And kind of lost its colour.

Your mobile was vibrating on the table
And the cat got so mad
That she knocked it off and it smashed.

The bath overflowed and is leaking through the walls
Because the shampoo bottle fell on top of the tap.

The cat tied me up to the chair
So I couldn't wash out the bin and it got maggots.

I was being good, honest,
But I think the house is haunted.
So, knowing you're going to have a fit,
I've gone over to Gran's to lie low for a bit.

Nisha Jones (10) & Sarah Hamilton (11)
Ashleigh CE (VC) Primary School, Barnstaple

Dear Mum

While you were out:
The fridge opened
And the ice cream flew into my hands.
The road workers used their rollers
And the vibration knocked the vases over.
The cat was watching Discovery Real Time
And decided to do DIY on the cupboards.
The fish jumped out of the tank
And into the toilet.
The dog was watching Match Of The Day
And kicked the football through the window.
The money fell down the drain.
The shoes went out in the mud
And walked all over the house.
I was being good (honest).
Knowing you are going to have a fit,
I am lying low at Gran's.

Josh Whalley (11)
Ashleigh CE (VC) Primary School, Barnstaple

Dear Mum

While you were out:
The berries from the garden got all over the floor,
Along with the flower buds
And the vase just flew off the cabinet
And got all over the floor.
I have no idea why there is wax
All over the new, cream carpet
And I have not been in the kitchen,
So I have no idea why there is flour
All over the floor.
Um, I did clean out the hamster cage,
But there was a big tornado
And so it looks just like it did before,
So I think you should definitely clean him.
I was trying to feed the cat
And his food just spilled out all over the floor magically.
I tried to clean it up, but, um, all the biscuits came out too.
Yeah, and Harrison came round,
Then ate all the sweets, then left.
I don't think you will ever find the culprit for these crimes,
So knowing you'll have a fit,
I have gone to Nan's to lie low for a bit.

Love from your *innocent* daughter, Jess.

Jessica Parker (11)
Ashleigh CE (VC) Primary School, Barnstaple

Dear Mum

While you were out:
My bedroom was nice and clean,
But then the cat came and, um, disappeared.

Somehow, a chocolate bar managed to fly from a cupboard to my mouth
And magically, there were brown smudges around my mouth!

Then, you wouldn't believe it,
The dog managed to kick a football through the window,
Knocking over your bookshelf and vases!
But, as quick as a flash, the floor was messed up,
Then your lipstick was being used by little sis!
Also, the hamster kinda stained your bed sheets
With blackcurrant juice.
I was being good (honest),
But I think the house is haunted.
So, knowing you're going to have a fit,
I've gone over to Gran's to lie low for a bit.

Heather Wroe (11)
Ashleigh CE (VC) Primary School, Barnstaple

Prayers And Poems From Around The World

I want to be your friend
Forever and ever without break or . . .
Until the leaves fall off in spring
Until the cliffs all vanish into the sea
Until the sky closes its eyes
Until history becomes the future
Until the sun rises at midnight
Until the Earth ceases to orbit the sun
That is how long I want to be your friend.

Class 9
Ashleigh CE (VC) Primary School, Barnstaple

My Pet

My pet is called Benji
But we call him Benji Bin
As he always has his head stuck in the bin.

He has big, floppy ears
And a black, shiny nose
That follows him where he goes.

He likes to go walkies
And always punctures my footballs.
He's twelve years old
I love my Benji Bin and he knows.

Aron Blight (7)
Ashleigh CE (VC) Primary School, Barnstaple

My Rabbit

I have a rabbit called Spots
And I love him lots and lots.

In my garden is where he plays
But his hutch is where he stays.

His fur is brown and white
He cleans himself every night.

Spots is four years old
He doesn't like the cold.

Joe Hastie (7)
Ashleigh CE (VC) Primary School, Barnstaple

Orks From Lord Of The Rings

Old, walking zombies
Rotten flesh of a dead man
A fierce roar of an angry lion in pain
The slimy trail of an old, wet snail
Blood from an old man with diseases
An alligator that has been teased
Slimy toads' eyes
A faulty fire bell in an army camp.

Zachary Coates (10)
Ashleigh CE (VC) Primary School, Barnstaple

Sitting In My Bed

Sitting in my bed with my cat
Along comes Mum
Takes her out!

Don't feel happy
Sad as a salt drop in my soup.

Cheerless
Glum
Not happy at all
All of the cuddly cat going, going, gone
Not a hair in sight!

So I go to bed
Fall asleep
Fast as a bolt of lightning.

Emily Hart (8)
Becket Primary School, Weston-super-Mare

Blue

Blue, blue, what is blue?
I don't know, so it's up to you.

The seaside sea that shimmers at night,
The sky so high,
Our painted walls,
Pencils, rulers and pens, of course.

Our teddies, our pillows and our CDs,
Our jeans, our pyjamas and our painted knees.

Katie Davies (9)
Becket Primary School, Weston-super-Mare

All Alone Felt Like Grey

Once,
I lost my
Father and mother.

I screamed,
Howled,
Mumbled,
But nobody came to help.

Heartbroken girl.

Some say I'm lonely,
Some say I'm gloomy.

My mother mumbles
Like a monkey.
Love is like a stone
You can never break.

My howl was as wild as a car.
My scream was as loud as a lion's roar.
My mumble was as quiet as a mouse
Stuck in a bramble bush.

Tearful,
Gloomy,
Disappointed.

My dad came to my rescue
With my dog and cat.

Lana Willis (9)
Becket Primary School, Weston-super-Mare

Sand Bay

Last Sunday
We went to Sand Bay
For three hours.

Went upstairs
Went to the rock part
Went on the rocks.

I went up higher
I went very high up
Stepped on seaweed and slipped.

Fell over
Fell down
Fell onto a rock
Fell and broke my back.

Andrew Lambert (9)
Becket Primary School, Weston-super-Mare

Birthday

Birds singing
Sun is out
Jump out of bed
Zoom downstairs
Guess what?
Guess what is in front of me?
Lots
And lots
Of toys
For me
I shout, 'Yippeeee!'
Wake up my parents
'I'm sorry!' I say
Open my presents
Can't believe my eyes
My very
First
Ramp
I take it outside
I hurt myself

But anyway . . .

Oliver Rogers-Hargreaves (9)
Becket Primary School, Weston-super-Mare

Me And Will

Me and Will
Met in playschool
Never left each other alone
Or the teachers.

Me and Will
Were allowed to work in any corner
Our choice.

One day
Our families met
After playschool
And went for a talk, while

Me and Will
Scattered silently in the summerhouse
As joyful as cheerleaders.

Jamaul O'Connor (8)
Becket Primary School, Weston-super-Mare

33

One Misty Day

One misty day
I scaredly approached
The pier
Nan drinking beer
With her friend Mia
Then amazingly
Nan shouted at me
I couldn't believe my ears
I was gloomy
I cried
Nan in despair walked off
I was upset
Screamed
Shrieked
Nan didn't care about me anymore
All up to me.

Sophie Swain (8)
Becket Primary School, Weston-super-Mare

A Very Hurtful Poem

At the Mad Monkey Paradise
Going on a rope swing
I was swinging

I noticed it was
Slippery
As a slug

I slipped into the air and
Hit
The ground
Really, really hard . . .

For the rest of the day
My face
Was really red

For the next day too
My face
Was really red.

Adam Griffin (8)
Becket Primary School, Weston-super-Mare

A Cat Dies

I hate it
When a cat dies.
Usually whoever
Sees it,
Cries with crystal tears
Of transparent blood.
It disturbs me.

The cats who died
Are Super Skelly
And Elite Ellie.

Usually,
I get a toy
To remember the cat who died
With a grave
In the garden.

Sam Leece (9)
Becket Primary School, Weston-super-Mare

My Sad Feelings

My grandad died before I came to school.
When my grandad died I was miserably glum,
A gloomy girl.

I remembered I could not speak to him,
But I can remember him in my heart,
Soul, mind, forever.
I will not forget him.

Rebekah Stead (9)
Becket Primary School, Weston-super-Mare

Morning - Cinquain

Tiredness
Dawn breaks like glass
The postman comes with post
Birds sing as loud as opera
Times pass.

Linden Ough (9)
Black Torrington CE Primary School, Beaworthy

Lullaby

Sleep, sleep, tomorrow will bring
A delectable hot fudge sundae
With chocolate syrup.

Sleep, sleep, tomorrow will bring
A beautiful, hot summer so I can
Surf on the beach.

Sleep, sleep, tomorrow will bring
A space shuttle and spacesuit
So I can explore space.

Sleep, sleep, tomorrow will bring
A precious gift for all.

Sleep, sleep, tomorrow will bring
A pair of skis
For the snowy winter.

Sleep, sleep, tomorrow will bring
A frosty day
That blossoms.

Tudor Filer-Gale (9)
Black Torrington CE Primary School, Beaworthy

Lullaby

Sleep, sleep,
Tomorrow will bring
A huge box of delicious, creamy chocolate.
Sleep, sleep,
Tomorrow will bring
A really full belly.
Sleep, sleep,
Tomorrow will bring
Delicious food from cooking club.
Sleep, sleep,
Tomorrow will bring
A tremendous diamond ring.
Sleep, sleep,
Tomorrow will bring
A colossal, elegant, multicoloured flower.
Sleep, sleep,
Tomorrow will bring
A humungous house bought by my mum and dad.

Kristal Braund (8)
Black Torrington CE Primary School, Beaworthy

Tongue Twisting Numbers

One orderly overtaking ox
Two tangle twisting tangerines
Three thundery thinking thumbs
Four fiddly feeling felines
Five fussily flipping fleas
Six slowly seeing snakes
Seven silently seeking salamanders
Eight adventurously ace apes
Nine neatly kneading gnats
Ten tiredly tipping tepees.

Tamsin Haywood (7)
Black Torrington CE Primary School, Beaworthy

Lullaby

Sleep, tomorrow will bring
A delicious hot fudge sundae
With sprinkles and delightful melting chocolate.

Sleep, tomorrow will bring
A pleasing day achieving in my writing.

Sleep, tomorrow will bring
A superb day doing my job every day
Morning and night.

Sleep, tomorrow will bring
Scientists working out the wave of gravity once again.

Sebastian Filer-Gale (9)
Black Torrington CE Primary School, Beaworthy

Tongue Tickling Tongue Twisters

One oddly overlooking orange
Two twinkly telephoning tangerines
Three thinly threading threads
Four fast flying frogs
Five far flying fleas
Six sadly sizzling sausages
Seven silently scraping celeries
Eight avariciously adventuring apes
Nine neatly kneading needles
Ten tightly tying TVs.

Jared Duff (8)
Black Torrington CE Primary School, Beaworthy

Loopy Miss Coopey

My teacher is called Miss Coopey
I think she is rather loopy
Mornings she jumps around
She falls hard to the ground
And after school she is droopy.

Peter Braund (11)
Black Torrington CE Primary School, Beaworthy

Happy Christmas, Ho, Ho

H appy Christmas, ho, ho
A nd Happy New Year
P ieces of pie smelling like blueberries
P resents and gifts wrapped in paper
Y ippee!

C razy children rolling in the snow
H ooray!
R eindeer with antlers like a tree
I t's Christmas Day once again
S leighs being pulled
T riggers and buttons on cars and planes
M assive snowmen being blown down
A cosy, warm home to come to
S nowball fights are making people go crazy

H urray for Christmas
O h yeah!

H ooray for Christmas
O h yeah!

Daniel Iggulden (8)
Blisland CP School, Bodmin

The Raven

T hick and sharp claws like a chisel,
H allowe'en spooky that makes me feel weird,
E verlasting bird prints in the window.

R aven affects like a boomerang,
A nnoying and squeaky like a mouse,
V ery spooky like falling through a trapdoor,
E verlasting effects that spook people out,
N ot good luck, unlike winning a football match.

Jonty Colman (8)
Blisland CP School, Bodmin

Hands To The Future

I see hands to the future,
Hands that hold a key,
Hands that hold the answers,
The answers for you and me.

The key fits to a trunk,
A trunk so secret to be,
A trunk that holds the answers,
The answers to you and me.

I turn the key lightly,
I hear the clunk, clunk,
I then open fearfully,
The old trunk, trunk, trunk.

It opens very slowly,
Dust flutters out,
Then I hear behind me,
My mother shout, shout, shout.

I realise where I am,
Back in my own room,
My little brother screaming,
Acting like a baboon.

'Alice, come lay the table.'
'Coming Mum, coming!'
I race down the stairway,
My sister's music humming.

I wish I knew what that trunk held,
Those hands as well holding the key,
But all I see from now on,
Are the secrets to you and me!

Eden Phillips (10)
Blisland CP School, Bodmin

Screaming

Go to the house,
Walk up the stair,
Trudge through the courtyard,
Thistles in your hair.

In the graveyard,
You hear a shout,
Turn to the tombstone,
A ghost's coming out.

You fall in a pit,
So deep you can't see,
The bottom of it,
And you find a tree.

The tree holds a key,
To get out of this dream,
Reach up and get it,
But don't forget to scream.

Deanna Pengelly (10)
Blisland CP School, Bodmin

The House Of Doom

There I was standing in my living room doorway sipping tea
Suddenly there came a tapping from my window afar
I went to the old window expecting to see a tree
Then a blackbird flew into my living room
It fluttered like a butterfly
And was as dark as night
The bird sat upon my chair and stared at me
It made me feel scared

I told it to fly away but all it did was fly to another chair
It opened its beak and I heard it laugh
Then it flew out of my window
Never to be seen again!

Oliver Brotherhood (10)
Blisland CP School, Bodmin

I Walked Along

I walked along the street one day
Along a beach and a sandy bay
When I saw something square and big
It might have actually been wearing a wig
I am tiny, wincy and small
It is gigantic, ginormous and tall
And now I really don't know what to do
I now have started to need the loo
I asked this thing if it would tell me its name
It said, 'Yes, if we play a good game'
We played a game of monstrous dodge ball
But all the giant did was jump and fall
I started on the long way home
Then the giant just wailed and moaned
It had no friends, unlike me
I then sat and stared at a bee
A bit later I came back
To hear something go *quack, quack, quack*
The giant had found a new friend, it was a duck!
Oh, what such great luck
Now I don't feel that bad
That the giant is not sad.

Ellie Parsons (7)
Bolham Primary School, Tiverton

A Funny Rhyme

There once was a princess called Sleeping Beauty,
Whose mother thought she was a bit of a cutie.
She loved eating strawberry sweets,
This made her grow up to ten feet.
Her husband, Prince Phillip, built a house,
Which made her so happy, she squeaked like a mouse!
She always wore the colour pink,
Which made the boys wink.
Her dog made a funny stink that went into the garden,
And the dog said, 'I beg your pardon!'
Sleeping Beauty came out
And picked the dog up and made him say *ouch!*
What a silly rhyme to write about.

Stephanie Symns (7)
Bolham Primary School, Tiverton

Months Of The Year

In January there is ice and snow
In February cold winds blow.

In March first daffodils peep
In April hedgehogs wake from sleep.

In May the sun starts to shine
In June crows like to whine.

In July rooks start to rest
In August seagulls are a pest.

In September birthdays come by
In October along come the flies.

In November fireworks go *bang*
In December Christmas bells clang.

Finn Cracknell (9)
Bowhill Primary School, Exeter

The River

A river is a winding snake
Twisting across the country.
It never stops like a bumblebee,
It's as elegant as a cat on a fence
Until the winter winds blow!
The river roars up like a lion
Ready to strike
And a shark chasing its prey.
When it comes to the great falls,
Like a falcon, it falls.

Emma King (10)
Bowhill Primary School, Exeter

A River

A river is a cheetah,
Long and blue.
It twists around the city and countryside
Like a long snake.
A river is a bee that never stops
Until it gets to the big, wide ocean
And does it over again.

Adam Smale (9)
Bowhill Primary School, Exeter

The Neglected House

In the cellar
There is a gory, sickening, rotting skeleton
A crooked wooden crate
A stale bowl of milk
A coarse, uneven, rocky wall
And a gloomy looking one-eyed cat
In the kitchen
There is a crooked, rocky cooker
A rotting bowl of cereal
A mouldy skeleton eating it
A gloomy, antique mirror
And a dead mouse hanging from the light
In the bathroom
There is a smashed up, mouldy bath
A rotting, old bar of soap
A snapped, mouldy nail brush
A broken non-working tap
And a brown, dirty toad.

Jordan Hayman (9)
Bowhill Primary School, Exeter

The River

The river is a wild horse,
Powerful and free.
He canters forever, never stopping,
With his powerful legs and long mane.
Hour upon hour he gallops,
The stones fly up behind him
And twigs crack behind his back.
But no one knows the true identity of the
River horse.

Laura Hardman (10)
Bowhill Primary School, Exeter

Sadness

Sadness is blue
It tastes of old crisps
It smells like an old pair of socks
It looks like people crying
And sounds like the rain hitting the ground
Sadness feels like a puddle of tears.

Laura Walton (9)
Bowhill Primary School, Exeter

Flame Of The Fire

A fire is like a roaring lion
Orange, yellow and red
He is flaming all day
With his sharp teeth and furry mane
He spreads, he spreads and spreads
The dangerous, hot fire makes a noise
Like a lion is trying to get out of his cage
Roar, roar goes the fire
Licking his flaming paws
And when the lion is hungry
Hunting its prey
Like a fire hunting where to flame next.

Jennifer Okoro (9)
Bowhill Primary School, Exeter

Months Of The Year

In January there is ice and snow
In February cold winds blow.

In March first daffodils peep
In April hedgehogs wake from sleep.

In May it is a warm place to stay
In June is when children play.

In July there is a great sky
In August the children say hi.

In September the sky gets darker
In October we get scarier.

In November the winds blow
In December it sometimes snows.

Mason Bartlett (9)
Bowhill Primary School, Exeter

The Fire

Fire is a roaring lion,
Red and orange.
It roars all day until it dies down,
With its roaring voice and rapid flames,
It's like a bat spreading its wings,
A howling dog,
Not everyone knows what fire is like.

Alysha Antat (10)
Bowhill Primary School, Exeter

A Tree

A tree is a sweet robin,
Tweeting all day long,
Racing through the wind to get her prey,
With her red breast that twinkles as she flies,
As the babies keep guard of the nest,
The sweet robin,
Tweet, tweet, tweets,
The robin catches its prey
And takes it back to her babies.

Hannah Down (10)
Bowhill Primary School, Exeter

The River

The river is like a busy bee,
Two different colours.
He's busy all the time,
With his little wings and his big, fat body.
Day upon day he's busy,
Flying by the soft banks of the river.
Buzz, buzz, buzz, buzz,
The little bumblebee says,
Collecting things as he goes along.
And when the winter comes
And the winds start to roar,
He buzzes home,
Gathering more and more things,
He *buzz, buzz, buzzes* home.

Maisie Weller (9)
Bowhill Primary School, Exeter

The Sea Water/Lightning

The sea is like a horse,
Galloping for the end of the beach,
Standing on his back two legs,
Like a wave crashing furiously on the ground.

Lightning is like a roaring cheetah,
Leaping to attack a tiny mouse,
But it's looking next to catch its prey,
So quickly, but how will you notice?

Freya Gant (10)
Bowhill Primary School, Exeter

Loneliness

Loneliness is blue.
It tastes like the salt from the tears you cry.
It smells like the bit of soggy tissue you've been drying your eyes with
For the past 20 minutes.
Loneliness looks like the horrible snigger from a bully's face,
Like he's going to get you, for you have no friends to stick up for you.
It sounds like the scream of your mum when she died,
That's why your loneliness is so dreadful.
It feels loud and sad.

Aimee Kenshole (10)
Bowhill Primary School, Exeter

The Fire Is A Herd Of Wild Horses

Fire is wild horses galloping around,
Big and red,
They gallop around all day
With their tails right up.
Hour upon hour they buck and rear.
When the rain comes they roll on the ground,
Like the sound of pebbles being scattered on the floor
And the thunder sounds like you're trying to break through a door.

Rebecca Pratt (10)
Bowhill Primary School, Exeter

Rain

Rain is a thousand twinkling stars falling from the sky.
They flicker and flutter, amazing you and I.
If it's raining and you go out, you'll need to wear a coat,
But when you get back home, you can put a glass of it right down your throat.

Daisy Saunders (10)
Bowhill Primary School, Exeter

Storm

A storm is a lion roaring in the middle of the tropical forest
And lightning is a crocodile snapping its strong jaws.
But thunder is a massive *oink* from a pig
And rain is like a cobra spitting venom.
But the storm is grey and dark like a never-ending headache.

Harry Cody (10)
Bowhill Primary School, Exeter

Happiness

Happiness is yellow
It tastes like a marshmallow
It smells like popcorn
It looks like my hamster
It sounds like birds singing
It feels like a hot, sunny day.

Charlie Lloyd-O'Keeffe (10)
Bowhill Primary School, Exeter

Happiness

Happiness is sunny yellow
It tastes like chocolate
It smells like sweet chocolates
It looks like sunshine
It sounds like laughter
It feels like the sun shining.

Charlotte Houghton (9)
Bowhill Primary School, Exeter

Bad Wind!

Wind, when it's bad, gets sent to its room
Where it thunders the floor like a bear in a cage,
Too small to even lie down.
It howls like a werewolf at midnight on Hallowe'en,
It sounds like it's about to drown.
Wind is like a lion, growling for food.
It looks like a tree, crashing to the ground.

Bethany Sluman (9)
Bowhill Primary School, Exeter

Calm

Calm is pale green.
It tastes like fresh cucumber
And smells like fir trees.
Calm looks like bamboo in China
And sounds like trickling water.
Calm feels like no cares at all.

Molly Driscoll (10)
Bowhill Primary School, Exeter

Gales

Gales are wild wolves,
Unexpected and grey,
Bounding round and howling to the moon,
Fearful and windy.
He breaks down trees,
Running round and round chasing his friends.
But on quiet days, he lies on his back
And just tickles your hair and toes.

Tess Bryant (10)
Bowhill Primary School, Exeter

Lightning

Lightning is a fast cheetah,
Fast and furious.
He flashes and crashes all day
With his charming teeth and bright colours.
Hour upon hour running wildly.
The rumbling and tumbling when the cheetah snores,
Crash, clash, crash.

Abbie Frankum (9)
Bowhill Primary School, Exeter

Bullying

Bullying is dark green
It tastes like mouldy apples
It smells of rotten cheese
And feels like a spider crawling up your leg.

Daniel Ensor (9)
Bowhill Primary School, Exeter

Sea

The sea is a jumping horse, it is strong and brown
It jumps on the sea and then gallops onto the sand
It is a furious horse that is very, very angry
It springs like a giant piece of wild fire
But slowly it falls into a sleeping motion and snores quietly.

Lewis Carrera (9)
Bowhill Primary School, Exeter

The Neglected House

In the front room
There's a gruesome, gory TV
And a disgusting, sickening sofa
There's an oily, fatty wall
A horrible, nasty table
In a cage there are phantom chinchillas.

In the bathroom
There's a half-broken mirror
And a smashed, old light
There's a bent, mouldy toothbrush
Mucky, filthy walls
And a stuffed, dead cat.

In the loft
There's a broken bed
And a web-covered skeleton
A slimy, wooden box
A bloodstained knife
And a giant rat.

Stan Clarke (9)
Bowhill Primary School, Exeter

My Image Poem

The sun is like a crispy pancake
Waiting to be thrown
Onto a plate.

The moon is like a saucer of milk
Waiting to be lapped
By a black cat.

The snow is like a million ice creams
Sitting on the ground
Getting eaten by a white rabbit.

Christopher Roast (9)
Bowhill Primary School, Exeter

Fire

Fire is rage like no other.
Fire is an artist going mad like Van Gogh.
Fire is a spitting cobra killing its prey.
Fire is a horse bucking up and down.
Fire is an angry bumblebee stinging.

Ben Martin (10)
Bowhill Primary School, Exeter

Months Of The Year

In January there is ice and snow
In February cold winds blow.

In March first daffodils peep
In April hedgehogs wake from sleep.

In May people plant seeds
In June they turn into trees.

In July people go to the beach
In August people try to sleep.

In September the flowers stop growing
In October the farmers are ploughing.

In November it is fireworks night
In December the children sleep tight.

Liam Wardle (9)
Bowhill Primary School, Exeter

Months Of The Year

In January there is ice and snow
In February cold winds blow.

In March first daffodils peep
In April hedgehogs wake from sleep.

In May children play
In June I go on holiday.

In July birds start to fly
In August Mum makes pie.

In September flowers continue to grow
In October I watch the Brownies' show.

In November the sun goes
In December it snows.

Ellie Passmore (8)
Bowhill Primary School, Exeter

Loneliness

Loneliness is navy blue,
It tastes like snails
And it smells like a sweaty sock.
It looks like a bare tree
And sounds like a million sirens.
It feels like a branding iron
Touching your skin.

Merrily Kirton (10)
Bowhill Primary School, Exeter

The Months Of The Year

In January there is ice and snow
In February cold winds blow.

In March first daffodils peep
In April hedgehogs wake from sleep.

In May birds make their nests
In June the sun shines its best.

In July everyone is on their holiday
In August people go out to play.

In September there are lots of showers
In October fields are ploughed by all the farmers.

In November it's fireworks night
In December there are Christmas lights.

Zoe Barter (8)
Bowhill Primary School, Exeter

The Months Of The Year

In January there is ice and snow
In February cold winds blow.

In March first daffodils peep
In April hedgehogs wake from sleep.

In May leaves drop
In June the rain plops.

In July the sand raises
In August the water blazes.

In September school starts
In October we do arts.

In November the snow falls
In December there is Santa Claus.

Jordan Matthews (9)
Bowhill Primary School, Exeter

Lightning

Lightning is like a zebra running along the desert,
Running as fast as it can, getting chased by a cheetah.
A zebra's stripes don't camouflage it in the trees.
Zebras running all night, playing with its zebra friends.
Lightning strikes, the zebras run until they find a shelter,
But in the summer zebras sleep comfortably all day.

Niambi Ross (10)
Bowhill Primary School, Exeter

The Months Of The Year Poem

In January there is ice and snow
In February cold winds blow.

In March first daffodils peep
In April hedgehogs wake from sleep.

In May the leaves start to blow
In June the waves start to flow.

In July everyone is on their holiday
In August people go out to play.

In September children go back to school
In October I am normally a fool.

In November it's fireworks night
In December it's not very light.

Jessica Commins (8)
Bowhill Primary School, Exeter

Love At First Sight

Love is pinky-red
And it will light up your day.
Love tastes like chocolate
Given by a boy.
It smells like roses
Out of a boy's hand.
Love is like a heart
Between each other
And it sounds like your heart
Beating wildly.
It feels like you're in Heaven.

Dalya Erdogan (9)
Bowhill Primary School, Exeter

The Moon Is Like . . .

The moon glimmers in the starlit sky
Waiting to explode
And burst into silver fireworks.

The moon is as beautiful
As an opera of the great blue whales
Singing at dawn.

The moon is like glittering cats' eyes
In the pitch-black
With rats and bats howling in the woods.

Brandon Smith (8)
Bowhill Primary School, Exeter

Months Of The Year Poem

In January there is ice and snow
In February cold winds blow.

In March first daffodils peep
In April hedgehogs wake from sleep.

In May the animals weep
In June roses come out from their sleep.

In July wasps fly
In August my mum makes a pie.

In September people sigh because summer ends
In October I go to my den.

In November it's fireworks night
In December there are Christmas lights.

Lauren Raw (9)
Bowhill Primary School, Exeter

Months Of The Year

In January there is ice and snow
In February cold winds blow.

In March first daffodils peep
In April hedgehogs wake from sleep.

In May the plants start to flower
In June the wind has power.

In July children break up for school
In August you can take a dip in a swimming pool.

In September it's Leah's birthday
In October I hear children play.

In November it's my birthday
In December it's Christmas Day.

Lucy Griffin (9)
Bowhill Primary School, Exeter

Lightning!

Lightning is like a snapping dog.
Lightning is like a loud flash of a camera.
Lightning is like a vampire.
Lightning is like death.

Ebony Davey (10)
Bowhill Primary School, Exeter

Neglected House

In the basement:
There is an old, crumbled box,
Broken, sharp basket full of clothes,
There is a deep, deep, dark hole,
There is an overflowing plastic bin,
A smashed, fogged up window
And rats running very, very fast across the basement floor.

In the garden:
The grass dried up and dead,
Broken, wet, slimy fencing,
Rusty, black car,
Frozen, muddy sandpit,
Creepy spiderwebbed tree house,
Spooky, black, bloodsucking bats hanging from the tree.

In the bathroom:
There is a broken, shattered window,
Green, smelly towels,
Stinky, revolting perfume,
Green, bogey-looking water,
Paper scattered over the floor,
Slimy, green frogs swimming in the sink.

Lilly May (8)
Bowhill Primary School, Exeter

The Months Of The Year

In January there is ice and snow
In February cold winds blow
In March first daffodils peep
In April hedgehogs wake from sleep
In May I go to the shop and pay
In June I go to the stable and hear a horse neigh
In July everybody gets their deckchairs out
In August everybody shouts
In September I do a description of me
In October I have some tea
In November the days are getting shorter
In December I have some cake but I have a quarter.

Callum Griffin (9)
Bowhill Primary School, Exeter

The Neglected House

There is a gloomy, smashed up bottle
There is a big, giant cobweb
There is a black, greasy coffin
There is a long, oily exhaust pipe
There is an old, scary toy
There is an ancient, dusty skeleton.

In the bathroom
There is a clogged up sink
There is a greasy shower
There is a mouldy, squished lump of soap
There is a muddy bath
There is a smashed up bottle of shower gel
There is an elderly, dead rat.

In the dining room
There is a chewed up old slipper
There is oily, broken furniture
There is a scratched up old sofa
There is a black, dusty, worn out telly
There is a smashed, shabby mirror
There is a dead cat.

Tom Robinson (8)
Bowhill Primary School, Exeter

The Months Of The Year

In January there is ice and snow
In February cold winds blow.

In March first daffodils peep
In April hedgehogs wake from sleep.

In May daffodils grow
In June the farmers sow.

In July it is warm and cosy
In August there is a summer posy.

In September people have a nice hot cup of tea
In October people get big stings from bees.

In November snow falls
In December someone comes called Santa Claus.

Lewis Stutt (9)
Bowhill Primary School, Exeter

Snow is Like . . .

Snow is like
A pillow
Waiting to be
Slept on at night.

Snow is like
A cloud of
Candyfloss
Waiting to be eaten.

Snow is like
A white piece
Of paper
Waiting to be written on.

Snow is like
A white wall
Waiting to be painted
A different colour.

Maxine Welch (9)
Bowhill Primary School, Exeter

Snow Is Like . . .

Snow is like
A brilliant white polar bear
Glimmering in the sun,
Like a huge diamond in front of a fire
Beaming and shining.

Snow is like
Pearls falling from the sky
Falling heavily
Like crisps being stepped on.

Snow is like
Children making angels in their imagination
They fly swiftly
Dodging birds on the way.

Bethany-May Hammond (8)
Bowhill Primary School, Exeter

A Poem About My Grandad

My grandad's like a giant but cuddly in a way,
He likes going to Lyme and walking along the bay.
His prize money is ours when he wins the show,
When I'm stuck on a question he'll say 'I know'.
If you get mud on the car he'll tell you off bad,
When it happens you get upset, very sad.
He likes to play football, scored most goals for the team,
He's retired now but still full of steam.
Onions and leaks he does grow,
When he is in the paper he really, really glows!
Every year he has a trip on a cruise,
He can get away from us and have a snooze.
When Grandma goes to France he makes a mess,
But overall . . . he is the greatest grandad!

Jack Elliott (10)
Combe St Nicholas CE Primary School, Chard

A Poem About My Dad

My daddy is Dean, he's an engineer,
I don't like it but he likes ginger beer.
When he tells me off it is crystal clear,
But deep down inside, to me he is dear.
Dad gets up for breakfast, the dog goes berserk,
Then after that he gets ready for work.
He calls up from downstairs to say goodbye,
He goes out the front door, I want to cry.
The day has just started, now it's my turn,
Get dressed, have breakfast and prepare to learn.
The day has just ended and Dad gets home,
He undoes his hair, no need for a comb!
He helps with my homework, now time for bed,
I love my daddy, as much as my ted.

Maya Bruce (11)
Combe St Nicholas CE Primary School, Chard

A Poem About My Grandpa

I know an old man, my grandpa
He is the funniest man I know.
He's a whizz at fixing metal!
My grandpa is the best blacksmith around,
Our house, drive and lane is full of his work,
From candle holders to metal flowers,
He can also fix the broken showers.
He can make up poems and rhymes on the spot,
He's not that friendly with horses (trot, trot).
He does this special breakfast, I love it,
Crusties he calls them, with Marmite and jam.
He also does this potato mash mash.
He always make me laugh, I love him so,
He's the best grandpa in the world, don't go.

Meg Lawrence (11)
Combe St Nicholas CE Primary School, Chard

A Poem About My Dad

My dad, he's a really cool geezer,
His feet are the factor of a smelly old cheese.
He walks into school with unshaven beard,
But then he dances really cool, but weird.
When it's time for bed, he's still out working,
I love him so much, I'm happy and chirping.
Some days he will go singing with bongo,
He likes lots of juice, his favourite is mango.
Dad is the smartest, he is a great artist,
His dogs are probably the largest I know,
He cheers you up when you're feeling low.
My daddy likes a band called Dragens Fly,
Probably his favourite bread is rye.

Yola Gonzalez (10)
Combe St Nicholas CE Primary School, Chard

A Poem About My Mum

My mum's called Ginni, she wears a pinny
She likes making up loads of recipes
She's a qualified chef, she's got a friend called Beth
She is at that old age of thirty-six
She likes making loads of ginger biscuits
She runs round like a busy buzzing bee
Mum runs around looking after us three
She likes drawing and is always roaring
She likes watching soaps but never can cope
Her bad habit is eating chocolate
Her most favourite sport is netball, cool
She is everyone's karaoke queen
So she is my mummy who is called Ginni
That lady that always wears a pinny.

Chloe Addison (11)
Combe St Nicholas CE Primary School, Chard

A Poem About Chris

My friend's name is Chris, he is so much fun,
He likes playing football and scoring goals.
He also likes biting the skin around his nails,
My friend Christopher likes to collect snails.
When he is having fun he eats a bun,
In his garden he keeps a pet called Mole.
He likes watching telly and PS2,
When Chris went to school he drew an igloo!
When Chris came to Combe he brushed with a broom,
When he came home he had seen a new moon.
When he is sick he wants to come to school,
Because he loves his work and football.
When he came back to school he looked so cool,
Then he played a trick - April fools.

Kyle Anderson (8)
Combe St Nicholas CE Primary School, Chard

A Poem About My Sister

My sis likes drama, singing and dancing,
She likes music and plays the piano.
It's a miracle when she is listening.
But a good thing, she helps other people.
She likes to skip and cook at the same time.
Some gymnastics she does are exciting!
With her pointed toes and strength in her arms,
In a way she is my great lucky charm.
In her ballet lesson she dances with grace,
She scoffs down her food when we have pancakes.
She doesn't really like to have a race.
She has really long, beautiful brown hair,
When she is singing, it isn't rare.
What a good thing she's my little sister.

Benjamin Johnson (10)
Combe St Nicholas CE Primary School, Chard

The Phantoms' Eclipse

I have a story
Might be legend or true
But it's one I must share with you.

In a town, an ordinary town
An eclipse appeared in the sky
But I swore I heard someone shout, 'Fly phantoms, fly.'

I ran through the woods
But the phantoms were too fast
Although they flew as high as a ship's mast.

So I sprinted through the wilderness
But I could not get past
The trees were too tall and vast.

I saw a light in the distance
But it was too far
I could not see the phantoms because they were the colour of tar.

I did not know what happened
Maybe a curse was on the town
I heard someone say the people will drown.

So this is it
My story has ended at last
But I will not forget my horrible past.

Stephen Bush (9)
Coxley Primary School, Wells

Cheerful Days

When I smile
My eyes are bright
The sun shines
Like a yellow light

Laughing and giggling
All day long
Merrily singing
A happy song

Jumping and skipping
Around and around
Children's chatter
Makes a happy sound

When everybody's happy
The world's a better place
So forget all your worries
And put a smile on your face.

Kirsty Densley (9)
Coxley Primary School, Wells

Happiness

When I'm in my garden
Feeling very blue
I memorise my feelings
That seems very new.

The thing I'm going to write about
On this cold spring morning
Is the springtime happiness
That lasts right through May.

When you hear a whistle
At the garden gate
I guess it's the postman
Running late.

My dream might come true
Even though it's new
As long as you can smile
I can laugh with you.

Rachel Churches (10)
Coxley Primary School, Wells

Love

As I stand in my room
And I feel like doom
I think about love
How it makes people smile
With its secret dial.

Just imagine the kiss
That you miss
And the magical laughter that it brings
With its whispers of dreams.

When that day comes, the 14th of Feb
It brings people together to show how much others desire them
Others will give cards and gifts
To show their love and affection.

Love!

Lily Kidner (11)
Coxley Primary School, Wells

Wiggling And Giggling

Tickles in your tummy
Like swallowing honey
You laugh so much, you feel everything's funny

Bobbing up and down
Listening to sound
Laughter has no limited bounds

Laughing, giggling,
Rolling, wiggling
Happy sounds mingling

Happiness flows
Giggling grows
Tittering where everyone knows

Tingles down your spine
Life feels fine
My laughter is mine.

Devina Walker (9)
Coxley Primary School, Wells

Nervous

Biting my lip
Waiting in line
My non-stop fidgeting
It's nearly time

Butterflies in my tummy
Kissing goodbye to my mummy
Pulling my hair
Taking great care

My teeth are chattering
A tingle down my spine
Trembled all day
I hope I do fine.

Joelle Henstridge (10)
Coxley Primary School, Wells

Love

Love doves in the air
Someone is kissing over there
Love birds are twittering in the blue sky
Love feels like a butterfly
But sometimes love can break your heart
The boys can leave you in the dark.

Daisy Andrews (10)
Coxley Primary School, Wells

Laughter

The bees fly over the trees
The fleas like to climb my knees
The birds fly over Devon
A boy is almost seven
Someone drinks wine
When they're only nine
When your mum giggles
A worm wiggles
School is very boring
My dad loves snoring
I love eating Mars bars
A spaceman fell off Mars.

Owen Ricketts (8)
Coxley Primary School, Wells

Sickness

You feel your brain curl,
Then you might want to hurl,
You don't know what to do,
Suddenly you need to go to the loo.

Your head feels dizzy,
Your tummy is fizzy,
You feel you're going to faint,
In a load of paint.

Your mother said,
You'd better go to bed,
If you feel better,
You might get a letter.

If you feel worse,
You might need a nurse,
If you've got spots,
You might have polka dots.

Rachel Best (8)
Coxley Primary School, Wells

Fear

My face is pale with fear,
I feel a running tear,
Funny feelings in my tummy,
I sure do want my mummy,
There are weird noises in the cellar,
They're cooking pizza, *mmmm* mozzarella.

The key is jammed in the door,
I can't get it out, my hands are sore,
The boiler's on, it's very hot,
I think I'm stuck on the spot.

My mum's shouting, 'It's dinner time,'
I am stuck, there's nowhere to climb,
I'm panting and puffing saying,
'Mum, I'm in the cellar,
That means no mozzarella.'

Natalie Hill (10)
Coxley Primary School, Wells

Nightmare

Ghostly trees looking like skeletons
Strange sounds all around me
Hoping I won't get caught
Getting more scared every step I take.
Trying to hide from that monstrous creature
That lurks in the night
With nowhere to go.
I can just about work out
The beast that haunts me every night
People looking out their windows
Hoping they will help me.
I am the predator's prey.

William Patten (9)
East Coker Primary School, Yeovil

Midnight In The Garden

The moon illuminates the cat
He has spotted his prey, a white mouse
Unexpectedly being watched by the predator
Licking his lips and sharpening his claws
The cat jumps up onto the hedge and then onto the tree
Jumping from branch to branch, keeping the prey in sight
Suddenly, the branch breaks, the cat lands cleanly on its feet
The prey has spotted the predator
The cat pounces, but misses
The mouse has got away.

Robert Trickey (11)
East Coker Primary School, Yeovil

Hunger

I camouflaged myself in the deep grass
Silently sneaking behind my prey.
It looked left, it looked right
But I stayed out of the mouse's sight.
I waited until he got closer to me
Then I leapt from the floor, aiming for my prey.
Unfortunately for me, it ran away
I crawled back home thinking, *no food for me today.*

Callum Cooper (9)
East Coker Primary School, Yeovil

The Hunter

The hunter creeps silently,
Prowling, growling,
His tail slides through the undergrowth,
He jumps onto the high wall,
He scans his victim,
Owls warn in the distance,
Danger is all around,
Eyes like emeralds illuminate the night,
He cautiously slides across the high wall,
He pounces and grabs his victim,
The prey is caught.
He walks elegantly back through the grass,
Who will be his next victim?

Sophie Extance (11)
East Coker Primary School, Yeovil

Night-Time Cat

She moves swiftly through the long grass,
Her soft, smooth body slides across the ground.
The moonlight shines down on her slim figure,
Her sapphire eyes glisten under the stars.
The claws are out of her paws and her ears are alert,
Everything is quiet - all you can hear is the swaying of the trees.
Suddenly, she leaps into the air to catch her prey,
The victim is dead and the cat has won the battle.

Laura Nitti (10)
East Coker Primary School, Yeovil

The Beast

The beast in the jungle grass,
The trees talking in the wind,
The grass moving.
Eyes like rubies, locked onto its prey,
Tail slipping along the muddy ground.
Pouncing, stealing the creature's life.
Suddenly, the air's silence is broken.
Dropping its prey, the beast leaps from the ground.
In a stealthy position, it moves through the grass.
Trees, now like fierce blades in the roaring wind,
Shadows stealing the beast's presence,
Eyes pierce the murky darkness.

Jake Firstbrook (10)
East Coker Primary School, Yeovil

Night

Crawling through the jungle,
The predator watching its prey,
Eyes like diamonds,
Tail dragging along the floor,
Never to be seen.
The prey not knowing what's going on.
An owl hooting in the distance,
Trying to warn all around.
Is the prey moving?
He'd better get to safe land.
The predator about to strike,
Pounces on his victim.
Does he get away?
Will he survive another day?

Sophie Chappell (10)
East Coker Primary School, Yeovil

Gloomy Night

As the sun goes down
The beast approaches
The trees looking like ghosts
He gracefully jumps from branch to branch
The predator has spotted its prey
Quietly the beast leaps
Landing with a thump on the ground
The prey does not know what's going on
The beast down on its tummy, not making any sound
Suddenly the beast pounces, but the prey is too fast
The beast walks dejectedly back to his lair with an empty stomach.

Zoe Durnan-Steer (11)
East Coker Primary School, Yeovil

Jungle Cat

Dark clouds pass the glowing moon
I run through the jungle, tail very low
I see my prey, a little mouse
I roar like a lion, breaking the silence of the night
I feel a drop of water on my outstretched paw
A flash of lightning illuminates my prey
Stalking him, I creep closer and closer, then pounce
Stealing his life, I grab him
Running back to my lair in victory.

Annabelle Rashley (11)
East Coker Primary School, Yeovil

Predator

In the moonlight,
The predator creeps,
Creeps towards the ebony shadows,
In search of its prey.
Looking with his fierce eyes,
Which glow like stars in the wondrous sky,
Listening to the sounds of the moonlit jungle.
His nervous heart beats furiously,
As he searches for the prey that is his.
Hoot goes the owl,
Warning the land to hide,
Hide from the demon that strikes
In the pitch-black world that is night.
With a deadly swipe, he catches his prey,
Dangling from his mouth,
He proudly takes it back to his lair.

Ellie Dunning (11)
East Coker Primary School, Yeovil

In The Mighty Jungle

The lion crept up slowly,
I saw him coming,
Coming closer.
He jumped,
I ran,
Bang!
The lion hit the floor,
I got away this time,
I might not be so lucky
Next time.

Erica Chambers (11)
East Coker Primary School, Yeovil

The Beast

It peers through the shadows at night
Trees still as a rock
While stalking its prey
The prey swims as fast as it can
But the beast is still too close
Suddenly, when the fish thinks the cat's gone . . .
In dives the vicious killer, eliminating its prey,
Before crawling back to its lair.

Tom Green (10)
East Coker Primary School, Yeovil

The Deep, Dark Night

Dark, glowing eyes far ahead peering over the wall
The sound of swaying trees gently calling
The predator has to watch and wait
He can't make a sound
The prey looks like a ghostly monster against the wall
The mouse moves
The cat wiggles its body quickly before it jumps
But the prey hears a loud bark, warning the little mouse
It doesn't work
The cat leaps, catching its prey
The beastly cat scuttles home to show his owner his prize catch.

Hannah Dunston (10)
East Coker Primary School, Yeovil

Concrete Jungle

Darker and darker the night grew.
The beast crept out to play, it spotted its prey.
The lonely tiger had nowhere to run in his concrete jungle.
As the wild beast leapt from roof to roof,
The tiger's eyes lit up like stars, showing fear.
The chase was on between good and bad.
The beastly animal grew smaller as light grew stronger.
He could sense the presence of light.
He fled back to his lair,
Where he could remain safe until dusk,
When he could become king again.

Jordan Smith (10)
East Coker Primary School, Yeovil

Ruby Eyes

I looked out of my window
I opened it, all I could hear was the ghostly tree whistling
Out of the corner of my eye
I saw something - ruby eyes
Staring at me
It was on its belly
With its tail swaying from side to side
Watching, waiting
A mouse jumped out of the bush
The cat leapt
Bang!
The mouse was dead.

Paige Hext (11)
East Coker Primary School, Yeovil

69

The Cat At Night

The cat comes out of its lair
Into the big jungle
It peers through the dark
You see the shadow
Stalking through the grass
Now and then you hear a rustle
Which the prey does not hear
The prey looks round
The cat is nowhere to be seen
He is as still as a rock
The prey does not know it's being watched
You can hear the birds
They are calling a warning
But it does not take any notice
Suddenly the cat jumps out
Catching its victim
It brings it back to its lair
A winner.

Tegan Williams (11)
East Coker Primary School, Yeovil

The Haunted Night

As the night sets
The mice come out to play.
Big eyes beam at his prey, the beast perches in the silent tree
Watching over the forest-like garden.
Suddenly, the monster's eyes lock on to a mouse -
Watching its movements.
The mouse is unaware of the danger
The predator swoops from above
Not taking his eyes off the mouse.
He gets to maximum height and swoops like a kestrel
Finishing off the mouse.

Samuel Smith (9)
East Coker Primary School, Yeovil

The Feast

I slowly crept through the forest,
I caught a glimpse of a mouse,
My eyes were like splitting diamonds staring at my prey.
I never took my eyes off it,
My belly touched the floor,
Just waiting, waiting till my prey got closer.
It slowly came to me,
My tummy was tingling,
It saw me!
I chased it,
I was still ready to pounce,
I got close enough,
I jumped, I caught it,
The end of his life, but a great feast for me.

Alistair Dewfall (9)
East Coker Primary School, Yeovil

The Gloomy Night

The light flashed as the beast approached,
My heart pounded,
The glowing eyes of the beast widened,
I heard owls hooting,
Wolves howling, saying danger was coming,
The trees swayed side to side,
As the beast lowered its body,
It had found its prey,
I knew I was in danger.
The beast pounced!
It missed.
I had escaped.
The beast's eyes darkened,
As it crept fiercely
Back into the forest.

Maia White (9)
East Coker Primary School, Yeovil

My Prey

I crept out of the cat flap,
Saw a mouse at the end of the garden.
Silently I climbed a tree,
Never taking my eyes off my prey.
I was ready to pounce.
I did - and missed!
My prey had a chance to escape.
I chased it,
Sprinted like a cheetah,
Caught up with the mouse.
I jumped and caught my prey.
It was the end of his life,
But a feast for me.

Charlie Gamble (9)
East Coker Primary School, Yeovil

Monster At Night

As the beast creeps forward without a sound,
Moonlight shines down on its prey.
The cat watches, crawling around,
Like a tiger ready to pounce.
The mouse runs backwards into the forest of grass,
The predator follows into the jungle and drags its tail along the ground.
The cat is a monster ready to pounce,
The mouse is in danger, but does not know it.
Suddenly the beast spies his chance and pounces.
The mouse looks up and sees the paw slicing through the air.
The predator has it caught.
Now the monster's stomach is full,
He crawls back into his cave.

Emily White (10)
East Coker Primary School, Yeovil

Brownies

B rownies are fun,
R un and run all around,
O ur Brownie pack likes to sing,
W e love art and crafts,
N ever-ending fun,
I love Brownies,
E very Brownie should do a good turn every day,
S nowy Owl sometimes plays games with us.

Shannon Brown (8)
Eggbuckland Vale Primary School, Plymouth

Little, Little Collection

Little, little baby bat,
How I wonder what you're at,
Sleeping on a tiny, little mat.
Breathes in and out again,
Little, little baby bat,
Meeting a little baby cat.

Little, little baby cat,
How I wonder what you're at.
Chasing a little tiny mouse,
Catch it but it runs away.
Little, little baby cat,
Had no breakfast, had no tea.

Little, little tiny star,
How I wonder what you are.
How big are you I wonder?
Very big or very small?
Little, little tiny star,
Twinkling like a diamond gem.

Nicest, nicest my best friends,
Kindest people in the world.

Moeko Takane (11)
Eggbuckland Vale Primary School, Plymouth

If I Had A Cat

If I had a cat
He would be black
With a long, shiny tail.
I would call him Fred
And he would lie down on my bed
And sleep
Until it was time
To be fed.

Adam Thomas (8)
Eggbuckland Vale Primary School, Plymouth

Dragon In The Classroom

D angerous teeth and deadly roar
R un in through our classroom door
A ngry dragon trying to bite
G irls and boys trying to fight
O nly the teacher trying to shout
N ow the dragon walks out.

Emma Swain (9)
Eggbuckland Vale Primary School, Plymouth

Seasons

I like seasons because . . .

In winter you could have a snowball fight
Or get a present from Santa Claus,
But . . .

In spring you could see a natural world
Or you could see a chick cracking its egg,
But . . .

In summer you could see lovely green leaves
Or you could eat an ice cream,
But . . .

In autumn there are harvest festivals
And you could see red, yellow, orange and gold leaves,
But . . .

I like seasons because I could see a change in different seasons,
But . . .
I would say keep the natural world going forever!

Yuiko Takane (8)
Eggbuckland Vale Primary School, Plymouth

Little Stars

Little stars shine at night,
Little stars shine so bright,
Cover the whole sky with glitter,
Little stars sing and dance
Round and round, side to side,
When morning comes they hide away,
But when night comes back,
They put a smile on my face.

Holly Webb (8)
Eggbuckland Vale Primary School, Plymouth

Traffic

Beep! Beep!
Goes the massive horn
On the huge American truck.

Zooming motorbike
Goes whizzing by.

Zoom! Zoom!
Gliding aeroplanes
And their roaring engines.

Daniel Unsworth (8)
Eggbuckland Vale Primary School, Plymouth

My First Dream

My first dream was a special dream
A dream I'll never forget
I know what you think - a dream is a dream
But that's not all that it is
A dream is magical
It's better than the stars in the sky
Better than the beaming sun
Even better than the silky ocean
It's almost real
You don't have to be asleep to have a dream
You can have a special dream
A future for yourself
A lot of people's dreams come true
But a lot don't come true
We all love dreams
But there's one thing we all hate about dreams
Losing one
There's one thing that everyone in the world wants -
A dream.

Toni Lawrence (10)
Eggbuckland Vale Primary School, Plymouth

The Bunny

In my hidey-hole I stay,
Where all my worries fly away.
When I am out at night,
I see aeroplanes in flight.
Hopping, bouncing everywhere,
Hopping, bouncing without a care.
I like things that are funny,
Who am I? I am the bunny.

Nicole Rae (8)
Eggbuckland Vale Primary School, Plymouth

Sweets

Sweets are yummy,
They treat my tummy.
Sweets are sour and sweet,
They are perfect and neat.
Sweets are delicious,
They are nutritious.
Sweets are chewy and crunchy,
But best of all, they are lovely and munchy.

Natasha Stables (11)
Eggbuckland Vale Primary School, Plymouth

Horse

Yawn, yawn
Goes the furry horse
Clip-clop
Goes the friendly horse
Gallop, gallop
The rider goes faster and faster
Munch, munch
The horse eating its food
Neigh, neigh
Says the horse when it gets washed
Swish, swish
The horse's small tail goes
Bump, bump
Goes the horse trotting.

Lauren Street (8)
Eggbuckland Vale Primary School, Plymouth

Traffic

Blasting, zooming
The shiny planes are insane
Whooshing, gliding
It's trying to kill my brain
Beep, beep
Goes the traffic
Skidding, skidding
The powerful motorbike goes by
Running, drifting
Children stop and stare.

Tyler Mace (8)
Eggbuckland Vale Primary School, Plymouth

This Is My Family

There was a boy with black hair
And he was eating a very green pear.
The girl had a blue balloon,
Her friend said she would be there soon.
My dad was watching 'Who Wants To Be A Millionaire?'
While I was shouting, 'It's not fair!'
Mum was cooking my tea,
While I was not happy.
This is my family.

Charlotte Orr (9)
Eggbuckland Vale Primary School, Plymouth

My Afternoon

The sun was shining bright
A dog jumped up and gave me a fright
My mum cuddled me and said,
'I won't shout or put you to bed.

How would you like to go to the beach?'
I said, 'Yes please,' and it took half an hour to reach
I had a good afternoon in the sea
Before we came home and had tea.

Charlotte Allman (8)
Eggbuckland Vale Primary School, Plymouth

Holidays

H olidays are fun
O utside in the sun
L ots of people playing games
I n the park and swimming pool
D oing diving and running around
A lways playing all around
Y ou will always have fun
S eeing people making friends.

Keiran Patton (9)
Eggbuckland Vale Primary School, Plymouth

Fish

Fish are slimy,
Fish are wet,
Fish, you can catch them in a net.
You can keep them as a pet,
If they get ill you take them to the vet.
You put them in a bowl,
Swimming is their goal.

Celyn French (10)
Eggbuckland Vale Primary School, Plymouth

Spring Song

On the grassy banks
Lambkins at their pranks
Woolly sisters, woolly brothers
Jumping off their feet
While their woolly mothers
Watch them and bleat.

Tara Wells-McCulloch (9)
Eggbuckland Vale Primary School, Plymouth

Earth Song
(In the style of Dann Matt George)

Radiance of the rainbow
Freshness of the water
Waves of the deep blue sea
Give life to me

Rustling of the bushes
The blazing light of the sun
The torch from the moon
Give life to me

The starry night sky
Orange from the sunset
The galloping of the horse
Give life to me

Tapping of the waterfall
Sparks of the fire
The bang of the thunder
Give joy to me.

Samuel Buckley (9)
Eggbuckland Vale Primary School, Plymouth

And My Heart Cries With Joy
(Inspired by 'And My Heart Soars' by Chief Dan George)

The brightness of the sunrise,
The colours of the rainbow,
The radiance of the moonbeam,
    Shine to me.

The bud of the blossom,
The crunch of the leaves,
The scent of the roses,
    Shine to me.

The shiver of the ice,
The rush of the waterfall,
The yelp of the newborn animals,
    Shine to me.

The crash of lightning,
The warmth of fire,
The flaming colours of the sunset,
    Shine to me
    And my heart cries with joy.

Alice Bowden (9)
Eggbuckland Vale Primary School, Plymouth

And My Heart Blooms
(Inspired by 'And My Heart Soars' by Chief Dan George)

The beauty of the butterfly,
The scent of the waterfall,
The brightness in the stars,
    Sing to me.
The swaying of the snowflake,
The glamour of the deer,
The cleverness of the dolphin,
    Sing to me.
The strength of the eagle,
The gracefulness of the swan,
The shimmer of rain,
    Sing to me.
The love in the rainbow,
The colours of the sunset,
The fluffiness of the clouds,
And the life never goes away,
    They sing to me,
    And my heart blooms.

Jessica Owen (8)
Eggbuckland Vale Primary School, Plymouth

And My Heart Sings
(Inspired by 'And My Heart Soars' by Chief Dan George)

The exquisite deer,
The fluffy clouds,
The lovely leaves,
    Come to me.

The trotting horses,
The smooth streams,
The quick dragonfly,
    Come to me.

The elegant dolphin,
The glamorous whale,
The gorgeous coral,
    Come to me.

The splendid waterfalls,
The soft snow,
The melting snowflake
And the life that never goes away,
    Come to me
    And my heart sings.

Jordan Louise Watts (8)
Eggbuckland Vale Primary School, Plymouth

And My Heart Smiles

(Inspired by 'And My Heart Soars' by Chief Dan George)

The petal of the daisy
The patterns of the snowflake
The drizzle of the rain
  Shine to me!

The scent of the trees
The colours of the rainbow
The redness of the robin
  Shine to me!

The cheep of the blackbird
The twinkle of the stars
The greenness of the hills
  Shine to me!

The blowing of the breeze
The oldness of stone
The trickle of streams
And the life that never goes away
They shine to me
And my heart smiles!

Lauren Crawford (9)
Eggbuckland Vale Primary School, Plymouth

And My Heart Shines

(Inspired by 'And My Heart Soars' by Chief Dan George)

The elegance of the dolphin
The shine of the rivers
The singing of the birds
The roaring of the lions
The coldness of the frost
  Shine to me
The lightness of the moonlight
The smoothness of the pebbles
The brightness of the sun
The whiteness of the snow
The colours of the rainbow
The gracefulness of the butterfly
And the life that never goes away
  They shine to me.

Danielle Glover (9)
Eggbuckland Vale Primary School, Plymouth

And My Heart Smiles
(Inspired by 'And My Heart Soars' by Chief Dan George)

The colours of the rainbow
The amazement of the stars
The brightness of the sunset
    Shine to me

The fluffiness of the clouds
The gleaming of the stars
The darkness of the midnight sky
    Shine to me

The sound of the waterfall
The clatter of the pebbles
The swaying of the breeze
    Shine to me

The kindness of the dolphin
The softness of the lamb
The beauty of the deer
And the life that never goes away
    They shine to me
    And my heart smiles.

Marnie Dimmick (8)
Eggbuckland Vale Primary School, Plymouth

And My Heart Smiles
(Inspired by 'And My Heart Soars' by Chief Dan George)

The yellowness of the sunrise
The orange of the sunset
The colours of the rainbow
    Sing to me

The splash of the dolphin
The patter of the rain
The cotton of the cloud
    Sing to me

The speed of the waterfall
The swaying of the snowflake
The redness of the leaf
    Sing to me

The whiteness of the swan
The sound of the bluebird
The glitter of the stars
    Sing to me
    And my heart smiles.

Paul Manuel (8)
Eggbuckland Vale Primary School, Plymouth

And My Heart Cries With Joy
(Inspired by 'And My Heart Soars' by Chief Dan George)

The radiance of the sunset
The victory of the newborn
The magnificence of the sea
Shine to me

The glittering moon
The chill of the waterfall
The scent of the flowers
Shine to me

The small grains of the sandy beach
The soft cover of a pebble
The gracefulness of a swan
Shine to me

The candyfloss clouds
The detail on the shells
The cool breeze of the air
They shine to me
And my heart cries with joy.

Katie Martin (9)
Eggbuckland Vale Primary School, Plymouth

And My Heart Flies
(Inspired by 'And My Heart Soars' by Chief Dan George)

The magnificence of the volcano
The twinkle of the eye
The darkness of the moonlit sky
Understand me

The elegance of the snowflake
The radiance of the stars
The sparkle of the smile
Understand me

The colours of the sunset
The swishing of the sea
The splashing of the dolphin
Understand me

The galloping of the horse
The drift of the eagle
The grace of the swan
And the life that never goes away
And my heart flies.

Sarah Quirk (8)
Eggbuckland Vale Primary School, Plymouth

My Grandad

My grandad was funny
My grandad was nice
My grandad loved potatoes
But didn't like rice.
He used to pick me up from school
And take me home for tea
Then we'd all sit down
While Nanny made a pot of tea for three.
He used to take me to the park
And I played on the slide
Sometimes he took me in the car
And we'd go for a ride.
Grandad's up in Heaven now
So Nanny's on her own
But we all look after her
And make sure she's not alone.
Although I miss Grandad very much
One thing I know is true
He's looking down
On me and you.
So, Grandad I will make you proud
In everything I do
Because one thing that will never change
Is how much I love you.

Laura Williams (8)
Goosewell Primary School, Plymouth

The Flower

The flower sits so pretty
Upon the window box
Not sure where it came from
Perhaps it's a fairy's locks.

So lonely, yet not alone
And she doesn't make me sneeze
Swaying back and forth
Within the gentle breeze.

Her colour is as yellow
As the early morning sun
Her petals are as delicate
As a rabbit on the run.

I hope she's here forever
But fear it's a moment's stay
So I wish with all my power
For a fairy, please, I pray.

Sarah Tunley (9)
Goosewell Primary School, Plymouth

Match Day

It's the weekend
And I feel glad
Because I go to football
With my dad.

I watch Plymouth Argyle
It's a special treat
I'm really excited
As I take my seat.

The players are on the pitch
As they're practising for the game
I am really happy
And my dad feels the same.

It's not a league game
It's the FA Cup
The crowd going crazy
As Argyle go one-nil up.

The other team did a tackle
It was very, very hard
The ref had no choice
But to get out his yellow card.

The ref blows his whistle
To say it's half-time
As we're one-nil up
And I feel fine.

The second half begins
As the players run out
The crowd go mad
And they start to shout.

Argyle score again
Now they're two-nil up
I am really happy
I start to throw my hands up.

The ref blows his whistle
Because it's the end of the game
I am really pleased
And my dad feels the same.

Alex Hulbert (9)
Goosewell Primary School, Plymouth

What Would You Do?

If you had a penny, lad, what would you buy?
Since I haven't any penny, Mum, I can but cry.
If you had two pennies, lad, what would you do?
As I haven't got two pennies, Mum, I can't tell you.
If you had three pennies, lad, what then lad?
I haven't got three pennies, Mum, and I'm just sad.
Lad, here's a penny, and two pennies too -
And three pennies beside it - now what will you do?
I'll buy me a currant bun with sugar on top -
I'll buy me a white mouse to skip and to hop -
I'll buy me a kite, Mum, to fly in the sky,
I'll thank you and thank you and bid you goodbye!

Daniel Broom (8)
Goosewell Primary School, Plymouth

Ballet

Ballet is a wonderful thing
Where you dance and have fun.
It's very hard, but it can be done
All day long.

I turn, I jump, I point my toes
And bring my hands in front.
Sometimes I dance with my friends
And sometimes on my own.

Ballet is good for exercise
It isn't only fun,
I love to dance and jump about
Especially in front of Mum!

Sophie Maries (9)
Goosewell Primary School, Plymouth

My Best Friend

He's big and black with a bony back,
He's got a wet nose and claws for toes,
He sleeps all day when I want to play,
He's very old and does what he's told,
He eats his food in one minute flat,
I think that's why he's getting fat,
He likes to walk and doesn't talk,
He's not a boy or a frog,
My best friend is a *dog!*

Tom Day (8)
Goosewell Primary School, Plymouth

Swimming Race

As I dive in
The water hits my head
Suddenly I think I am dead
Oh no, I'm not
Sorry, I cannot stop
I'm in a swimming race
With my heart beating
At a very fast pace
All I can hear
Is me as I pound
And my arms
Flip-flapping around
Soon I can see
The end of the pool
And the winner
Looking cool.

Sally Moss (8)
Goosewell Primary School, Plymouth

Shoot Out Card Poem

Football cards are great
I swap them with my mate
To buy six it is thirty-five pence
For goalies, midfield, strikers and defence
I have to be good to get a pack
Sadly, swaps I have a stack
I think Fletcher and Rooney are the best
But hopefully I will get the rest
Mum won't let me take them to school
Still, I think shoot out cards are cool.

Oliver Pile (8)
Goosewell Primary School, Plymouth

The Silly Young Man

There was a young man from Rangoon
Who behaved like a silly baboon
He put on a black cape
And ran round like an ape
And was laughed at from midnight till noon.

Sean Lethbridge (9)
Goosewell Primary School, Plymouth

Around The World In 80 Days

I'm getting ready for a journey around the world,
The greatest record ever held.
It all started with a dash,
As I rolled down the path.
First to France. Bonjour! Bonjour!
Home of dancing girls galore.
Next on to Spain, paella again,
Huge sunny villa with rooms for games.
Now to Italy and on to Greece,
Where the ancients didn't live in peace.
Over to the USA I go,
Where sometimes the weather is 15 below.
Moving south to Cuba, Jamaica and Mexico,
Where they trade in fruit and cocoa.
Welcome to Brazil,
A country of football and carnival.
Now to Egypt, the land of the pharaoh,
A place I always wanted to go.
Travelling north to Russia,
That used to be part of USSR.
Down below is India,
Where the Taj Mahal lies.
Then going north to China,
The Great Wall stretches for miles.
To Australia and New Zealand
And finally back to England.
My 80 days have gone around the world
I travelled and I was the first one.

Christopher Biddle (9)
Goosewell Primary School, Plymouth

Bananas

They grow in big bunches on tropical trees
Get transported to England by boats over seas.

They taste great on their own, but we like to buy
Them for our mum to make banoffee pie.

They are healthy, nutritious and good for you
And you can use the skins to polish your shoes.

You peel them and mash them and sprinkle with sugar
But watch your waistline, they are no figure hugger.

They are especially loved by chimpanzees
So it's lucky for them that they do grow on trees.

**Benjamin Hunter (9)**
Goosewell Primary School, Plymouth

The Cat Poem

Curled asleep on the settee
Stretches and winks one eye at me
Pointy ears and sleek, smooth fur
Stroke him gently, hear him purr
Wide awake now, ready to eat
Miaowing, he gets under my feet
Silent and quick, he runs up a tree
He's kind of wild, he's always free
He hates the wet
I love my pets.

Corrine Trivett (8)
Goosewell Primary School, Plymouth

My Grandad

My grandad is cosy and warm
Like a *huge* teddy bear.
He is as cheeky as a monkey
And has grey, curly hair.
He is loved very much
And is as funny as a parrot.
He loves eating pasties
He says they taste better than a carrot.
My grandad can sometimes be a pest
But he is really the very *best!*

Chloe Swan (8)
Goosewell Primary School, Plymouth

Butterflies

Butterflies can fly
They float through the air
Soaring high into the sky
Their brightly coloured wings
Pinks, green, purples and blues
With mirrored patterns on them
They enter your garden
Landing on flowers
Blending into the background
Where are they?

Caitlin Neighbour (8)
Goosewell Primary School, Plymouth

The Mouse

There was a house
Where lived a mouse
Who sat all day long
Singing a song

This boring old place
With nothing to chase
There's nothing to eat
Savoury or sweet

I'm starving to death
And losing my breath
No bread for me
I'm not happy

I dream of another place
With ponies, fields and space
I get all in a flutter
When I'm washed down the gutter

I hate it when fireworks go *pop*
When inside I have to stop
That's what my life is about
So I sit and wriggle my snout

So don't leave me here all alone
Please take me back to your home!

Charlotte Thomson (9)
Goosewell Primary School, Plymouth

Help, It's A Monster!

There's a monster under my bed, Dad
It's giving me a fright
I'm not sure where it is now
Can we please turn on the light?

I think it must have sharp, red horns
Its teeth are rotten and brown
I can hear it snuffling on my roof
It chuckles like a clown.

Come on Dad, where are you?
It's giving me the creeps
I need a great big hug now
To help me go to sleep.

Oliver May (8)
Goosewell Primary School, Plymouth

Football

Saturday football, team arrives,
Nets up and warm up, team talk,
Ref's here, opponents come,
Whistle goes, game on.
Half-time, orange slices,
Nil-nil, don't want to draw,
Want to score! Back on the pitch,
Striker forward, pass the ball,
Goal!
Team cheers, parents roar,
One-nil up, time's up,
Whistle goes, shake their hands,
Man of the match? Must be me!

Jarrod Howes (8)
Goosewell Primary School, Plymouth

Dinosaur

There once was a dinosaur who loved to roar
His jaws were big, so were his claws
His roars were louder than an applause
He rowed his boat using the oars.

His mum told him to do his chores
But she thought this was a lost cause
So she told him to go out the back doors
And smacked his bum using the oars
His friends gave his mum a great big applause.

Tommy Dyer (8)
Goosewell Primary School, Plymouth

My Family

They laugh at everything I do and say
And they take away the clouds on a dark and dismal day.

We argue over the remote control and sometimes Grandpa wins
I reckon I should take that remote and throw it in the bin.

I make my family laugh when I am in the bath
That's the thing about my family, we always laugh and laugh and laugh!

Cameron Brett (9)
Goosewell Primary School, Plymouth

Bratz

The Bratz are hip, they are so cool,
A bunch of kids straight out of school.
We so enjoy our games and fun,
It's party time for everyone.
Roxxi's cool in Wonderland,
For Dan it's surf or in the sand.
As Yasmin holds her slumber party,
The fashion show must just have started.
Ethan swings on through the jungle,
Whilst Chloe, Jade and Sasha rumble.
In Hollywood meanwhile is Meygan,
Brad, Pirate of the Caribbean,
In panto Phoebe stars as Genie,
Whilst prom night brings that formal feeling.
Fianna stops to watch the clock,
Remember Bratz, these angels rock.

Amy Ashford (9)
Goosewell Primary School, Plymouth

It

It eats children's heads, especially girls
It looks like a toothbrush
It has a fish tail that whips people
It moves, it slides across the floor
And it jumps
It behaves really mean, really mad
It lives in the toilet.

Holly Alldridge (8)
Goosewell Primary School, Plymouth

Fat Fluff Cat

My cat, Sid, is a fat fluff cat
With big orange eyes
He won't chase a rat
But he loves chicken pies.

His tomato soup-coloured fur
And feather duster tail
When he is tickled he starts to purr
And when he is fat and full, he moves like a snail.

Madeleine Chaston (8)
Goosewell Primary School, Plymouth

The Seasons

A springtime tale
Is a time for new life
Sunshine tiptoes through the mist
A burst of colour to end winter's strife
Weather is warming up, this time is bliss.

A summer's tale
Is rather hot, especially outside
Pretty gardens tended for hours
Swimming trunks, ice cream and donkey rides
Beaches full, no sign of flowers.

An autumn tale
Leaves turning brown, orange and amber
Wet, pouring rain and clouds hide the sun
Squirrels collecting nuts, they clamber
Wind blows the leaves until there are none.

A winter's tale
The chill, Santa and frost are here
Hibernating animals bed down to sleep
Dark nights, Christmas tree lights
Logs on the fire all warm and cosy.

Emily King (8)
Goosewell Primary School, Plymouth

Walking To The Time Out Tree

Walking alone to the time out tree
I walk so alone
With all the woodland creatures behind me
And all the blossoms start to grow.

My footsteps turn to patterns
My head turns to song
And God is right behind me
Life itself carries on.

I edge a little further
My feet touch the ground
I grab the time out tree
And cuddle it with all my might.

The branches start to tickle me
There was no way out
And the trunk lays itself on my palm
I am no longer alone.

Amy Robinson (9)
Goosewell Primary School, Plymouth

My Dog, Lucy

I have a golden retriever
She is seven months old,
I like to take her for walks
Whether it is warm or cold.

She can be stubborn as a mule
As she sits down at the gate,
Refusing to walk
And making me wait.

At other times she's playful
And pulls on the lead,
I have to stroke her gently
And ask her not to speed.

I like to cuddle up with her
And give her lots of hugs,
She smells fresh and warm
As we sit together on the rug.

She runs in the garden
Bringing mud in everywhere,
Then sits in the corner
And doesn't seem to care.

At the end of the day
She lays down to rest,
Content in our kitchen
My Lucy is the best!

Catherine Fairbanks (9)
Goosewell Primary School, Plymouth

Stop Bullying

Staring
Watching
Seeing the tears he cries
So why?
Why walk on by?
When you see the tears he cries
Help me
Help him
Stand up to those bullies
Stand apart
But stand together
Reunite as one forever.

Luke Carns (9)
Goosewell Primary School, Plymouth

We Went To Visit Perth

We went to visit Perth,
We flew upon a jet,
To the other side of Earth,
To where it wasn't wet.

Australia is hot,
You have to put on lotion,
It's like a cooking pot,
So use the magic potion.

The barbeques were nice,
We had a brilliant time,
It had a bit of spice,
The adults drank some wine.

The koalas like to sleep,
They sleep up in the trees,
They are so very sweet,
And they eat lots of leaves.

My cousin is an Aussie,
When she's in her pool,
She wears a bright blue cozzie,
She thinks she is so cool.

We saw such pretty views,
And on the golfing green,
There were some kangaroos,
That's what my dad had seen.

Frankie-Jo Perrott (9)
Goosewell Primary School, Plymouth

My Monster

It's scary and hairy
It's furry and smelly and has sharp teeth
It has razor claws and its eyes are small
And it has wavy feet
It eats smelly socks, mean people
Bats, skin, bones, birds and cats
It moves slowly like snails and slugs and worms.

It gobbles, it sucks brains
And bones and skin
It lives in a shed with a bed
And a shelf and a door
It behaves badly and naughtily and horribly.

Chloe Spence (8)
Goosewell Primary School, Plymouth

Party

We all want one every week,
Lots of music and a thumping beat.
Balloons, cake, music and laughter,
Running, jumping, that's what we're after.
It's your birthday, then it's mine,
Doesn't matter if the sun don't shine.

Elliot Smith (8)
Goosewell Primary School, Plymouth

My 200 Armed Monster

Horns, scales, sharp teeth like blades,
Daggers for claws, dribbles red drool,
Screams and groans, big, fat and blue.
Three chins, 200 arms and legs like mountains,
Scary as he may seem to be,
He is a lot sweeter than you or me.

Ciaran McLeod (8)
Goosewell Primary School, Plymouth

It

It eats lots of children
It will also eat you too
It looks like an alien - so look out
It moves like a snake but only on its tentacles
It is very scary
It behaves like a horrible human, but even worse
It lives in a smelly, scary cave, so you'd better watch out
Because it will hypnotise you and paralyse you
So you'd better look out!

Bethany Kendall (7)
Goosewell Primary School, Plymouth

My Monster

It eats worms and slugs and boys and girls.
It looks scary and hairy and smelly.
It moves fast but quietly.
It always behaves badly.
It lives under my bed and in my shed.

Ashleigh Hemmins (7)
Goosewell Primary School, Plymouth

It

It
Eats
School charts and darts
And strawberry tarts
It drinks blood and mud
And water from a lake
And eats a cake.

It
Looks
Hairy and scary
A big nose to sniff toes
Sharp teeth to eat beef
It sits on chairs
And has lots of hairs.

It
Moves
Like a slug
And creepy-crawlie bugs
It flies like a bat
And wears a silly hat

It
Behaves
Very naughty
Last week it ate a kid
And ate a tin lid
It popped a balloon
And then ate a baboon
And flew to the moon.

It
Lives
In a dark cave
Full of spiders
And gliders.

Kane Williams (8)
Goosewell Primary School, Plymouth

My Monster

My monster is hairy and scary.
It lives in a dark and spooky cave.

It is very bad and not nice.
It is very smelly.

It is very sneaky and fast.
It eats people and blood.

Cade Rendle (8)
Goosewell Primary School, Plymouth

My Monster

What does my monster look like?
Wriggly and red and furry, has only two toes and big eyes,
That's what my monster looks like.

How does my monster move?
It moves slowly, walking across water, splashy-splash,
That's how my monster moves.

Where does my monster live?
In a cave in the fishpond at the bottom of the garden,
That's where my monster lives.

What does my monster eat?
It eats kids and bones,
That's what my monster eats.

George Nuttall (7)
Goosewell Primary School, Plymouth

My Monster

It eats stones and bones, eyes and flies
Children's feet and tasty meat, mud and blood
Buns and tongues, kids and cribs
It looks like a snotty nose with stinky toes
It's scary and hairy, smoky and chokey
It lives in a cold, stinky place where it stuffs its face
And makes lots of mess, a lot of mess!
It behaves very badly, it ate a child in one bite
It popped a balloon and ate a baboon with giant feet
And it stamped on meat
It moves quite quickly and stamps its feet.

Daniel Redding (8)
Goosewell Primary School, Plymouth

My Monster

It eats rotten garbage
It looks like a dustbin
It moves like a stealth cat
It behaves well
It lives in a sewer
It smells like aftershave.

Jonathan Bishop (7)
Goosewell Primary School, Plymouth

The Dustbin Monster

It eats other monsters
And it sloshes and crunches
It eats human brains
And swallows a whole one
It looks big and scary
And has got nine eyes
And a small mouth
With twelve terrifying teeth
And two big, disgusting ears
It behaves like a monster
Because it is a monster
It lives in a dustbin
With slime in it
People's rubbish
Dogs' and cats' hair
It jumps like a lunatic.

Christian White (7)
Goosewell Primary School, Plymouth

My Monster

It looks like a robot, but is a monster
Fuzzy hair to tickle people
And fuzzy arms and fuzzy legs.

It eats human brains
And little girls and monsters too.

It moves like a robot
And old people and monsters.

It behaves like rude people
And when you're at the table
It makes smells and you get sent to bed.

It lives in slimy dustbins
With fish heads and banana skins.

Joseph Allen (7)
Goosewell Primary School, Plymouth

It

It eats livers, kids' kidneys and human brains and blood
Its head looks like a rotten pumpkin and it has squid legs
It moves like a penguin and rolls and wobbles
It behaves like a gorilla or a caveman
It lives in the sink or my bed.

Lucy Harris (7)
Goosewell Primary School, Plymouth

The Under Bed Monster

It eats leftovers from my kitchen
It eats worms from my garden
It eats socks from my bedroom.

It looks like a crab with five eyes
A big, arched nose and a big, fat belly.

It moves sideways like a crab
With two pincers and eight legs
It is green and purple with black spots on its belly.

It behaves very mean
And throws socks at my friends
They think it's funny!

It lives under my bed in a bag that is red.
I like my monster.

Tabitha Patey (8)
Goosewell Primary School, Plymouth

It

It eats googly eyes and people's hearts
It looks like it has three shiny, blue eyes
One long tail and four small feet
With a small love-heart face
And a big, round belly with a love heart on
It moves really slowly when it crawls
And fast when it walks
And slides when it slithers
It behaves really horribly, really mean and mad
It lives underwater with the fish in a dark, dark cave.

Lauren Porter (7)
Goosewell Primary School, Plymouth

My Monster

It leaves a trail of blood and poison in your bedroom past midnight
Then it rises from under your bed
And it wakes you up and scares you to death
So you freeze into a block of ice
Then it picks you up and throws you out of the window
And you break out of the ice
Then it goes back into your wardrobe and goes to sleep
Then when you wake from that awful nightmare
And look in your wardrobe, nothing is there
When you go back to sleep, you never see it again.

Reece Kirkham (8)
Goosewell Primary School, Plymouth

It

It crunches bones and drinks blood
Eats human beings and leaves the brain on the ground.

It looks scary and hairy
And small and green.

It moves fast and slow
And runs most of the time.

It behaves badly, like a lion
And gets mad.

It lives in a dirty sewer
Under the ground.

Thomas Ribbons (7)
Goosewell Primary School, Plymouth

My Monster

What does my monster look like?
Well . . . clean, mean, spiky, spooky, sharp, smells
That's what my monster looks like.

How does my monster move?
Well . . . crawls and creeps,
Glides, hops and runs,
That's how my
monster moves.

Where does my monster live?
Well . . . garden, street, under my bed, shed,
That's where my monster lives.

What does my monster eat?
Well . . . slugs, worms, blood, bones,
Rotten eggs, banana skins,
That's what my monster eats.

Cameron Box (7)
Goosewell Primary School, Plymouth

It

It eats slimy worms and slugs
It behaves like a naughty dragon
It lives in a cave
It looks like a grenade has hit it
It moves like a grasshopper
It smells like my grandma's socks, well dirty socks.

Jack Lipman (8)
Goosewell Primary School, Plymouth

It

It eats slugs and worms
When it's half-term.
It eats fish and bats
Spiders and rats.
It looks scary and spooky
Wary and kooky.
It looks green
Like a bean.
It moves side to side
And it likes to glide.
It moves this way and that way
And into some hay.
It behaves silly
And ate Billy.
It behaves naughty
And is all warty.
It lives behind Mrs Yates' curtain
And with me for certain.
It hides under my bed
And bumps its head.

Molly Gibson (7)
Goosewell Primary School, Plymouth

It

It eats people at night
It looks like an alien frog with twelve eyes
It moves like a jumping frog
And runs when it wants to eat people at night
It behaves like an angry cheetah
It lives in a dark cave
Where it can hide and scare people at night.

Imran Azlisham (8)
Goosewell Primary School, Plymouth

It

It eats like a pig, it scoffs and it stuffs, it slobbers.
It looks gloomy, it looks purple, it looks slobbery,
It looks mean, it looks silly.
It behaves groany and moany,
It's moody, it's nasty, it's mean.
It moves, it slides and it glides, it wriggles and it giggles.
It lives under beds, it lives in sheds, it lives in my drawers.

Courtney-Jean Lee (7)
Goosewell Primary School, Plymouth

My Alien, Green

My alien, green, whatever that means,
But whenever I ask him, he starts to scream.
My alien, green, at six o'clock,
Watches the news whilst eating a sock.
He can't stand elephant shoes
And throws up while eating banana stew.
He has to wear a diaper,
As he goes very hyper
On crazy cauliflower ice cream
And it makes him scream like a baby.

My alien, green, loves to watch at seven,
Holiday Planet Earth, to him it's like Heaven!
But afterwards at eight, he goes on ExploringEarth.com,
Looking for an Earthling to date.

My alien, green, has one huge eye which has a dial,
To make his eyesight better for a while,
He also has a metal chest,
He thinks it makes him look the best!

Anna Brett (10)
Goosewell Primary School, Plymouth

My Monster

My monster eats flowers and towers
And naughty children like you.
My monster has got eleven eyes.
My monster has got ten ears
And his hands are very hairy.
His nose is very long.
My monster swims like a spider,
Swings with his tail like a monkey.
My monster is very cheeky
And naughty with other monsters.
My monster lives in the sewers with rats and bats.

Stacey Kelley (8)
Goosewell Primary School, Plymouth

My Monster

It eats nosy boys and teenagers
It looks scary and has big teeth
It moves like lightning
It behaves very cheekily
It lives under my bed.

Harriet Cope (7)
Goosewell Primary School, Plymouth

Monster

He has skinny legs,
Red heads,
He's hairy with a burly, pimply body,
He has a fuzzy lion tail,
He oozes,
He slouches,
He shuffles and toddles,
He creeps and trudges on tiptoe,
He lives in a garden shed,
Under beds, in pools, shoes
And even in wardrobes.
So now you know,
Beware of this terrible creature!

Jessica Horne (7)
Goosewell Primary School, Plymouth

The Grim Reaper

He is grim and miserable
He has bad breath because of gum disease
He reeks
He's got wrinkles around his eyes
His flesh sags
He dribbles and drools
He walks slowly like an old man
Then once he sees his prey, he's off!
He's super strong
And can snap any rope or chain built to hold him
He can even snap your bones
And suck up your blood before he eats your guts and heart!
He lives deep inside the hedge on top of a giant hill
He looks down and waits for someone to come
Then he breaks their neck.

Jamie Trueman & Jack Penwill (8)
Goosewell Primary School, Plymouth

Toe Eater

He gobbles toes and is terribly rude
But when you shout at him he gets in a mood.
He looks pimply, warty and very naughty
His body points forwards but his head looks back.
He ambles and rambles along many a track
He lives in the wardrobe in your bedroom
Beware for he is coming to your area quite soon!

Jamie Griffiths (7)
Goosewell Primary School, Plymouth

Monster

He scuttles under the creaky floorboards
He is called Narog
He has one eye that changes colour -
Sometimes red and sometimes blue
His teeth are sharp and dripping with blood
He has pointy ears, a spiky tail
And a horn on the end of his warty nose
His legs bulge like my grandma's jelly, all wobbly
He wears high heels to make him look tall
And even more frightening
He likes to destroy planets and eat children
So children, beware of this hideous monster
With a huge frame and a huge appetite!

John Polson & Alex Scott (8)
Goosewell Primary School, Plymouth

Vampire Devil

It has webbed feet, hairy but skinny legs
Tattered body, red and green striped eyes
A big, fat nose with spiky points on the end
And a spider head with pointed ears.
It gallops around at a fearful pace
Arriving home and slipping deep inside an enchanted cave.
Beware, for it can be seen down and around the beaches
Hiding in rock pools
Ready to pounce and gobble you up!
It has more than two million eyes.

Scout Wheeler (7)
Goosewell Primary School, Plymouth

I Saw A Monster

I saw a monster walking down the street
He looked like a pig with bulging eyes
He'd got a horribly spotty body
If you touched him he would turn horribly rude.

He moved like a snake slithering down deep
Into the dark green forest, spitting poison all around.
He lived in a dustbin
Wiggling his horrible, spotty body,
Rattling the smelly rubbish.

He eats people and spiders all in one slimy gulp.

Abbie Webb (8) & Kyra Cutler (7)
Goosewell Primary School, Plymouth

My Alien

My alien has six arms as short as a 15cm ruler.
I wonder how she brushes her teeth?
My alien has three long fingers, as thin as pencils.
She'd probably be good at playing the piano.
My alien has a giant head, as round as a plate.
Probably because she has a huge brain.
My alien has a nose as tiny as a mouse's eye.
I don't think she has a good sense of smell.
My alien has two long legs with giant webbed feet.
Maybe her planet has a lot of swamps.
My alien has three huge eyes that can see in the dark.
She often wakes up in the middle of the night.
My alien has two pointy ears, as sharp as knives.
I think she has a very good sense of hearing.
My alien has a giant smile.
She is a very happy creature.

Chloe Britton (9)
Goosewell Primary School, Plymouth

Animal Kennings

Fantastic swimmer
Fish fighter
Flipper flapper
Loud squeaker
Hoop performer
Sand roller
Cute looker
Friend winner
Child carer
Good jumper
Food hunter
Crowd lover.

Helen Springett (10)
Goosewell Primary School, Plymouth

I Saw A Monster

I saw a horrible monster
Walking down the street
Long feet
A spotty face
Hairy legs
Scaled body
He doesn't run, he lumbers.

Shae Moore (7) & Terry Fletcher (8)
Goosewell Primary School, Plymouth

Monster Poem

He's got webbed hands and feet
Two long ears
One bulging eye on each end of a long antenna
Two floppy wings hang down his back.

He glides stealthily, but when full of food
He waddles like a penguin
He zooms like a rocket underwater
Never taking a breath.

He lives in a dirty hole
In the beautiful reef
It smells like a dustbin
Full of rotten food.

He eats massive, beautiful fish
And never leaves a bit
But his favourite snack
Is naughty teenagers.

Toby Ogden & Rory Lethbridge (8)
Goosewell Primary School, Plymouth

Sadie

My dog called Sadie can sometimes be rather crazy.
She likes to go for walks and sometimes she likes to talk.
She likes sleeping in her bed when I am stroking her head.
She likes eating her food, although the noises can be rude.
I love my dog, Sadie!

Elizabeth Dawson (9)
Goosewell Primary School, Plymouth

Monster Man

He is scary
He's a bit hairy
He is mean and sneaky
He slithers like a snake
His dragon tail stretches out behind him
He flicks it when mad
When he does horrible things, he is never sorry
He lives in the shed
And he hides when people are around.

Sam Lipman (8)
Goosewell Primary School, Plymouth

The Evil Jumper

He eats like a pig
He's got disgusting manners.
He eats frogs' legs all in one!
He lives on his own in a cave, it is really smelly.
He waddles like a duck.
His body sways on short, stubby legs,
His eyes are like tiny marbles glistening in the darkness.
He behaves like a three-year-old having a temper tantrum,
Rolling on his back and waving his legs in the air.
He is a very lonely monster!

Polly Morfett (8)
Goosewell Primary School, Plymouth

The Ten-Headed Monster

He has ten heads and long, flowing hair.
He does not like to be seen.
He has loads of eyes, all colourful.
Have you ever seen a monster like this before?
He eats your fingers.
He hides behind the bushes.
He jumps out and gobbles your fingers all in one go.
He fills his mouth and then shuffles away,
Returning to his cave where they disappear in one gulp!

Holly Vincent (8)
Goosewell Primary School, Plymouth

Monster Poem

He has scruffy hair, a hairy face and jagged feet
He waddles like a penguin and oozes on the ground
He lives in a dustbin in an icy, deep cave
That melts in summer.
He eats Chinese and wastes food as well as teachers
He gobbles up teenagers and young girls as well.
So beware, he could mash you.

Theo Fuge (8) & Ben Chapman (7)
Goosewell Primary School, Plymouth

Animal Kennings

Quick mover
Meat eater
Funny looker
Rock climber
Fast killer
Deep sleeper
Long leaper
Deafening barker
Rough fighter
Brilliant builder.

What am I?
Ans: Tazmanian Devil.

Thomas Dimmick (10)
Goosewell Primary School, Plymouth

Animal Kennings

A tree climber
A swift swinger
A banana lover
A cheeky screamer
A tree hugger
A jungle jumper
A meat hater
A nest changer
A nit picker
A strong hitter
A leaf nester
A fruit muncher.

Ashley Scott (11)
Goosewell Primary School, Plymouth

What Am I? Kennings

School hater
Sport player
Home time lover
Lesson cryer
Playtime chaser
Book reader
Story teller
Hard worker
Mind thinker.

What am I?
School child.

Rebecca Jane (10)
Goosewell Primary School, Plymouth

Animal Kennings

A water spurter
A deep down diver
A krill eater
A loud singer
A big floater
A shipwreck gobbler
A smooth swimmer
A fast glider
An endangered creature
A clever thinker.

What am I?

Sophie Bannan (11)
Goosewell Primary School, Plymouth

Animal Kennings

A drool dripper
An echoing howler
A nasty killer
A sheep lover
A moon howler
A claw sharpener
A meat eater
A grandma lover
A fierce fighter.

Who am I?
A wolf.

Marnie List (11)
Goosewell Primary School, Plymouth

Animal Kennings

A hungry hunter
A lethal runner
A careful catcher
A cunning little player
A big jaw biter
A teeth cruncher
A fast-legged runner
A hard nut banger
A bone cracker
A sleeping slinger.

What am I?

Joe Moore (11)
Goosewell Primary School, Plymouth

Animal Kennings

A sly mover
A seabed crawler
A vicious biter
A skin shedder
A prey attacker
A silent belly crawler
A scary reptile
A body squasher
A silent creeper
A long creature.

Anaconda.

Ross Slinger (10)
Goosewell Primary School, Plymouth

Kennings

A meat eater
A good sneaker
A prey seeker
A sneaky pouncer
A mean looker
A vicious biter
A snow runner
A food swallower
A kid breeder
A pack leader
A man hunter
A cub feeder

Who am I?
White tiger.

Michael Donohue (11)
Goosewell Primary School, Plymouth

Cinquain

Hot days
Playing outside
Paddling in the pool
Eating ice cream makes your mouth cold
Brain freeze.

Samantha Stevens (11)
Goosewell Primary School, Plymouth

Animal Kennings

Meat eater
Animal killer
Dog avoider
Sound killer
Cat family
Family lover
Family teacher
Bad sleeper
Good killer
Family leader
Bullet avoider
Human killer.

What am I?

Meave Daly (10)
Goosewell Primary School, Plymouth

Animal Kennings

A creamy coloured fur coat wearer
A rough growler
A meat eater
A human killer
A bigger kitten
A fast runner
A fierce loner
A claw sharpener
A great fighter.
The king of the jungle.

What am I?

Rebecca Ward (10)
Goosewell Primary School, Plymouth

Cinquain

Sun out
In the summer
Sunbathing or swimming
Kids are out getting cold ice cream
Summer.

Kieran Reeves (10)
Goosewell Primary School, Plymouth

My Alien

My alien has more spikes than a porcupine,
His favourite number is number nine.
He likes the show Fetzza, along with Domino pizzas.

He likes to go to Asda for some lovely pasta,
He has a fat, green and purple tummy,
He also thinks maggots are yummy.

He has chunky, white whiskers,
He smells like a pig from Planet Big.

My alien has eyes as big as the moon,
His legs are as stubby as a penguin's,
He has a little tail, shaped like a nail.

My alien is called Zag Zook.

Jamie Mitchell (9)
Goosewell Primary School, Plymouth

Animal Kennings

Bird eater
Water hater
Tree climber
High jumper
Soft pillow
Strong hunter
Sharp clawer
Meat eater
Happy sleeper
Fur licker
Lazy animal.

Josh McLeod (10)
Goosewell Primary School, Plymouth

Cinquains

Damp day
Hard, crunchy leaves
It's not a day to play
People hate the wet, rainy day
Dry up.

Fog day
Leaves are falling
Wet and horrible day
Come sun it is really boring
It's wet.

Curtis Kelley (11)
Goosewell Primary School, Plymouth

What Am I?

An endangered species
A brown coat wearer
Has a big frown
A tusk charger
A ground thumper
A desert lover
A sad loner
A pain hater
On all-fours
A bullet avoider
Is a quiet mammal
Doesn't have fur like camels
They are very boring
A loud snorer
A very slow mover.

Jordan Airzee (10)
Goosewell Primary School, Plymouth

My Alien

My alien has six arms as long as giraffes,
Two for grappling, two for picking and two for crawling.

My alien has four long legs to jump as high as a kangaroo,
My alien is as high as a table.
I wonder what his house looks like.

My alien has teeth as sharp as a shark's.
Maybe it can destroy it.
He has four legs as wide as a human's head.

My alien has a long, curly tail, so he does swing,
My alien has two laser guns and he likes music.

Ryan Turner (9)
Goosewell Primary School, Plymouth

My Alien

My alien has six googly eyes
He is also lots of fun
My alien eats cow pies
And likes to watch aliens cook lots of pie
My alien likes to dance to rock music
He also has claws sharp as a six metre blade
My alien's skin is dark blue
He has real tight muscles
My alien is the most frightening alien you will ever see.

Lewis Slinger (9)
Goosewell Primary School, Plymouth

Exploring Zelchesenses

On the planet of Zelchesenses, two aliens arrive,
For the wars that raged elsewhere they had to survive.
They arrived at a quarter to ten,
They found what we call a hen in a pen.

They decided to explore the rest of the planet's wonders,
The planet was hot so they got very flustered.
As they went off deeper into the planet with a hop and a skip,
They went too fast, so the child alien had started to trip.

The two aliens were nowhere to be found,
Through the thick of the wood no thing made a sound.
As the old, fussy mother began to flip,
The relaxed child was taking a muddy, watery dip.

The aliens ran through the forest of trees,
When they discovered what we call leaves.
The old lady alien's spikes bombarded the leafy trees,
When suddenly she got an awful disease.

The aliens met up in the path of the rocket,
To find the mum's eye was out of its socket.
They flew out into the darkness of space,
With a fizz and a bang with no style or grace.

Ryan Bell (10)
Goosewell Primary School, Plymouth

The Friendly Alien

I was walking down the street,
When I saw some strange, green feet,
They were running after me,
And I ran to be safe.

The alien found me, we became friends,
Zig Zow Zee and me,
We had a picnic, *whoopee,*
He sounded like a chimpanzee.

Zig Zow Zee loves going to Tesco,
Not again, don't start being a stupid guy.
He also loves books.
Which one next, Zig Zow Zee?

He's half green and half blue,
And has lumps on his back.
He can even play the didgeridoo,
His favourite place to sleep is on a pile of goo.

Emma Bell (10)
Goosewell Primary School, Plymouth

My Alien

There's an alien I would like you to meet,
His best features are his massive feet.

His name is Alith Smice,
Although he is afraid of head lice.

His five evil eyes,
Are the size of giant pies.

His spiky, stony, silver, scaly skin,
Is as sharp as a pin.

He enjoys eating mouldy maggots,
But his favourite food is foul faggots.

His feet are enormous,
170 times larger than a mouse.

His tremendous teeth,
Are as pointy as holly in a wreath.

He thinks his twelve-nostrilled nose is great
And so does his best mate.

He lives in the wet, wild, windy woods,
So if he sees you, he might eat you as puds.

So next time you go down to the forest,
Make sure Alith Smice is having a rest.

Alice Smith (10)
Goosewell Primary School, Plymouth

Alien's Lair

There's a big alien's lair
And Maggie lives there.
She has a thousand blue, bloodshot eyes
All over her face,
A pointy nose like a red chilli
And a big mouth with sharp fangs
And what looks like worms inside.
She has bleeding flesh for skin,
Her neck is rock solid,
Her hands are six green, sharp claws.
She has red, spiky hair,
She is as tall as a tree,
She has two sharp legs
With points for feet.
Her favourite food is squirrels,
She likes killing them too.
Her favourite drink is swamp water.

Aaron Mannion (10)
Goosewell Primary School, Plymouth

Pineapple!

I once discovered
An uncovered
Pineapple. It was so crazy
But also lazy
He can walk and talk
Scream, sing and stalk
Also yummy
For my tummy
I did resist
To eat his fists
So we sat
And had a chat
He has prickly skin
But no fins
Eyes, mouth and a nose
He has hands and toes
He eats frogs' eyes
With shepherd's pie
He has a juicy body
He watches Noddy
I once discovered
An uncovered
Pineapple. It was so yummy
I found him in my tummy!

Jamie Howes (10)
Goosewell Primary School, Plymouth

Sharja

Sharja is an alien, pink and spotty green,
She lives on planet Oberzene, where it is hot and clean.
Her very small head is purple,
Her ears are bright green with a mouth the size of a dog,
She must be as loud as me!
Abacus is Sharja's pet, a little white dolphin,
Comes from planet Earth, she does,
Eats cheeseburgers with me.
Ro-Mo is Sharja's, his skin is scaly green,
His spots are orange, you know, he has seventeen.
Jupiter is Sharja's favourite place to go on holiday,
She loves it there, all slimy, purple, freezing and mean.
Abbacus and Sharja have a happy life,
But here is where we leave them to go home tonight.

Jessica Lethbridge (10)
Goosewell Primary School, Plymouth

The Alien, Zig Zag

Zig Zag lives on Jupiter
It spins and makes him dizzy
When he's watching GMTV.

Zig Zag hates aliens on Jupiter
Zig Zag hates them on there.

Zig Zag does not like sleeping
Because he thinks aliens
Will come to Jupiter to get him.

Zig Zag loves watching TV
Zig Zag has two TVs
Other aliens come and watch it with him
But they're friends.

Zig Zag doesn't like Jupiter that much
Because it has holes as big as skyscrapers
Zig Zag wishes he had a car
To get him around Jupiter quicker
But Zig Zag could fall off Jupiter.
The planet is brown, yellow like lemon and mad.

Zig Zag has five icy eyes
He has three long legs
He has a circular, knobbly nose
He has 5,000 tiny teeth.

Jack Wotton (10)
Goosewell Primary School, Plymouth

The Alien

Once in the night
I had a great fright

I saw a UFO
It came down quite low

In the cockpit I saw an alien
It was hard to understand because he was covered with uranium

He had a small, silver body
And his nose was spotty

He had a flat little nose
And three silver toes

He ate crushed sugar, salt with toffee
And he liked dipping it in some coffee

I watched him fly back into the sky
Then I wondered if he ever would die.

Michael Cook (9)
Goosewell Primary School, Plymouth

My Alien On Lar Jours

My alien's eyes are bigger than Uranus
When he gets stabbed he thinks it's painless.

On Saturdays he shops at Safeway
But he needs to cross the motorway.

He smells like rotten milk
And his feet smell like cheese.

He has 21 legs
But every day his skin he sheds.

His legs are fatter than an elephant's
But on his strange and weird planet
He has a dog with three heads.

His favourite TV programme is Star Wars
And he sure likes going to Lar Jours.

His name is Robbie.

Connor Mellody (10)
Goosewell Primary School, Plymouth

Animal Kennings

A sea creature
A flesh eater
A fast mover
A smashing sighter
A sharp hunter
A large fish
A boat destroyer
A human killer
A blood creature
A seal approacher.

Ryan Ball (11)
Goosewell Primary School, Plymouth

Sports

S pectacular skills
P erfect players
O ccasional injuries
R adical rulers
T alented teams
S uperb wins.

Ciarain Crook (10)
Goosewell Primary School, Plymouth

Monsters

It moves like a long, slithery snake
It looks like an ogre
It has a hairy nose
It has two stinky legs and two stilt legs
It lives under floorboards
And its stench causes rats to die and fall to the ground
It feasts on the poor creatures
It eats like a pig, snuffling and grunting in the darkness
It has worms and cockroaches growing out of its ears
It really is a fearsome beast!

Alex Yates, Stephanie Bourner (7) & Coral Bell (8)
Goosewell Primary School, Plymouth

I Saw A Monster

He is horrible,
Rude
And scary,
He looks like a slimy frog
And his teeth are sharp,
He moves like a snail
And wobbles to the side,
He lives in a dusty old bin,
He eats children,
Garbage
And boxes.

Nicholas Chapman & Aston Walker (7)
Goosewell Primary School, Plymouth

Beware Of The Terrifying Ogre

It has a humped back and a frog nose
It has 20 eyeballs that are squidgey
It has a fat tummy that is gooey
It has a fat head that has no hair
It has huge ears
It has loads of bogeys hanging out of its nose
It has hard legs
It has sharp teeth
It has hairy hands
It crawls when it walks
It is spooky and very scary.

Harry Pile & Charley Vaughan (7)
Goosewell Primary School, Plymouth

Monster Poem

He walks like an old monster
He has hair in his ears, he's scary
He has a hump on his back
He is fat and burly
He eats slugs, bats, bugs and rats
He lives in a dark cave
Sometimes he comes to children to crunch on their bones
He always roars into your ear, so watch out for him
He gobbles up teenagers
He always tells tales
He has frog feet.

Lucy Duffy (7)
Goosewell Primary School, Plymouth

There Is A Monster In My House

There is a monster in my house
He has a multicoloured, striped body
He has a million warts and no teeth
He moves like an elephant and wakes everyone up
I get mad
I am annoyed
I am tired
The next morning I get up
The monster is in the cellar eating like a pig
Dad blames me and I am sent to my room
There's a monster in my house.

Melisa Tucker-Cantez (8)
Goosewell Primary School, Plymouth

My Cat Called Daisy

I have a cat called Daisy,
She is very, very crazy.
Daisy swings in the trees
Like a chimpanzee.

She came to school like a big fool
And played with me in PE.
Crazy Daisy runs around the house
Chasing her tail.

Crazy Daisy scratches the settee
Whilst eating her spaghetti.
Crazy Daisy likes to nap in the afternoon sun,
Crazy Daisy is so lazy when bedtime has come.

Danni Rundle (9)
Goosewell Primary School, Plymouth

Football

F un for all the players
O ver the crossbar
O ut of the box
T rying to win the game
B rilliant when you score a goal
A mazing when you are running down the pitch
L ong before the end of the game
L egends are here.

David Ford (9)
Goosewell Primary School, Plymouth

Kayleigh

K is for being a kind friend
A is for liking animals
Y is for a young girl
L is for Leo
E is for excellent worker
I is for being an intelligent girl
G is for a great swimmer
H is for hilarious when I fell in a swimming pool.

Kayleigh Page (9)
Goosewell Primary School, Plymouth

Volume

V olume is loud
O ver the limits
L oudness around
U ndestructable noise
M ind-blowing volume
E arache of death.

Jack Chynoweth (10)
Goosewell Primary School, Plymouth

The Dive

Fearful as I look over the diving board
Tearful as I jump
Frightful as I go towards the pool
Careful as I splash into the pool
Boastful as I win a medal
Grateful that I won.

Ashlea Easton (10)
Goosewell Primary School, Plymouth

My Journey Through Space

When I flew into space
It was like a big race
With the planets, stars and moons
And all singing me tunes.

As I flew past Saturn
I was amazed by the pattern
As I flew past Mars
I could see lots of cars.

As I flew past the sun
I burnt my bum
As I flew past the moon
I knew I had to land soon.

Back at home on Earth
I thought it was really worth
The journey through space.

Ellice Stock (10)
Goosewell Primary School, Plymouth

Football Mad

N ewcastle United are the best
E very time we play a game
W e go out and beat the rest
C ould win the cup one day
A nd everyone would shout hooray
S ometimes we might lose a game
T hough we don't feel any shame
L ittle does anyone know
E very game we aim to win.

Louise Ross (9)
Goosewell Primary School, Plymouth

Rap Song

Hello, my name is Connor and this is my rap
So just shut up and listen to this funky track
It's on track 6 of my CD
If you put in you you'll be listening to me
My very amazing rap is about something great
It's a very long story including a lot of hate
If you buy my CD just put that track on
Listen to it hard, listen to that song
It will be the best thing you do
I guarantee to you.

Connor Rollings (10)
Goosewell Primary School, Plymouth

Ingredients For The Perfect Summer Holiday

A plane of excitement
A cup of sun
A wave of water
A bucket of sand
A spoonful of ice cream
A pool of happiness
A glass of orange cocktail
A suitcase of fun
A pocketful of friends.

Abi Purchase (10)
Goosewell Primary School, Plymouth

Mr And Mrs Bo Jelly

Mr and Mrs Bo Jelly
Won the world record for having a big belly
They sat on their chairs, unaware
Of the pins stabbing their bellies
They flopped and flipped and were blown to bits
To a place where there was no telly
And that was the end of Mr and Mrs Bo Jelly.

Daniel Roberts (10)
Goosewell Primary School, Plymouth

Lauren

L is for Leo
A is for animal lover
U is for unusually funny
R is for really interesting
E is for excitable
N is for nice.

Lauren Smith (9)
Goosewell Primary School, Plymouth

As I Stand On The Balcony I See . . .

Lazy lions bathing in the hot sun
Cautious crocodiles watching their prey
Ginormous giraffes eating the greenery
Enormous elephants walking in a line
Zipping zebras skipping away
Huffing hyenas playing around
Night-time arrives and all is silent.

Christopher Strydom (10)
Goosewell Primary School, Plymouth

Pain

Pain is black
Pain smells like death
Pain tastes like rotten eggs
Pain sounds like a howling dog
Pain lives in dark, mouldy caves.

Kayleigh Todd (10)
Goosewell Primary School, Plymouth

Rosemary

R estless at night-time
O bedient at school
S cared of spiders
E xcitable about drama
M anageable at home
A nimal lover
R eally interested in sports
Y ou always see me smile.

Rosemary Pryce (9)
Goosewell Primary School, Plymouth

Limerick

There was an old witch from a tree,
Whose nose always sneezed on me.
Her big bogeys, they splash,
She could sell them for cash,
But for me, they were always free.

Jade Pring (10)
Goosewell Primary School, Plymouth

Football

F ree kicks
O ffsides
O utrageous fouls
T errible misses
B rilliant skills
A mazing goals
L ong shots
L ovely saves.

Josh Ferme (10)
Goosewell Primary School, Plymouth

My Alien

My alien's name is Updown,
Although sometimes he does frown,
He is a savage killer,
Even though he is a good seller.

My alien shops at Asda,
But he does not like pasta,
My alien is a wrestler,
And he does pack a punch!

My alien's favourite TV programme is Coronation Street,
And he has stinky feet.
His whole body is purple,
And he lived for 5,000 years.

Sometimes he watches the animal channel,
Other times he's fixing the panel,
His hands are not hands, they are spiky balls,
And when he plays football, he always pops the ball.

Updown is a savage beast,
And he loves massive feasts.
He has eagle eyes,
And comes from the planet Hell 2!

Macauley Waites (9)
Goosewell Primary School, Plymouth

My Alien

My alien has four eyes
Two are red, two are silver
His hair is loads of spikes
Half are red, half are silver
He has two legs and two arms.

His fingers, his toes,
His half eaten nose.
He lives on planet Zok
And his name is Log.

His teeth are as sharp
As a sabre-toothed tiger's,
His favourite food is human flesh.
His favourite drink is alien juice.
His arms stretch as far as the moon
And he eats it.

Kieran Lukehurst (9)
Goosewell Primary School, Plymouth

My Football

My passion is football
My favourite team is Liverpool
To watch them is exciting
Their players are so cool.

Saturday mornings
I take my ball to the field
Me and my dad
We're winning the Charity Shield.

Mum gets all moody
We're covered in mud
She picks up my football
And throws it with a thud.

When I am big
I'm going to play for England
Mum won't be moody
I'm fulfilling my dreams.

I'll be famous
And have a great big drink
Out of the World Cup!

Luke Easton (8)
Goosewell Primary School, Plymouth

Daisies

Summer's coming
Hip hip hooray
Sun is shining
Every day
Say goodbye
To winter chills
Say hello to daffodils
Roses, tulips, daisies too
Nod their heads at me and you.

Courtney Chick (9)
Goosewell Primary School, Plymouth

Little Monster

I'm a little monster
And I live under your bed

I'm a little monster
With a very ugly head

I'm a little monster
Who makes crashes and bangs

I'm a little monster
And I've got big fangs

I'm a little monster
Who's just a bit scary

I'm a little monster
Who's just a bit hairy

I'm a little monster
And I'm short and stout

I'm a little monster
I'm around when the light's out

I'm a little monster
And I'm the only one

So switch on the light
And I'll be gone.

Robert Lanham (8)
Goosewell Primary School, Plymouth

My Brother

I have a little brother
Stanley is his name
In bed asleep I was
When he came
He was born on the 21st December
That's an easy day
For me to remember
He looks like me and my sister
And a man asked my dad
'What did you have, Mister?'
'A little boy,' my dad replied
Smiling from ear to ear
With pride.

Abigail Horne (8)
Goosewell Primary School, Plymouth

Washing Day

The washing machine goes round and round
Like a merry-go-round
The washing inside goes up and round
Like a tumbling clown.

While the bubbles fizz and froth
The clothes are getting clean
Then the water flows away
Do you know what this means?

The dirty water has gone down the drain
The clean water's coming through
Now the machine has started rinsing
The clothes are soon going to look like new.

Then it starts spinning round and round
Like a spinning top
Faster and faster and faster it goes
Then suddenly it stops.

Connie McGregor (9)
Goosewell Primary School, Plymouth

Newfoundlands

Newfoundlands are lovely
They are big and black
You tickle them on the belly
When they lie on their back.
Some of them are black and white
And some of them are red
But whatever one you get
They will have massive heads.
They slobber, drool and bark
And bite and nibble at your toes
You buy them when they're nice and small
And they grow and grow and grow.

Conor Moy (8)
Goosewell Primary School, Plymouth

The Ghost Train

There's a tumbledown old station,
Where a ghost train waits to go,
All aboard, ghostly ghouls and goblins,
Watch the engine brightly glow.

In its cab a phantom fireman,
Helps the engine get up steam,
Chuff-chuff-chuff, it's moving slowly,
Hear its whistle, like a scream!

Ghostly guards are whistling wildly,
Bony fingers wave goodbye,
As along the rails the ghost train glides,
Beneath the moonlit sky.

Witches shriek along the rail cars,
While inside the dining car,
Vampires munch and crunch with monsters,
Sipping cocktails at the bar!

On they speed through misty marshes,
What a chilling sight to see,
Ghostly faces at the windows,
Silent wheels turn eerily!

If there were tickets for the ghost train,
Would you dare take a ride
Or would you quickly leave
And find somewhere to hide?

Macauley Bridgman (9)
Goosewell Primary School, Plymouth

Up, Up And Away

Up, up goes my helicopter
Spinning around and around
Up, up high into the sky.

Going right, going left
Forwards and backwards
Then falling down
It hovers for a moment
Before crashing to the ground.

Jonathan Holland (8)
Goosewell Primary School, Plymouth

The Dark Night

When I'm in the dark
I really get scared
So when I go to the toilet
My shadow looks like a bear.

When I'm in bed all alone
With the curtains closed
And the lights out
I get so scared I shout and shout.

When night comes and light fades
When everything is left in the shade
I can see the dark come from afar
But there is some light, I can see a star.

The dark, dark night is coming to a close
The scary shadows are no more
The light is starting to appear
I'm safe now daylight is here.

Nathan Garlick (9)
Goosewell Primary School, Plymouth

The Human Cat

My pet is a big, hairy cat
He likes to wear spotty pink hats
He walks on his two back legs
He always gets his own way when he begs.

Flash likes doing the washing up
But he only does it when people aren't there
I've seen him eating
Cucumber sandwiches and pears.

He's very, very fat
And he picks on rats
Just like any other cat
But he's not as normal as you think.

Kirsty Evans (9)
Goosewell Primary School, Plymouth

String Rock

I got an electric guitar for Christmas,
It's as loud as it can be,
When I play the notes with my fingers,
The noise vibrates me.

Learning to play the notes is hard,
I practise every day to get really good,
I always use a plectrum,
I pluck it as I should.

I want to become a rock star,
So I will become really rich,
I always have to use my brain,
Because if I don't, I will get a stitch.

Amelia Chaston (8)
Goosewell Primary School, Plymouth

Books, Books

They are everywhere,
They come in different colours,
They come in different sizes,
Fat ones, thin ones,
Scary, funny,
Happy ones, sad ones.
Which other ones are there?
Books, books here and there,
They are made out of everything,
Anything you can imagine.
Books, books.

Shannon Murtagh (9)
Goosewell Primary School, Plymouth

Football Is So Nice

Football is so nice
You can play it more than twice
I play it with my friends
Until lunchtime ends.

The aim is to score some goals
In between the poles
Every time we win
We all start to grin.

Jordan Wozencroft (9)
Goosewell Primary School, Plymouth

Charlie My Cat

Charlie is my cat
Her fur is soft and lovely
She's so pretty for a cat
And she's so cuddly.

When she looks out of the door
She makes a funny noise
And scratches with her paw
So she can play with her toys.

She runs around the house
With her tail between her legs
When she plays with her mouse
She sits up and begs.

Bethany Neil (8)
Goosewell Primary School, Plymouth

Henry VIII

Henry VIII was a very fat man,
He had six wives, one named Anne.
Two were beheaded,
Three of them died
And in the end one survived.

Catherine of Aragon would not produce an heir,
Henry got mad and lost all his hair.
But then Jane Seymour came along,
And alas, Henry's son was born.
A few days later Jane Seymour died
And Henry VIII hardly ever cried.

Liana-Maria Brett (10)
Goosewell Primary School, Plymouth

RAF Fighter Pilot

RAF fighter pilot rises above the rest
Exciting as can be,
Low level flying through the mountains.
Complicated buttons,
Which one should he press?
Roller coaster riding 'Excitement Express'.

Daniel Langman (9)
Goosewell Primary School, Plymouth

Football Crazy

I only started football last week,
I was so shy I could not get much sleep.

Football was slow, football was fast,
I had to move, I didn't want to be last.

Once I had the ball, another player made me fall,
Football is fun for everyone.

A penalty was given by the ref,
I scored the goal, the crowd made me deaf.

Football is good for your heart,
So come on and take part.

Oliver Green (9)
Goosewell Primary School, Plymouth

Homework

H istory homework is so old-fashioned
O n geography I'm all over the place
M aths doesn't always add up to me
E nglish, I can't describe how good it is
W ork is alright I suppose
O n science homework I daydream into space
R ight answers make you want to celebrate
K eep your hands off my homework, I've tried hard at this.

Megan Overall (8)
Goosewell Primary School, Plymouth

Fairy Poem

F airies are very pretty
A nd they help other fairies
I n forests you can find fairies and they live in a ring of toadstools
R ead fairy books and the fairies will be happy with you
I like fairies, do you?
E very day fairies will play
S ome fairies have crowns.

Beth Luscombe (9)
Goosewell Primary School, Plymouth

Thank You Letter

(Based on 'Christmas Thank Yous' by Mick Gowar)

Dear Great Great Granny

Thanks for the underpants,
I've always liked luminous orange and green.
What beautiful underwear,
How did you know the ones you sent last year were getting too small?
I have always adored stripy underwear.
Whenever I wear them, I'll always be seen.

Gemma Williams & Rebecca Jones (11)
Goosewell Primary School, Plymouth

Climbing A Tree

Climbing a tree is great fun for me,
Climbing up high and climbing down low,
I climb up high, reaching up to the clear, blue sky,
Down I go to see the green, velvety grass far below.
My mum calls me in for tea,
Bye-bye, see you tomorrow, tree!

Amber Swan (8)
Goosewell Primary School, Plymouth

My Nana

N ana is far away, but it's always wonderful to see her
A lways giving us treats!
N ana is always fun and makes us laugh on our adventures
A lways kissing and cuddling me and makes me smile!

Bethany Elliott (9)
Goosewell Primary School, Plymouth

Monkey Business

Tree swinger
Banana flinger
Tree topper
Belly flopper
Noise filler
Jumping thriller
Grows bigger
Weird figure
Rope hanger
Big banger
Quick mover
Eating hoover
Stick snapper
Class rapper
Messy runner
Escapes the gunner.

Michael Guy (10)
Goosewell Primary School, Plymouth

What Am I?

Swimmer killer
Ferocious diver
Bone cruncher
Silent approacher
Man eater
Flesh tearer
Blood sensor
Turtle eater
Ocean scarer
Razor teether
Moving actor
Ship wrecker.

A: a shark.

Jamie Ranger (10)
Goosewell Primary School, Plymouth

The Old Man And His Dog

There was an old man with a dog,
Who got tired and sat on a log,
When all of a sudden,
A couple of dozen
Ants crawled over the man and his dog.

Ruth Taylor (11)
Goosewell Primary School, Plymouth

What Am I?

A tree climber
A rope swinger
A bug eater
A loud screecher
A banana fiend
A fast mover
A fur festerer
A jungle swinger
A chest beater
A play fighter.

William Cook (11)
Goosewell Primary School, Plymouth

Christmas

C rackers crackled by the tree
H olly sat on the bushes
R eindeer flew away
I went to bed early
S tockings hung by the fire
T he snow fell on my garden
M erry Christmas
A big sack full of presents
S anta came to town.

Harvey Selwood (10)
Goosewell Primary School, Plymouth

What Am I?

Sun lover
Strong fighter
Grass chewer
Fast runner
Quick killer
Grass lover
Bullet hater.

Jake Ley (10)
Goosewell Primary School, Plymouth

Acrostic Poem

C hristmas has come to town
H olly sways in the wind
R udolph is pulling Santa's sleigh
I n the snow Santa falls off the roof
S now is falling
T own has Christmas spirit
M istletoe above every door
A nd Santa gives presents to everyone
S izzling pudding in the oven.

Jordon Pryke (10)
Goosewell Primary School, Plymouth

Cinquain

Brown leaves,
There's a cold breeze,
The temperature's dropped,
Trees are as bare as skeletons,
Carpet.

Whitney Williams (11)
Goosewell Primary School, Plymouth

Jack Ronalds

There once was a man called Jack Ronalds
He always went to McDonald's
He had a cat called Luke
Who always used to puke
That pet of the man called Jack Ronalds.

Billy Gibson (10)
Goosewell Primary School, Plymouth

Cinquain

Splash! splash!
Time for swimming
Jumping in the cool pool
Kids eating ice cream all the time
Good fun!

Hannah Ludwell (11)
Goosewell Primary School, Plymouth

My Puppy Casper

A hand licker,
A playful baby,
A cat chaser,
A fast chaser,
A quick racer,
A cheeky chewer,
A lazy snoozer,
A cuddly cushion,
A treat taker,
A strong sniffer,
A rope tugger,
A swift swimmer.

Imogen Clench (10)
Goosewell Primary School, Plymouth

The Panther

Black hunter
Meat eater
Prey stalker
Loud growler
Good swimmer
Gazelle muncher
Bone cruncher
Water lapper
Serial killer
Life taker
Stunning prowler
Throat piercer.

Eloise Redman (10)
Goosewell Primary School, Plymouth

What Am I?

Fast runner,
Meat eater,
Good hunter,
Spot wearer,
Tree climber,
Smart chaser,
Cute looker,
Vicious starer.

Rebecca Nicholson (10)
Goosewell Primary School, Plymouth

Kennings

Fatal biter
Poison spitter
Belly slitherer
Prey stalker
Tail rattler
Sand lover
Skin shedder
Tree climber
Tunnel burrower
Loud hisser
Animal eater
Cage hater
Music lover.

Alex Gilbert-Smith (10)
Goosewell Primary School, Plymouth

Kennings Duck

Quick swimmer
Bread eater
Loud quacker
Corn lover
Egg layer
Swift flyer
Head ducker
Land waddler
Great looker
Speedy flapper.

George Salisbury (11)
Goosewell Primary School, Plymouth

Summer - Cinquain

Summer
Has come with lots
Of fun swimming and games
Surfing and volleyball are fun
Today.

Richard Lang (11)
Goosewell Primary School, Plymouth

The Jaguar

Skilful mover,
Swift runner,
Meat tearer,
Brilliant climber,
Good pouncer,
Horrible roarer,
Sneaky crawler,
Jungle liver,
Rainforest hunter,
Gunshot hearer,
Deer chaser.

Lydia Gannon (11)
Goosewell Primary School, Plymouth

Kennings

Meat eater
Tree climber
Speedy runner
Deer catcher
Non stopper
Spotty pouncer
Big bouncer
Quick killer
Blood spiller.

Elliott Trivett (11)
Goosewell Primary School, Plymouth

Autumn - Cinquain

Listen,
Leaves are dropping,
The puddles are splashing,
Moods are changing to the season,
Cooling.

Jedd Evans (10)
Goosewell Primary School, Plymouth

A Turtle

A swift swimmer,
An egg layer,
A sea lover,
A slow walker,
A shell shocker,
A belly slider,
A small fish eater,
A solo liver,
A shark hater,
A seaweed gobbler.

Ben Polson (11)
Goosewell Primary School, Plymouth

Kennings

Belly banger,
Rope swinger,
Tree hanger,
Ugly minger,
Banana eater,
Swift runner,
Double seater,
Non stunner,
Cage dweller,
Long liver.

Kieran Jones (10)
Goosewell Primary School, Plymouth

Autumn - Cinquain

Dark sky
The trees are bare
Puddles are emerging
The fog is like a big, white quilt
It's cold.

Ethan Street 10)
Goosewell Primary School, Plymouth

What Am I?

A tree swinger,
A noisy scratcher,
A jungle king,
An arm dragger,
A chest beater,
A tic picker,
A black fur beast,
A loud creature,
A banana eater.

What am I?

Lily Hawkins (11)
Goosewell Primary School, Plymouth

Raindrops - Cinquain

Listen,
To the raining,
It is very wet here,
On the trees, the rain drips on me,
Listen.

Paige Emerson (10)
Goosewell Primary School, Plymouth

The Starving Dog

There once was an old, staving dog,
Who lived in a hollow log,
When it got dark,
He started to bark
And then he ran home in the fog.

Zoe Hamilton (11)
Goosewell Primary School, Plymouth

A Hot Day On A Beach - Cinquain

Big waves
Crashing on beach
Shiny shells in the sand
People having fun on the beach
Hot day.

Robert Tunley (10)
Goosewell Primary School, Plymouth

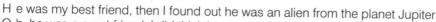

My Best Friend

H e was my best friend, then I found out he was an alien from the planet Jupiter
O h, he was a great friend, I did think he was very odd
L uke he was called
A lways cheery, always funny

C oca-Cola was his favourite drink, he never ate, he always drank Coca-Cola
O n his planet Hola Cola, he was the boss of the mongooses
L aughing to all the mongooses all the time
A h, he was a great friend
    Luke always wore a clown suit his teeth were like razors.

Sophie Bolt (10)
Goosewell Primary School, Plymouth

Tenth Planet?

Satellites hovering through space,
Travelling at an incredible pace,
Trying to find a tenth planet is harder than you think,
Every time we find something,
It appears to be negative and our hopes sink.

But there's more out there
In different galaxies expanding right now!
Who knows, you may find it,
You may be the one to make people say *wow!*

Ryan Hardy (9)
Goosewell Primary School, Plymouth

The Planet Of Planets

Saturn's ring
Twice Jupiter's size
A giant planet
Covered in flies.
Mars has aliens
Mercury's heat
Venus is love
And aliens with cheesy feet.

George Willcocks-King (9)
Goosewell Primary School, Plymouth

My Monster Poem

Watch out, my monster is in my kitchen.
It's spotty, green and blue, hard and bumpy.
It's very, very good at singing and very bad at dancing.
It lives in the kitchen and comes out at night,
Eats food and even gets thirsty,
So then it gets a drink quietly.
Its language is French,
Its behaviour is funny and silly.
It can walk,
My monster eats children and adults.

Megan Lang (8)
Goosewell Primary School, Plymouth

Salaboga

S ad aliens, with excited people
A ll together in one place
L ively child aliens with upset children
A ll under one roof
B ogs, marshes and water
O h no! Blue rain and purple sun, both in one sky
'G oners! We're goners!' aliens shout!
'A mazing! How are we goners?' humans scream.

Amber Clark (9)
Goosewell Primary School, Plymouth

Stormy Weather - Cinquain

Listen
To the rain on
The ground making puddles
With the thunder and lightning too
Listen!

Caitlyn Anderson (10)
Goosewell Primary School, Plymouth

Up In Space!

When I travelled up to space in a spaceship,
At first I was frightened.

I met the alien and asked what was his name?
He said he was called Globeyva, then we both made friends.

After we had made friends, I wasn't so frightened,
Although he did look weird!
I'll tell you what he looked like,
That's if you want to hear.

He is green, has three purple arms and one blue eye,
Two ears on his hands and three fingers on each hand,
Five legs which each have five feet on them and warts.
He doesn't have any toes.

Sounds horrible doesn't it?
But once you get to know him, he's OK.

We sat down for a snack
And Globeyva picked up his food with his feet
And shoved it down his ear.

But there we go, maybe one day
You'll find out that your friend is an alien too!

Jemima Hosking (9)
Goosewell Primary School, Plymouth

Scary Monsters In School

There was a scary monster in school
In the corner of the classroom
I think it came from Pluto, or somewhere else.

It was as big as an elephant
And it smelt like dead fish!
The teachers said he was just little.

He had big, colourful eyes
And his body was green, blue and orange
And very fat.
His legs were gold.

His ears were like water
And his arms were made out of metal.
His lips were bright blue,
Like he had been in water for years!

He had wooden fingers that were teensy
And had a flat nose
That looked like it was squashed,
And his name was Cutey Pie!

Anna Fox (9)
Goosewell Primary School, Plymouth

A Holiday Tour Of Space

Come on, get into the rocket,
Sorry madam, please don't wear that locket.

First the lowly moon,
If it crashes into Earth, we're all doomed.

Now Mars,
If you look at those rocks you'll see they look like cars.

Then Jupiter and Saturn,
And Saturn's rings got flattened.

And next Uranus and Neptune, both a bit blue,
They're also great at solving clues.

And the last one on this side,
Pluto, right let's go back in a swift glide.

And on the other side it's the sun,
Hot enough to set fire to my bun.

Then Mercury and Venus, they're the last,
Let's get home now very fast.

That's the end of my tour by rocket,
Here madam, you can have back your locket.

Kerry Hayes (9)
Goosewell Primary School, Plymouth

My Planet, Jello

My planet is a red, blue and green planet,
Cube, square and rainbow planet,
Jelly monsters rule that place,
Jelly monsters win every race.
They speak every language,
Especially jelly language,
The weather is sunny,
The weather is crummy.
They live in huts,
They watch TV known as the Muts,
Their favourite food is jelly pizza,
With lovely toppings of Margherita.

Hannah Taylor (9)
Goosewell Primary School, Plymouth

My Poem

The sun is not a planet, it's a star big and bright,
It also provides heat and light.
Now Mercury is small and hot,
No wonder, it's the closest planet to the sun.
On Venus, very, very hot it is,
You wouldn't like it there, you'd burn to a crisp.
On Earth here you live,
It's a wicked planet, don't you think?
Well, Mars is small and hot,
Lots of volcanoes and lava, it smells like molten rock.
Jupiter, the biggest planet of them all,
It can fit all the planets in its core.
Saturn belongs to the gas giants,
Can you guess why?
Uranus is a twin to Neptune,
They have lots of things in common.
Neptune is a big planet,
It's blue and fairly giant in size.
Pluto is the smallest planet,
Freezing cold and pink like a piggy.

Connor Clarke (10)
Goosewell Primary School, Plymouth

The Alien City

Last night a mist took over the sky,
When the mist had cleared I saw an alien city,
I looked left and saw a pink planet,
It was shaped like a pig and was raining money,
I guessed it was a piggy bank planet
And on it were walking, talking pigs.

Then I looked right,
I saw a planet shaped like a turkey
And next to it I saw swede, carrots and potatoes,
I saw talking chicken legs and walking chicken legs,
Talking potatoes and swede
And don't forget the gravy waterfall,
Then it disappeared.
It was the best night ever!

Dylan Wheeler (9)
Goosewell Primary School, Plymouth

My Monster

Deep in the sewer you might see a river
Damn cold and very, very stinky.

Deep in the river you might see a monster
He has got three eyes
Funny, orange lips
Bat ears and last but not least
Three weird spikes on top of his head.

My monster lives in the stinky sewer.

My monster's behaviour is very bad
He eats human brains
Eats spiderweb spaghetti
He likes to steal hair dye.

He is brilliant at tricking people
The trick is shaking your hand
Then pulling you and drinking your blood.

His language is Fulucia.

Sam Holland (8)
Goosewell Primary School, Plymouth

I Am An Alien

I am an alien on Mars
They have very big spas
I have seven fingers and seventeen toes
My bum looks big and so does my nose
I look at the moon, it's monsoon season
If you want to go there, you must have a reason.

The sport that we play is minimay
Saturn and Jupiter are near me
They are very clear to see
Venus has got a fly trap
Ooh! It's time for nap-nap.

Samuel Knight (9)
Goosewell Primary School, Plymouth

Oops, It's In Mrs King's Hair

Deep down in the classroom drawer
A little monster lay
With his long, spooky eyes peeping
As the night-time darkens.

At the stroke of midnight
He would jump out
And hide all the long yellow and black pencils
And the short, short rubbers
And hide them behind the speakers and then go to sleep.
Googly has small, dark blue spots and he's very famous too.
He has bumpy skin too.
Googly has wavy arms and legs and small, small wings.
He has an ugly, ugly mouth and short, short legs,
He even has lots of scary eyes.
Googly changes into different colours.

Hannah Rowse (8)
Goosewell Primary School, Plymouth

The Seven Planets

Pluto's size
Half our moon
Jupiter's size, what a surprise
Saturn's aliens with cheesy feet
Uranus' aliens love to eat meat
Venus' heat, got to be doom
And Neptune is big, but nowhere to live
But Mars is a home for Ryan's imaginary friend, Biv.

Luke Reardon (9)
Goosewell Primary School, Plymouth

Mjupiter

M y planet is called Mjupiter.
J ack rabbits live on it with astronauts, moles and ghosts
U would not want to go on it
P eople don't live on it, only astronauts
I t is sunny all year round, all day long
T wo of each creature live on it, eight altogether
E very creature loves it
R eally loves it, a lot.

Lottie Hunt (9)
Goosewell Primary School, Plymouth

My Monster

My monster looks ugly
Hard and slimy
Especially the face
My monster's language is Locumunguse
My monster eats teachers
Girls and boys
Dogs and cats
And fish
My monster
Lives in a haunted house
My monster
Is bad at being good
My monster
Is good at being bad
So watch out!

Yasmin Tucker Cantez (8)
Goosewell Primary School, Plymouth

My Monster

Deep down in the drainpipe
You might see an eleven-eyed monster
Down in the drainpipe
And so -
Watch out, he might eat you!

My monster has eleven eyes
Four long legs
A really big mouth
Twenty-seven teeth
And small, pink wings.

My monster is naughty
He eats teachers and girls.

Aaron Graham (8)
Goosewell Primary School, Plymouth

My Monster Poem

Ben is a very clumsy monster,
He trips up on his feet.
When you come to meet him,
He'll tumble to the ground,
As he's tumbling to the ground,
He'll make a loud sound.
He has big glasses on his blue eyes,
Flies surround him.
He'll trip up on his feet.
His nose is hairy,
But not that scary.
His mouth is covered in drool,
So he won't go to school.
He has a very messy den,
So everyone calls him messy Ben.
He has clothes everywhere,
Even on the stairs.

Jessica Kelly (8)
Goosewell Primary School, Plymouth

My Monster Poem

Watch out for it!
It can hurt you
It is dangerous and eats humans
Its language is Flabadaber
And it is clumsy.

It is good at painting itself.
My monster looks like a crocodile.
It lives in a cave
And it is called Eating Machine.

Paige Bradley (7)
Goosewell Primary School, Plymouth

My Monster

My monster likes eating people
Even junk food,
You will always, always
Have to do what he says
You will regret it if you don't
So mind where you go
He might be there
Right in front of your eyes.

James Oldham (7)
Goosewell Primary School, Plymouth

My Monster Poem

Watch out, it's in your underwear
My monster lives under your bed
She does.
Deep in your sleep
My monster eats
When I'm asleep
She peeps.
She is evil
And good at looking ugly.
She is bad at singing.

Jade Norsworthy (7)
Goosewell Primary School, Plymouth

Aliens

They are smelly
They are bad
They are selfish
They are mad
They are childish
They are green
They are big
They are mean.

Chantal Williams (9)
Goosewell Primary School, Plymouth

A Monster

A monster, a monster
A bloodthirsty monster
He's red and yellow
With razor-sharp teeth
He's fat and ugly
He sleeps under girls' beds
He eats 8-year-olds and drinks their blood.

Scott Lawton (7)
Goosewell Primary School, Plymouth

My Monster

My monster looks like
He has spots on his belly

My monster sounds like
He sounds like a tummy rumbling

My monster moves
He moves carefully

My monster can
Play a guitar with a drink in his hand

My monster lives in
He lives in France

My monster eats
He eats grown-ups.

Ryan Fishlock (7)
Goosewell Primary School, Plymouth

My Monster

Deep in Mrs King's pocket
There is a dribbling, slimy monster.
Watch out!
He might eat you!
He will fly out at night
And whisper bad dreams into your ear.
My monster will be kind to you
If you are kind to him,
So don't get too close
To Mrs King.

Catherine Slope (7)
Goosewell Primary School, Plymouth

My Monster

My monster is furry and funny
And very, very silly
My monster speaks Spanish
And sleeps in your bedroom.
So *watch out* for that monster.

In the daytime
He goes in the kitchen
And then he goes to school.
He is very, very funny
And he makes people laugh.

Leah Tunney (8)
Goosewell Primary School, Plymouth

Four Hundred Mountains

I've never been to a place
Where four hundred mountains lay on the thick, white snow.
Animals in the jungles,
Trees on the islands with no fear.
The beauty of nature
Is like a whole new world spinning in the air.
Then special occasions flash by in your heart.
The time comes when we have to say goodbye to our memories
That will always live strongly in our hearts, deep down.
Our families that will never forget
The crystals of beauty of you as their child,
Because we are all one of a kind.
I've never been to a place
Where four hundred mountains lay on the thick, white snow.

Jasmine Fenn (10)
Grass Royal Junior School, Yeovil

T-Rex

He charges through thick jungle,
With eyes the size of boulders.
He stalks through the darkness of the swamps.

He has found his weak prey.
As fast as lightning he grabs it by the neck
And throws it around like a doll.

He rules his jungle,
A violent king.
Before he sleeps, he roars louder than a lion
To his prehistoric kingdom.

Ross Giles (10)
Grass Royal Junior School, Yeovil

My Cat, Charlie

Charlie wants to sit in a chair, but Barney's sitting there.
Charlie pushes him off just like Garfield, but he doesn't care.
So he just sits there and stares!
Ten o'clock in the morning, Charlie disappeared,
Oh look, I see over there he's asleep on my bed.
Charlie goes and attacks me just on my head.
Ten o'clock at night, all asleep except Charlie,
Charlie's running around Marilyn's instead.
Seven thirty in the morning, Charlie comes home,
Sits in front of the hamster wondering where did he go.
Half an hour later, where did he go?
Guess where he went.
Sound asleep on Mum's bed!

Karla Turner (10)
Grass Royal Junior School, Yeovil

My Dog, Chance

My dog, Chance
His fur is as dark as the sky on a cold winter's night
His eyes are twinkling stars
Now most dogs are kind and playful
And my dog's number one,
But if you are not careful
He'll drool right on your bum!
My dog, Chance
May be cuter than the rest,
But I'd love it so much
If he could play fetch!

Paige De Roeper (10)
Grass Royal Junior School, Yeovil

Summer

Summer glides
Melting ice lollies
Walks through layers of green grass
But never speaks.

Summer skipping
Touching the people and boats
Swaying from east to west
She never frowns.

Summer strolling
By the warm seas
Playing in the sea
Waving goodbye
Before going to sleep.

Beth Wasiewicz (10)
Grass Royal Junior School, Yeovil

Sonic Heroes

S onic in the lead with great speed
O ver cold mountains, a hot desert
N ever to be beaten
I know he will be there for you
C ome to save the world soon

H e's a hero
E very day
R ushing miles away
O pen your heart to this hero
E Xcellent hero
S ave your day because he's coming your way.

Lily Byron-Helyar (10)
Grass Royal Junior School, Yeovil

Summer!

Summer is a glazing bright light
Shining and staring gloriously into gazing eyes.
Summer is as hot as a ruby,
Burning fire heating and warming Earth
In all its heavenly glory.
Summer is when ice creams melt
And drip down sides of cones
Like slow flowing rivers.
Sounds of families playing on the beach.
Colours bloom and sing from leafy trees.
Brings cold gardens to life.
Summer is when misery is put to an end.
Dullness and grey change to a sparkling, golden season.

Dayna Whittingham (10)
Grass Royal Junior School, Yeovil

A Blind One's Colours

A blind man came to me happily and said
'What are colours like dear friend, please tell me.'

Red is like a chilli, smells like fresh strawberries,
Feels like fire, tastes spicy.

Green is like grass swishing by,
Smells like grape juice, feels like peas, tastes sweet.

Yellow is like the sun.
Smells like bananas, feels like a lemon, tastes sour.

Blue is like the sea, crashing.
Smells like a glass of fresh air, tastes like blueberries.

Elisha Davies (10)
Grass Royal Junior School, Yeovil

The Car

The car zooms fast as light without a sound to be heard.
You could hear a pin drop and the whistle of the wind.
You can smell the wind blowing out of the pipes and smashing your nose to pieces.
The bright dazzling colour wakes you up to a happy day.
People think life's a waste. We should be happy once in a while.

Liam Taylor (10)
Grass Royal Junior School, Yeovil

I Have Three Friends

I have three friends
In my home and garden,
One cat, one guinea pig, one fish too
My home and garden is like a zoo.

Love and care and clean and feed,
That's what friends always need.
Chester the cat climbs up the walls,
It helps him to sharpen his healthy claws.

Hamish the guinea pig loves to dig,
His fur is like a wig.
Dec is a goldfish as shiny as can be,
He blows kisses for you and me.

Jack Overy (11)
Grass Royal Junior School, Yeovil

My Grandma

My grandma is good and kind
My grandma is nearly blind.

My grandma is my father's mum
We always have lots of fun.

She is a fantastic dancer but,
Once she had the evil cancer,
It was in her chest, but now it's gone.

And now she's a brilliant grandma to my brother and I,
She looks after us nearly every weekend
And makes us crispy steak pie.

Charlotte Reilly (10)
Grass Royal Junior School, Yeovil

Summer

In the summer it's scorching hot,
Melted, dripping ice lollies we have forgot.
Swimming in the warm ocean-blue water,
Eating scrummy sandwiches that have been cut into quarters.
Playing in the arcades, having lots of fun,
Off to the fish and chip shop as the day is nearly done.
Soon time to get snug in my bed,
Where there's another hot summer's day ahead.

Kalehsha Murphy (11)
Grass Royal Junior School, Yeovil

All My Colours
(Based on 'What is Pink?' by Christina Rossetti)

What is pink?
Lemonade is pink
It's my favourite drink

What is green?
The grass is green
That's all I've seen

What is white?
The cloud is white
So is my kite

What is blue
The sky is blue
Where lots of birds flew

What is red
My Arsenal cover is red
And the hat on my head

What is brown?
My hands are brown
So is my mum's frown

What is orange?
An orange is orange.

Bradley Harris (8)
Grass Royal Junior School, Yeovil

School Time

S chool is a special time of life
C ome along and see what it's like
H ometime children like the most
O ver there's my loving class
O ver there are my excellent friends
L ove school while you're still there

T wo of my friends don't like school
I think deep down they really do
M um and Dad say they do too
E veryone I think really does, so should you.

Jack Palmer (10)
Grass Royal Junior School, Yeovil

Colour Poem

(Based on 'What is Pink?' by Christina Rossetti)

What is pink?
My mum's rubber gloves lying on the sink

What is red?
My Arsenal cover covering my bed

What is blue?
My T-shirt is blue, so is my shoe

What is white?
The cloud is white, so is my kite

What is green?
The grass is green, so is a bean

What is brown?
My hands are brown, it makes my mum frown

What is orange?
Why an orange, just an orange.

Dion Calway (9)
Grass Royal Junior School, Yeovil

Summer

S ummer is a time to chill out
U nder the shimmering tree where blossoms grow
M um goes out to water the sunny sunflower plant
M aybe the shining sun will come out to play
E ating all the juicy fruits of the light green tree
R ainbows come from soft, cushion clouds.

Anna Gullis (11)
Grass Royal Junior School, Yeovil

Muppet

The way he gallops through the field,
The way he trots in the breeze,
The way he makes you yield,
It sometimes catches you,
It makes you sneeze,
But this is a noble horse
And we will always be friends.

Abigail Hayward (10)
Grass Royal Junior School, Yeovil

The Sun

Smiling, glowing now the sun
Floats the day in his golden light.
This way and that, he looks and sees
Golden stalls on shimmering sand.

When he falls to the west,
A slumber he is in,
But when morning comes,
His bed is in the east,
To greet everyone.
Another summer's day.

Joseph Vickers (11)
Grass Royal Junior School, Yeovil

Wings

(Based on 'Wings' by Pie Corbett)

If I had wings
I would swoop down to the ocean floor.

If I had wings
I would stare at the fishes in the ocean.

If I had wings
I would taste the juicy clouds in the sky.

If I had wings
I would touch the end of the clouds.

If I had wings
I would think about a hamster.

Bethany Moore (7)
Hatherleigh Primary School, Hatherleigh

Wings
(Based on 'Wings' by Pie Corbett)

If I had wings
I would hover across the light blue ocean.

If I had wings
I would taste a chunk of the beautiful white clouds like marshmallows.

If I had wings
I would touch the fingertips of the cheesy moon.

If I had wings
I would swoop across the scorching deserts.

If I had wings
I would smell the scent of chocolate cake.

If I had wings
I would dream of flying to the moon.

Ryan Fulford (8)
Hatherleigh Primary School, Hatherleigh

Wings
(Based on 'Wings' by Pie Corbett)

If I had wings
I would glide through the white, milky yellow clouds.

If I had wings
I would munch on the ice like it is ice cream.

If I had wings
I would watch the beautiful animals run around the fields.

If I had wings
I would sniff the fresh air.

If I had wings
I would feel the tops of every house.

If I had wings
I would dream all of the houses are chocolate.

Charlotte Johnson (8)
Hatherleigh Primary School, Hatherleigh

Wings
(Based on 'Wings' by Pie Corbett)

If I had wings
I would sniff the whiff of the cloud's breeze.

If I had wings
I would skim on top of the desert sands.

If I had wings
I would envisage drifting through the cotton clouds.

If I had wings
I would feel the stars with the fingertips of my fingers.

If I had wings
I would devour a chunk of the burning sun.

If I had wings
I would gaze at the seas twinkling in the moonlight.

William Bedford (8)
Hatherleigh Primary School, Hatherleigh

Wings
(Based on 'Wings' by Pie Corbett)

If I had wings
I would hover over the deep blue sea.

If I had wings
I would try to feel the soft, fluffy clouds.

If I had wings
I would try to taste a bite of the fluffy candyfloss clouds.

If I had wings
I would look at the tiny people that look like ants.

If I had wings
I would dream of having a pet rhino.

Kathryn Croom (7)
Hatherleigh Primary School, Hatherleigh

Wings

(Based on 'Wings' by Pie Corbett)

If I had wings
I would swoop through the swishing breeze and across the frying hot desert.

If I had wings
I would kiss the tips of the clouds and swim in the living seas.

If I had wings
I would bite the marshmallow clouds and stuff myself with it until it's gone.

If I had wings
I would stare at the boiling hot sun and stare at the lovely clouds.

If I had wings
I would smell the scent of chocolate and smell the roses.

If I had wings
I would dream of leaping over the moon and swimming through the doors.

Shannon Netherway (9)
Hatherleigh Primary School, Hatherleigh

Wings

(Based on 'Wings' by Pie Corbett)

If I had wings
I would soar through the atmosphere and touch a cloud's thumb.

If I had wings
I would skim across the fluffy waves that pour down.

If I had wings
I would sniff the scent of forming clouds to rain down again.

If I had wings
I would fly to Mars to do my shopping.

If I had wings
I would breathe the aroma of sheep consuming the blue.

If I had wings
I would dream of walking in the air and swimming the Earth.

Chris Meardon (9)
Hatherleigh Primary School, Hatherleigh

Wings
(Based on 'Wings' by Pie Corbett)

If I had wings
I would fly over tropical beaches and stare at the people below.

If I had wings
I would go to the night sky and talk to the man on the moon.

If I had wings
I would swoop over bright blue seas and gaze at the colourful fish.

If I had wings
I would taste a slice of Mars and investigate if it tasted of Mars bars.

If I had wings
I would touch the ends of the oceans.

If I had wings
I would dream of having a ride on a buzzard.

Daniel Rooney (7)
Hatherleigh Primary School, Hatherleigh

Wings
(Based on 'Wings' by Pie Corbett)

If I had wings
I would hover over the warm deserts and the deep blue seas.

If I had wings
I would try to push my beak through the worm holes and munch them.

If I had wings
I would sniff the sweet air.

If I had wings
I would taste the candy clouds.

Benjamin Williams (8)
Hatherleigh Primary School, Hatherleigh

Wings

(Based on 'Wings' by Pie Corbett)

If I had wings
I would glide over the puffy, fluffy clouds.

If I had wings
I would tickle the scorching hot sun.

If I had wings
I would gobble a bite of the cold icy sea.

If I had wings
I would sniff the scent of dripping green trees.

If I had wings
I would glance at the soft milky clouds.

If I had wings
I would daydream of a chocolate world with everybody made of chocolate.

Rachel Boyland (9)
Hatherleigh Primary School, Hatherleigh

Wings

(Based on 'Wings' by Pie Corbett)

If I had wings
I would glide through the fluffy clouds.

If I had wings
I would rise up and nibble the moon.

If I had wings
I would hover and examine the sun.

If I had wings
I would imagine flying over the ocean.

Naomi Chaney (7)
Hatherleigh Primary School, Hatherleigh

Wings
(Based on 'Wings' by Pie Corbett)

If I had wings
I would swoop down to the oceans and stare at the fish.

If I had wings
I would fly in the air to taste the milky clouds.

If I had wings
I would touch the sky.

If I had wings
I would taste the shiny sun.

If I had wings
I would rise over the boiling deserts.

If I had wings
I would dream of going to the circus.

Shannon Leahy (8)
Hatherleigh Primary School, Hatherleigh

Wings
(Based on 'Wings' by Pie Corbett)

If I had wings
I would kiss the sweet candy on the clouds.

If I had wings
I would pop in homes and taste the roast.

If I had wings
I would glide round the stars.

If I had wings
I would rise like the sun.

If I had wings
I would dream of walking the sky and swimming the earth.

Joshua Chaney (8)
Hatherleigh Primary School, Hatherleigh

Christmas Time

At Christmas time
I can see Santa's
Radical reindeers
Running.

At Christmas time
I can hear the
Golden bells ringing.

At Christmas time
I can smell the
Taste of turkey.

At Christmas time
I can touch the
Squidgy pudding.

Ellie-Mae Hayman (7)
Hatherleigh Primary School, Hatherleigh

Wings
(Based on 'Wings' by Pie Corbett)

If I had wings
I would doze on the cushion of the clouds.

If I had wings
I would guzzle the marshmallow of the clouds.

If I had wings
I would feel the wool of the clouds.

If I had wings
I would stare at the boats that sail across the sea.

If I had wings
I would glance at the bright moon.

Austin Guest (9)
Hatherleigh Primary School, Hatherleigh

Wings
(Based on 'Wings' by Pie Corbett)

If I had wings
I would swoop through the veil of darkness and emerge
Into dazzling sunlight.

If I had wings
I would skim the murky seas with my wingtips
And open into a glittering archway.

If I had wings
I would taste a chunk of sun,
As hot as a green chilli.

If I had wings
I would drift through the sun's golden rays
And gaze into the heavens.

If I had wings
I would stroke the tips
Of the wispy clouds.

If I had wings
I would dream of breathing earth
And drinking air.

Esther Feaver (9)
Hatherleigh Primary School, Hatherleigh

Wings
(Based on 'Wings' by Pie Corbett)

If I had wings
I would rise over the boiling deserts.

If I had wings
I would intake a smell of the swishing breeze.

If I had wings
I would kiss the edge of the milky clouds.

If I had wings
I would nibble a tiny bit of the moon.

If I had wings
I would go into the dancing circus.

If I had wings
I would imagine marrying an elephant.

Harriet van Houben (8)
Hatherleigh Primary School, Hatherleigh

Wings
(Based on 'Wings' by Pie Corbett)

If I had wings
I would drift over the boiling desert and over the seven seas.

If I had wings
I would chew the milky clouds of cotton candy.

If I had wings
I would shake the hand of the raindrops.

If I had wings
I would glance at the Milky Way.

If I had wings
I would sniff the chocolatey smell of Mars.

If I had wings
I would imagine that I could walk through the walls
And find myself in another land.

Claire Munn (8)
Hatherleigh Primary School, Hatherleigh

Wings
(Based on 'Wings' by Pie Corbett)

If I had wings
I would rise through the sky.

If I had wings
I would swoop through the air.

If I had wings
I would watch the worms peck out of their muddy holes.

If I had wings
I would hover to see what's going on.

Abigail Piper (8)
Hatherleigh Primary School, Hatherleigh

Wings
(Based on 'Wings' by Pie Corbett)

If I had wings
I would swoop down to the wide open seas.

If I had wings
I would have a taste of Venus.

If I had wings
I would stare at the rooftops.

If I had wings
I would cuddle the edges of the clouds.

If I had wings
I would imagine diving into a swimming pool.

Tom Strawbridge (7)
Hatherleigh Primary School, Hatherleigh

Wings
(Based on 'Wings' by Pie Corbett)

If I had wings
I would swoop through the town
And see the people walking.

If I had wings
I would fly through woods
I would skim the seas
And touch the Milky Way.

If I had wings
I would taste the cheese of the moon.

Dan Friend (8)
Hatherleigh Primary School, Hatherleigh

Wings
(Based on 'Wings' by Pie Corbett)

If I had wings
I would swoop over the white summer seaside.

If I had wings
I would feel the yellow hot sun.

If I had wings
I would handle the spongy jumpy milk clouds.

If I had wings
I would view people playing football.

Roxanne Hall (8)
Hatherleigh Primary School, Hatherleigh

Wings
(Based on 'Wings' by Pie Corbett)

If I had wings
I would hover over the seven seas.

If I had wings
I would breathe through the clouds.

If I had wings
I would munch the moon.

If I had wings
I would swoop around the sun.

If I had wings
I would drift around the world.

If I had wings
I would stare at the people on the ground.

Sam Halsted-Cann (9)
Hatherleigh Primary School, Hatherleigh

Wings
(Based on 'Wings' by Pie Corbett)

If I had wings
I would glide to the oceans.

If I had wings
I would stuff myself with the cheesy moon.

If I had wings
I would touch the fingertips of the stars.

If I had wings
I would fly to the chocolate factory.

If I had wings
I would dream about Man U winning.

Nicolas Orbell (9)
Hatherleigh Primary School, Hatherleigh

Wings
(Based on 'Wings' by Pie Corbett)

If I had wings
I would swoop over the clouds.

If I had wings
I would inhale the air.

If I had wings
I would chew the cheesy moon.

If I had wings
I would glance at the animals below me.

If I had wings
I would daydream that I was in outer space.

Tiffany Wheeler (8)
Hatherleigh Primary School, Hatherleigh

There Once Was A Girl Called Ems

There once was a girl called Ems
Who swallowed a packet of pens,
They drew on her tummy,
So she called for her mummy
But fell into the River Thames.

Emily Jayne Speed (10)
Hazeldown Primary School, Teignmouth

There Was An Old Man From Bude

There was an old man from Bude,
Who was incredibly rude,
He stuck out his tongue,
And rolled in some dung,
Then ended by running round nude!

Tania Jeffrey (10)
Hazeldown Primary School, Teignmouth

Stationery Rap

This is the stationery rap (rap)
This rap has no mishap (mishap)
If you're thinking of departing,
When we're already starting,
Then you'd better stay right here.

Pencils dance around like mad
Rubbers bounce on the stationery pad,
Scissors do the splits up high
Look at the crayon fly, *oh my!*

Rulers happily do the cancan
Sharpeners sizzle like a frying pan,
Handwriting pens jig to the beat
I can tap the beat with both my feet.

Clap-clap, clap-clap-clap!

Gel pens jiggle across the page
The sellotape's dying of old age,
Fountain pens go *splat, splat, splat!*
My pencil case is fat, fat!

Anastasia Cope (10) & Amelia Laxton (11)
Hazeldown Primary School, Teignmouth

Kennings Eagle

Rodent eater
Prey beater
High flyer
Rare crier
Graceful soarer
Meat gnawer
Egg layer
Food slayer
Deep thinker
Water drinker
Powerful catcher
Bird snatcher.

Harry Driscoll (10)
Hazeldown Primary School, Teignmouth

Cheeky Monkeys!

When cheeky monkeys come out to play
They goof around most of the day
But sometimes they will love to eat
A big yellow banana as a treat!
The boy monkeys will play in dirt
When the girl monkeys just want to flirt
They climb the trees and fool around
The mums and dads just stand and frown.
They swing and sing out happily
We're all cheeky monkeys, you and me!
When they get home they have their tea
They are very tired, you would be
If you were a cheeky monkey!

Heidi Oliver (11)
Hazeldown Primary School, Teignmouth

Hamster Kennings

Food cruncher
Tube muncher
Late sleeper
Night creeper
Wheel spinner
Scoffs dinner
Paw patter
Sawdust scatter
Warm hugger
Bed tugger.

Fiona Riches (10)
Hazeldown Primary School, Teignmouth

Please Mrs Mintey
(Based on 'Please Mrs Butler' by Allen Ahlberg)

'Please Mrs Mintey
This boy Colin Kay,
Keeps calling me a fat head Miss
How can I get away?'

'Hide in the toilet dear
Run across the hall,
Climb over the fence dear
Hide under someone tall.'

'Please Mrs Mintey
This boy Colin Kay,
Keeps grabbing me by the neck Miss,
How can I get away?'

'Jump off a mountain dear
Whack him in the head,
Hide under the table dear
Run home and go to bed.'

'Please Mrs Mintey
This boy Colin Kay,
Keeps sneezing on my work Miss
How can I get away?'

'Work on the roof dear
Call him silly names,
Do what he did to you dear
Or just shut up and run away.'

'Please Mrs Mintey
This boy Colin Kay
Keeps hitting me with a pencil Miss
How can I get away?'

'Jump out the window dear
Put poison in his food,
Tell the headmaster dear
You can even be rude.'

Elliott Simpson (10)
Holway Park Primary School, Taunton

Wings
(Based on 'Wings' by Pie Corbett)

If I had wings
I would soar through the soft milky clouds.

If I had wings
I would spy down on the people that are sticking to the Earth.

If I had wings
I would swoop down to the oceans and watch the fish down below me.

If I had wings
I would sweep over the school and watch the children playing in the playground.

If I had wings
I would sweep on the wind's breath.

If I had wings
I would dream of being a human.

Megan Hobson (8)
Hatherleigh Primary School, Hatherleigh

Wings
(Based on 'Wings' by Pie Corbett)

If I had wings
I would fly across
Oceans and swoop over the mountains.

If I had wings
I would stare at people
And grab milky clouds.

If I had wings
I would hover above the town
And look through the windows.

If I had wings
I would cut through the clouds and ride on them.

Ben Anstey (7)
Hatherleigh Primary School, Hatherleigh

Please Mrs Hughes
(Based on 'Please Mrs Butler' by Allen Ahlberg)

'Please Mrs Hughes
This boy Steven Drew
Shoved me down the toilet Miss
What shall I do?'

'Hide in a cupboard dear,
Climb up a tree,
Lock yourself in the shed, my dear
But don't bother me.'

'Please Mrs Hughes
This boy Steven Drew,
Kicked me under the table Miss
What shall I do?'

'Go and work in the garden dear,
Go and work in a tree,
Go and work in the playground dear
But don't bother me!'

Kelsey Dalley (10)
Holway Park Primary School, Taunton

Please Mrs Cutler
(Based on 'Please Mrs Butler' by Allen Ahlberg)

'Please Mrs Cutler
This boy Andy Lou,
Keeps hitting me Miss
What shall I do?'

'Runaway home love
Hit him with a bone
Or maybe a comb dear
But I want to be alone.'

'Please Mrs Cutler
This boy Andy Lou,
Keeps throwing rubbers Miss
What shall I do?'

'Hurt him with a broom love
Hurt him all night,
Put him in a dark room dear
But I'm going for a bite.'

Harry Stannett (11)
Holway Park Primary School, Taunton

The Rugby Wocky
(Inspired by 'Jabberwocky' by Lewis Carroll)

The match is about to start,
The players are signing autographs,
The teams are going apart
The fans are taking photographs.

Beware of the Johnny my son!
The tackles that hurt,
The kicks that punish,
The runs that make people eat dirt.

The ref takes his whistle in his hand,
The kicker starts the game off,
The crowds are going mad
One of the TV cameras gets broken.

The front row's bound to make a big hit
It makes all the backs fall over
The scrum collapses and makes a pit
A player scores a try and kills the rugby wocky
The player gets the conversion
The match has ended
The players are signing autographs.

Billy Massingham (10)
Holway Park Primary School, Taunton

Please Mrs Gould
(Based on 'Please Mrs Butler' by Allen Ahlberg)

'Please Mrs Gould
This girl Danny Drew
Keeps hitting me Miss,
What shall I do?'

'Go and sit in the corner dear
Go and sit in the sink,
Take your work onto the window my sweet
Do whatever you think.'

'Please Mrs Gould
This girl Danny Drew
Keeps calling me rude names Miss,
What shall I do?'

'Lock yourself away my dear
Run away to sea,
Do whatever you can my son,
But don't ask me!'

Connie Carter (10)
Holway Park Primary School, Taunton

179

When I Am Old
(Based on 'Warning' by Jenny Joseph)

When I am old I shall have wrinkles and smell of violet.
I shall sit in my cosy chair reading my book and wearing my purple satin slippers.
I will wear a lilac frock with a light blue hat
With cream gloves and a wooden walking stick.
I shall not use it much but it's just in case.
I will wear a red brooch on my favourite cardigan.
I will keep a stack of hot-cross buns in my cupboard which no one will know.
I shall keep sweets for people who visit.
I will be a kind old lady, I will miss my childhood.
When I go out for my daily walk
I will greet people with a happy hello.
I'll pop in to the shops to get a few things
Perhaps buy myself a packet of marshmallows.

Hannah Cook (10)
Holway Park Primary School, Taunton

When I Am Old
(Based on 'Warning' by Jenny Joseph)

When I am old I shall eat bread, butter and jam
And all I will drink is red wine.

But my outfit will be completely different to anyone else's,
It will be some suede shoes with my blue shirt and my long black cloak.

As I walk in the street in a bad mood
People who annoy me I will poke them with my stick (unlucky for them!)

When I walk through the park I will see children playing football just like me
I used to play for Holloway FC.

As I used to go to the seaside and throw stones in the sea
I can't do that anymore but I do enjoy watching other children throw stones
And while I enjoy the sun I'm the luckiest man ever.

Joseph Coombes (10)
Holway Park Primary School, Taunton

When I Am Old
(Based on 'Warning' by Jenny Joseph)

When I am old I want to be wise
And have everything nice,
Singing an old time classic song
In my chair rocking.

When I see a pig
Which is very big
I ride on its back
As if I am on horseback.

I will go to town and go shopping
For something good for eating,
I pick up non-solid foods,
I pick up liquid foods.

Why? Because I have no teeth
Because I want to feed
To satisfy my need,
To ease the pressure on my feet.

I will wear oversized shirts and grow fatter,
I will have my old friends come for dinner
And read newspapers, listening to the music cassette
And dance all day until the American sunset.

Rumbidzai Dozwa (11)
Holway Park Primary School, Taunton

Chocowocky
(Inspired by 'Jabberwocky' by Lewis Carroll)

It was crammed in the newsagents
As I went to get my éclairs,
I could smell the Cadbury's at the counter
And at the Mars I stared.

Beware my son, don't eat too much
Or you will have a filling,
And you will have to bear the brunt
Of all the dentist's drilling!

I took the Toffee crisp in hand
And stood a while in thought,
As I stared at the Minstrel stack
And there I stood and bought.

And coming out of the shop I saw
A Cadbury on the floor,
I picked it up and took it home
And left it in the drawer.

Pagan Ferguson (10)
Holway Park Primary School, Taunton

Trains

Whizzing around the tiny track,
Shiny trains shunting back.
Large and small,
Crossing huge bridges
They must not fall.
Dirty and clean,
Their smoke stacks gleam,
Watching the engines going around the track.

Creeping slowly up steep hills
And racing down the other side,
Peep! Peep! Goes the whistle,
Whoosh! Replies the escaping steam,
Like a cloud of white cotton wool.
Amazing trains carrying goods
And people to far away places.

Shooting around the bend,
Into the silent station,
Slowly screeching to a halt,
People jumping in and out,
Wheels start rolling,
Faster and faster
To a new destination.

Bradley Chant (7)
Horsington CE Primary School, Templecombe

Reflections On Winter

Frosty fields and snowy benches,
Sparkly webs on gates and fences,
Icy ponds in the park,
We go home early because of the dark.

Morning coming the snow is gone
I hope that winter goes on and on,
Snow is coming; we dress up to go outside,
Crunching sounds from the fresh snow,
Snow angels and snowballs,
Splintering ice on the pond,
Ducks and birds skating along,
Children slipping on the ice.

Alison Jeans (7)
Horsington CE Primary School, Templecombe

Snow

Snow sparkles like the sun on a river,
Snow sparkles down like icing
Just like the jewels on the Queen's crown.

Snow sparkles,
Skates shine like a glowing sun,
Skates shimmer on the shining ice,
Spinning around
It is so much fun!

Wellies splash like a whale in a pool,
Wellies crunch in the snow,
Keeping us warm with hats and scarves.

Kicking up the twinkling snow,
Throwing crunchy snowballs,
Building amazing snowmen,
Winter's always fun!

Millie Powell-Thomas (7)
Horsington CE Primary School, Templecombe

My Favourite Things

I have many favourite things,
Some have shiny wings.
Enormous-headed baby dolls
And card tricks to amaze.
Turning handles on my bubblegum machine.
Yummy, coloured, sugary sweets from my shop,
Sliding skateboard flipping up,
Wheelies on my gleaming bike,
Whizzing down the hills
On my smashing scooter.
But most of all
I love my pretty pink pig.

Chloe Hannigan (8)
Horsington CE Primary School, Templecombe

Snow

Shiny, snow, sparking snow, shimmering snow,
Spreads across the wonderful world like a gigantic white blanket.
Faster and faster the glittering snowflakes drift down.
Tiny flakes together make huge snowdrifts.
Making freezing snowballs out of fairy dust.
Building crazy snowmen, icicles twist in the breeze.
Excited children playing with white icing.

Daisy Liddle (7)
Horsington CE Primary School, Templecombe

Rugby

Rugby is a deadly war,
It's tough!
You might end up on the floor,
Rugby is a brilliant sport,
Running as fast as a cheetah,
Feel the wind try to catch you,
You'll get grubby!

Tag rugby is fun for all,
Groovy girls and bossy boys,
Rushing to catch the spaceship shaped ball,
Tails wagging round and round,
Pulling, pushing and running around
The enormous pitch as big as a calm sea!

My team scores a try
The crazy crowds go wild
As they jump for joy
My fabulous team wins!

Lauren Armson (8)
Horsington CE Primary School, Templecombe

Snow

The white soft snow
Covers the marvellous world
Like a smooth sparkling duvet.
Shiny snowflakes drifting down like beautiful bubbles.
Transparent icicles
Hanging from the evergreen trees,
Like Christmas baubles.
Ice skaters skating on frozen lakes,
Their fingers tingle as they spin around,
Silent snowmen wait sadly for the thaw!

Phoebe Smith (7)
Horsington CE Primary School, Templecombe

Dragons

Black smoke fills the air,
Blotting out the shining sun
As the flying dragon attacks the village.
Dragons are like massive tanks,
Smashing down riverbanks,
Dragons have fiery breath,
Bringing people to a painful death
Shiny swords and mighty lords,
Armoured horses and heavy forces,
All of which have lots of power
But the dreadful dragon is as large as a castle tower!

One brave knight picked up his metal lance,
He saw he had a fair chance,
The shining brave knight aimed at the scaly belly
He turned the dreadful dragon into jelly,
Now that the deed was done
The smoke cleared
So they could see the sun!

Hugh Johnson (8)
Horsington CE Primary School, Templecombe

Winter

Rushing outside,
I noticed many things,
Ice patterns on the windowpane,
Snow crumbles and ice smashes,
Icicles hanging from the roof,
Smoke weaving from the chimney,
Footprints arriving at the door,
Birds dragging for some food,
And me outside building a snowman.

Georgie Thorne (8)
Horsington CE Primary School, Templecombe

Crazy Tennis

The great court on the school playground
It is like a wall of net.
As the mighty nets are set up
The game will soon commence.
As I get my Raven racket
My opponent collects his huge racket,
I pluck my strings,
Nervously,
My serve is *out!*

Second service in,
Backwards and forwards,
We return the yellow ball to each other
Out! As the ball skids out
I dance with joy,
But soon he is returning my service
With a tremendous backhand.
I smash it hard onto the ground.
There is no rebound.
Joy, as I finally win!

William Jackson (8)
Horsington CE Primary School, Templecombe

Insects In The Bathroom

Lying in my bath
Imagining many things,
Earwigs counting their feet
They look really neat.
Imagine woodlice waving at me,
Spiders jumping into the sink
Where ants had discovered a skating rink.
A yellow ladybird was skiing on the side of the bath
A purple butterfly was applying her make-up on each eye,
I shouted, 'Hey, all of you, when you have finished
Splishing and splashing, shaving and washing, misbehaving
Can I come in, for just one minute please?'

Thomas Crabb (8)
Horsington CE Primary School, Templecombe

Fantastic Football

Football is great,
Football is fun,
But it will never be better than my dad and mum!
A football is like a ball of string,
Fantastic football is an amazing thing.

Football is great,
Football is fun,
But it will never be better than my dad and mum!
The sphere-shaped football is caked in mud,
Which makes it hit the ground with a thumping thud,
Here comes the referee with a shining new ball,
That looks like a ball of wool,
The darkness of the night begins to fall,
The keeper makes a save and hits his head,
The crazy fans are roaring, 'Is he dead?'
One of the players is feeling ill,
So they give him a special pill!

Football is great,
Football is fun,
But it will never be better than my dad and mum!
Winning is a brilliant thing,
But don't get upset if you keep on losing
The green grass shimmering in the sun,
Everyone is having fun,
Eating their hot meat pies,
The ball gets kicked into the shining sky!

Charlie Martin (9)
Horsington CE Primary School, Templecombe

Snowflakes

Snow is falling making everything white
Children laughing
Eating snowflakes that land on their tongues
Freezing toes and cold noses
Splashing ice and tingling icicles
Frozen locks on the car
Icy windows need de-icing
Skating and sliding on the ice
Paying snowball fights
Building snowmen
Snow crunches underfoot.

Selina Targett (8)
Horsington CE Primary School, Templecombe

Football

Football is my favourite activity,
Because it is so exciting,
I like kicking the ball
Smashing it into the corner of the net.
The emerald and apple green grass
Like the rainforest paint,
Always greener than before.

Football brings me so much fun
You can be sure
Just kicking the ball
Around on the muddy ground
Using my skills
Makes me feel head over heels.
Taking penalties is so exciting
As long as they cross the line just in time.
The greatest feeling
Is when I'm playing well
Curling the ball into the net
Just like the speed of a jet.

Robin Batchelor (9)
Horsington CE Primary School, Templecombe

My Kite

I love my beautiful blue and white kite
Watching it parade in the fierce wind
Running with the end of the string held tightly
Soaring high in the blue sky
Twisting and turning
Climbing higher
Catching on finger-like branches on the oak tree
It suddenly rips and tears
My sad kite flaps around
No more will it soar!

Lizzie King (8)
Horsington CE Primary School, Templecombe

A Great Game

Football is the greatest game in the world,
It's even better than smashing school!
The referee comes out of the tunnel
With a shining, glimmering ball,
Covered with black and white hexagonal shapes.

The two skippers shake shivering hands,
While the musical band go to sit in the noisy stand.
The grass is green,
The players gleam
And the excited fans are settling down.

Light is fading,
Night is gaining,
Time is marching on.

The second half starts
And the stocky Rooney scores an amazing goal.
One minute till the end
And fortunes change with a goal from Celtic's skipper.
'What a great game!' chant all the fantastic fans.

Jack Wingate (9)
Horsington CE Primary School, Templecombe

Kennings Who Am I?

Very rare
Bamboo lover
Black 'n' white
China liver
Mountain roamer
Snow leopard enemy
Cub haver
Daxiogmao namer
Award winner.

Katie Walker (11)
Hugh Sexey Middle School, Wedmore

Hoof Prints In The Snow

It's freezing cold as we walk down the lane
There's nothing but white as it's snowed again.
Icicles line the branches of trees
Glitter and twinkle in the cool breeze.
I've taken to the common and across the snow
Leaving trails of hoof prints as we go.
Making a soft and crunching sound
That seems so loud in the silence around.
We head to the hill and I push you to trot
And we chase the cold all the way to the top.
Where we stand and look at the beautiful scene
Of a country pure white, where once it was green.
I glance behind us back down the slope
And see all our patterns defacing the snow.
Then the wind blows a flurry again down the lane
The prints vanish it's pure once again.
So we laugh at Jack Frost and your excitement mounts high
And as the snow falls you rear to the sky.
Challenging the winter to this new sport
We walk down the hill but share the same thought.
I tip you to canter across the common we go
Once again leaving hoof prints in the snow.

Caitlin Horsnett-Bowley (10)
Hugh Sexey Middle School, Wedmore

What Am I?

Sound hunter
Good chanter
Dripping jaws
Spiky claws
Fox eater
Stomach heater
Hunting horn
Whip's worn.

Sally Eccles (11)
Hugh Sexey Middle School, Wedmore

A Book Of Rhymes And Limericks

There was a young man called Jake
Who fell in a very big lake
He couldn't swim
He made a very big din
And then he got bitten by a snake.

There was a young man called Len
Who stabbed himself with a pen
It was like an injection
He got an infection
And he met some men.

There was a young lady called Jane
Who was a very big pain
She put powder down the teacher's pants
In the lavatory she puts ants
And very often got the cane.

Sarah Bale (10)
Hugh Sexey Middle School, Wedmore

A Diamond

A
Diamond
Is the hardest
Thing on the planet
The only thing that can
Crack it is itself. So
Don't try and crack
It because you
Will fail.

Ashley Brill (10)
Hugh Sexey Middle School, Wedmore

The Strange Maid Called Peach

There was an old maid called Peach
Who liked going to the beach,
She took her bucket and spade
Sandcastles she made,
That unusual maid called Peach.

Danielle Callow (11)
Hugh Sexey Middle School, Wedmore

Match Winner

Get ready
Prepare kit bag
Travel in car
Nice and steady.

Warm up
Sign in
Spin the racket
Play to win.

Keep cool
Break at set
Work hard
Running sweat.

Now it's time
Forehand inner
Down the line
Match winner!

Toby Mitchell (11)
Hugh Sexey Middle School, Wedmore

Monkey - Kennings

Flea picker
Banana licker
Rope swinger
Tree clinger
Brown and hairy
Not that scary
Jungle muncher
Nut cruncher
Sometimes chunky
I'm a monkey!

Laura Baker (10)
Hugh Sexey Middle School, Wedmore

My Dog - Cinquain

My dog
Four furry legs
Two big, shining, brown eyes
Long, pink tongue and smelly bad breath
But cute!

Emily Thorowgood (11)
Hugh Sexey Middle School, Wedmore

Colour Monster

Crowd killer
Frightening footsteps
Roadrunner
Jumping jogger
Very dumb
Massive destroyer
Long nails
Weird wings
Flexible belly
Brown thumbs
Grumpy and green
Purple fingers
Red eyes
Colour monster!

Chris Spittal (11)
Hugh Sexey Middle School, Wedmore

Always Eat Your Toenails

Always eat your toenails,
Cos you will grow up big and strong.
Your parents might think you're weird
But I don't think it's wrong.

Always eat your eyelashes,
Cos they taste really nice.
If you don't eat them
Share them with your mice.

Always eat your earwax
Cos you'll get really cool.
It may seem strange
But believe me it's the rule.

Lucy Woodman (10)
Hugh Sexey Middle School, Wedmore

My Kennings

Humans' hell
Crunch crack
Snap scream
Dark death
Clever clinger
Long locker
Long liver
High hider
Mean killer
Risk life
You die
What am I?
I'm an anaconda.

Jordan Southey (10)
Hugh Sexey Middle School, Wedmore

Dolphin

Ocean bullet
Sea jumper
Deep diver
Fish teaser
Shark's dinner
Ocean skimmer
Intelligent swimmer
Trapped by trawler
Clicking caller.

Daniel Bond (11)
Hugh Sexey Middle School, Wedmore

My Crocodile

Here lies my crocodile
He had such a lovely smile,
With glinting teeth and warm eyes,
It came as such a surprise
When my mum came to say
'Crocodile has gone away.'

Thomas Day (11)
Hugh Sexey Middle School, Wedmore

The Ballad Of Private Peaceful

Charlie and Tommo were brothers,
A tree fell one day on their father,
It's sad but they'd still got their mother,
Their father was a carpenter and carver.

The colonel had good land for fishing,
The boys went out and poached there,
They sat under the bridge wishing,
That the colonel wouldn't find them there.

He caught them there one day,
It turned out he was very cross,
They said they were there just to play,
He shot their dog and part of their family was lost.

A parade came down the road and played,
Their instruments were solid gold,
They kept on marching and didn't stay,
It was about the war but you had to be seventeen years old.

Charlie went, so did Tommo,
They went off on their first train trip,
A man said they would start tomorrow,
They had to fill in an age slip.

They both got through and they were glad,
But they realised they were homesick,
They found out that it was very bad,
The time went by tick-tock-tick.

They went to France and then to Germany,
It was horrible and unexpected,
They didn't do what they were told so they were told off firmly,
Their trenches were by Hanley inspected.

Charlie went to prison for not obeying,
Tommo came to visit him a lot,
Goodbye and sorry they were saying,
Then Charlie was taken to be shot!

Molly Efford (11)
Hugh Sexey Middle School, Wedmore

Bugs - Cinquain

Slimy
Creepy-crawlies
Crawling along the ground
Biting, itchy and poisonous
Yuck bugs!

Elizabeth Bradley (11)
Hugh Sexey Middle School, Wedmore

Nutmeg, Nutmeg

Here is the grave
Of hamster Nutmeg.
The things we saw over the years
Like the time she won the best pet prize.
We've shared laughter and tears
All she said was true not lies.

Her scent was sweet and pure
Her eyes emerald-green.
Glossy and soft was her fur
She was the loveliest thing ever seen.

When she died, oh when she died
Deathly fog descended.
As much as I have really tried
The hole in my heart never mended.

Saddened and lonely was our town
'Please don't die,' we did beg,
We buried her deep in the ground
But a cat saw her leg.

He dug her up
And ate her whole
So in that cat
Lies Nutmeg's soul.

Katie Richards (10)
Hugh Sexey Middle School, Wedmore

There Was An Old King From Tring

There was an old king from Tring
Who thought it was fun to sing
The queen didn't agree
And put poison in his tea
And that was the end of the king.

Lily Madsen (11)
Hugh Sexey Middle School, Wedmore

My Pet Rabbit

I'll never see him again
I feel so sad.
I've cried and cried
Once I found out my rabbit had died.
He made me laugh he was so funny
And he died though he was only a bunny.
I had him for a year
Since I got him, him dying was always my fear.
I love to see him playing around
On the soft, moist ground.
It was a lovely pet
Who was loved even by his vet.
I loved to see him lie on my lap
Sometimes he even snoozed into an afternoon nap.
I love him with all my heart
My heart would be broken if we were split apart.
Now he's six feet under the ground
Where on top of him there is an earthy, soil mound.
I just want to see him one more time
One more stroke, one more cuddle before he died.

Rachel Wilson (10)
Hugh Sexey Middle School, Wedmore

Always . . .

Always eat your bogies
You'll grow up green and strong
Some people may think you're ugly
But I don't think it's wrong.

Always suck your blood
It will taste of iron
You'll grow up a stud
If your name is Brian!

Callum McKenzie (11)
Hugh Sexey Middle School, Wedmore

Tongue Twister

Red robin robbed a rubber from a robber.
Then Robert the robber ran from the red robin right into rubbish.
The red robin rummaged through the rubbish then found some rhubarb.
Then the red robin robbed more rubbers from the robber.

William Richardson (10)
Hugh Sexey Middle School, Wedmore

Wangeep

The land of the wangeep we go,
The scary trees whisper and blow,
It's as dark as the night
Would give you a fright
We enter his house, oh no!

But as we got into the cave
We suddenly got a skin shave,
He can fly in the skies
And eats human pies,
But then he disappeared, he'd gone!

We sprinted back to our boat
But our ship was not afloat
The wangeep came along
Singing his song,
But he drowned us in his moat.

Joshua Page (10)
Hugh Sexey Middle School, Wedmore

Sometimes

Sometimes I hate my mate.
Sometimes I go to the park in the dark.
Sometimes I'm bored with the Lord.
Sometimes I'm late for my date.
Sometimes I'm done with having fun.
Sometimes I'm mad when I'm sad.
Sometimes my buddy gets muddy.
Sometimes I play all day.
Sometimes I need a nappy when I'm happy.
Sometimes . . .
But only sometimes . . .
I'm not!

Chelsea Mitchell (10)
Hugh Sexey Middle School, Wedmore

My Kite

Swooping in the air
Surfing the sky
Chasing the clouds
Way up high
See my kite fly
It will never die.

Lucy Burgess (10)
Hugh Sexey Middle School, Wedmore

Witches' Potion
(Based on 'Macbeth')

Double, double, toil and trouble,
Fire burn and cauldron bubble.

A touch of hair
From a moody mare,
Children's nails
And rotten bales.
Cows' brains
Sprinkled with poisoned rain.

Double, double, toil and trouble,
Fire burn and cauldron bubble.

Witches' knuckles
And someone's buckles.
Pig dung,
Mixed with sticks from Ker-plunk.
Cigarette smoke,
Combined with guts from your old folks.

Double, double, toil and trouble,
Fire burn and cauldron bubble.

Bats' lips
And the king's hips.
Eyes from a frog
And a tail from a dog.
Cat's nose
And someone's toes.

Double, double, toil and trouble,
Fire burn and cauldron bubble.

Lauren Reason (10)
Hugh Sexey Middle School, Wedmore

My Poor Hamster

My poor hamster
Is now deep down
He lives in the soil
All wet and brown
All he is now
Is a big fat bone
Me and my mum always
Moan, moan, moan!

Melissa Noble (10)
Hugh Sexey Middle School, Wedmore

Kennings Who Am I?

Bone hunter
Food muncher
Amazing swimmer
Great fetcher
Toy player
Cat chaser
Wicked walker
Racing runner

Funny walker
Diver dude
Warm blooded
Ice lover
Fantastic swimmer
Funky flipper
Spectacular skier
Chocolate cupboard.

Olivia Evans (10)
Hugh Sexey Middle School, Wedmore

Who Am I?

Tree swinger
Emergency singer
Flea eater
Friend beater
Female taker
Nonsense maker
Baboon killer
Storm chiller
Baby snatcher
Fly catcher
Fruit picking
Juice licking.

Clare Kieft (11)
Hugh Sexey Middle School, Wedmore

The Volcano Creature And The Sea Creature

In the volcano
The creature sleeps
After a battle
With a creature of the sea.

Only a red orb
Can awaken the creature
Meanwhile
Someone steals one.

They go to the creature
And the orb starts glowing
As the ground rumbled
And the creature awakens.

In the sea
Someone else has a blue orb
It starts glowing and the sea shakes
As the sea creature awakens.

The volcano creature roars
And shows its spiky back
And rock solid body
As it prepares for battle.

The sea creature sends waves
And shows its shiny back
And strengthened body
As it prepares for battle.

The land creature
Speedily jumps
Towards the angry sea
And the sea creature.

The sea creature
Swims briskly
Towards the rumbling land
And the land creature.

The creatures meet
And start to clash
The land creature throws lava
The sea creature throws water.

Meanwhile
The people swap orbs
And they start glowing
Sending the creatures back to sleep.

Ben Sutlieff (10)
Hugh Sexey Middle School, Wedmore

In The Jungle

In the jungle
Two red pandas,
Stay together and groom each other,
Quietly, gently they sleep like mice
While, not too far away
Brothers kill and sisters fight.

As they climb up in a tree
They do not fight like you and others
Collecting fruits and nuts
They watch and stare
Whilst mothers hit and fathers swear
They are watched by this little bear.

Georgina Mason (10)
Hugh Sexey Middle School, Wedmore

My Elegy Of John The Slug

Here lies the body of John the slug,
I loved my old pet John,
When I did slug races he always won.
He caught a very bad disease,
The thing is he had no knees.
He got fatter then fatter and fatter more
Until his chest was rubbing the floor.
Finally he left me
I hope he's well and free.

Sam Hanlon (11)
Hugh Sexey Middle School, Wedmore

My Kite

My kite's not just a kite
But a kite which soars across the sky taking charge of the field.
My kite's not just a kite
But a kite which knows every bird and tree and tells the clouds where to be.
My kite's not just a kite
But a kite which sings with the breeze and dances with the wind.
My kite's not just a kite
But a kite which is colourful, beautiful and magic but above all it's *my kite*.

Naomi Taylor (10)
Hugh Sexey Middle School, Wedmore

Chelsea

C helsea are the best
H ernan Crespo is our main striker
E ngland international Frank Lampard, he's our star player
L iverpool beat Chelsea one-nil in Europe
S tamford Bridge is our stadium
E ngland defender John Terry is captain of Chelsea
A bramovich is our chairman.

Anthony Cleave (10)
Hugh Sexey Middle School, Wedmore

Limericks

There was a young man called Jake
Who choked on a little cornflake.
The dead boy was dumped,
He was found bruised and bumped,
And his fingers were used in a cake.

Aimee Driscoll (10)
Hugh Sexey Middle School, Wedmore

My Crocodile Matt

Here lies my crocodile Matt
His favourite food was rat
He loved to play any day
No matter what you say
I threw him sticks
He broke them to bits
I loved my crocodile Matt.

James Chinnock (11)
Hugh Sexey Middle School, Wedmore

Tortoise

T ough, tottering along
O blivious to what's going on
R oaming around
T reading the ground
O bserving the view
I nquisitive what's new!
S lowly, on all-fours
E arth's dinosaurs.

Demelza Mitchell (8)
Indian Queens Primary School, St Columb

203

Animals

Fluffy rabbits hopping and skipping
Cute dolphins jumping and splashing
Big dogs barking fiercely
Little kittens playing quietly
Sweet guinea pigs squeaking loudly
Funny squirrels scurrying fast
Friendly ferrets running wildly
Quiet hare hiding silently
Sly snakes slithering secretly
Fluttering butterflies flying high
Fierce lions roaring and snarling
Wise owls hooting eerily
Weird armadillos scuttle and hide
Chestnut horses galloping beautifully
Slow tortoise walking slowly
Silly monkeys chattering and swinging.

Jess Keatley (7)
Indian Queens Primary School, St Columb

Gadget Man

My dad is a gadget man
He watches the TV
While he is eating his tea
His favourite channel is QVC
Gadgets are his favourite toys
Mummy says he is like one of the boys
Always buying expensive toys
I love my gadget dad
Because he is gadget mad.

Katie Wells (8)
Indian Queens Primary School, St Columb

Friendship

Friendship is fun
Like dancing in the sun.
Friendship is kind
Like the innards of your mind.
Friendship is good
Like the man in the red hood.
Friendship is till the end
Like the time we will spend.

Lauren Wass (8)
Indian Queens Primary School, St Columb

Animals

Animals, animals, animals.
Happy, hoppy rabbits jumping for joy.
Horses galloping gaily along the sand.
Cuddly cats curling up together.
Animals, animals, animals.
Barking dogs dancing playfully.
Fluffy, white sheep wander through the woods.
Squirrels scampering skilfully along the branches.
Animals, animals, animals.
I love animals.

Grace Williams (8)
Indian Queens Primary School, St Columb

My Pony

My little pony
All day he's lonely
Until it's time to see him
Then he moves all his limbs
Off we go to the park
Until it's dark
Then it's time to be fed
Then he goes off to bed.

Kirsty Syms (8)
Indian Queens Primary School, St Columb

Fairies

F airies are beautiful
A nd they're happy and kind
I love fairies and I will for the rest of my life
R aindrops make fairies wings glisten
Y oung fairies are the most beautiful of them all.

Holly Hindley (8)
Indian Queens Primary School, St Columb

Monkey

I was in the jungle
Inspecting the trees
Suddenly
Out of nowhere
Appeared a dark shadow
With two eyes
Like chocolate drops
Melting my heart.

I stood there
Watching him or her stare back at me
It swung its tail over a low branch
Up,
Up,
Up,
Until it swung its tail to the top of the tree
And glanced back at me
His or her mouth dribbled until
Splat!
Saliva fall on me.

I stood back
Then I started to back off cowardly
Here in his or her environment it was fierce
I wish I could be a monkey
Wild and free.

Charlotte Martin (8)
Keyham Barton Catholic Primary School, Plymouth

The Bully

When the clock hits 10.40
We all go out
And we all watch out
For him we do not like
And we don't sleep easy at night.

Again at 12.15
We go and get some air
And he is also waiting there
Finally the day is over
It's time to go
And tomorrow it starts all over.

Kieron Kelly (10)
Keyham Barton Catholic Primary School, Plymouth

Lion

In the plains of Africa,
I saw a blur of orange,
Peering closer,
I made out a mane of hair.
Fire like in its colour.
Fire like in its flickering movements.
His great body,
Was covered in smooth, furry skin.
A lion!

It pounded out
My heart pounded too,
Faster than an Olympic runner.
It turned and glared at me,
Its muddy brown eyes, piercing.
I gazed back,
Half scared, half fascinated.

He threw back his mane,
And roared!
Louder than a volcano erupting,
Louder than drums banging,
Louder, even, than an earthquake.
His thin, bright red lips
Revealed saliva dribbling down.
And his fangs, his fangs were pointed,
And as sharp as scissor ends.

He sniffed the air with his black, leathery nose.
Then padded away,
I wish I could be a lion,
With a great, flowing mane
And maybe some day, a magical day, I might be.

Eleanor Borthwick (9)
Keyham Barton Catholic Primary School, Plymouth

Cheetah

Down in the scrubs
In the plains of Africa
Sounded a rustle in a bush,
Yellow eyes glaring at me,
As the face came out,
First I thought it was a tiger,
Then realised it was a cheetah,
Its skinny long legs walked slowly toward me,
Tap, tap.
Its mouth came wide open,
It showed its sharp pointed teeth,
Its black spots showing in the sunlight.
It looked at me as if it were going to chase me,
Behind that cheetah, a cheetah cub,
Little growls
One little step,
Getting ready to pounce,
His legs bending down,
It pounced,
To the side,
It was beginning to get dark,
So while the cheetahs were asleep,
I sneaked off,
Yes, I was gone,
But the cheetah weren't
Gone from my mind.

Aaron Bevan (9)
Keyham Barton Catholic Primary School, Plymouth

The Cheetah

In the middle of the desert
In the corner of my eye,
I saw a cheetah creeping around
It stared into the centre of my eyes,
I stared back.

It slowly
Stepped forward and . . .
Leapt onto a buffalo running past
It ripped off its flesh,
With its razor-sharp teeth,
Slashed its neck with claws
As jagged as rocks
Eventually killing its prey,
It ate some.
Then it ran and ran,
As fast as lightning,
I followed it into some shade
It lay peacefully until it woke.
Then it walked proudly around the tree
It stopped,
Dashed away,
Out of sight,
But not forgotten.

Oliver Roberts (9)
Keyham Barton Catholic Primary School, Plymouth

Dog

I was on my own,
Walking in a park
When,
It started getting dark.
All of a sudden
There came a big, black dog
Behind me.

It licked its thin, slobbery lips,
It grinned at me,
I could see its razor-sharp teeth,
Then it tramped slowly towards me.
At this point I took a good look at it.
Its fur like a piece of torn rag
Its eyes like a little cave,
With a glimpse of light in the middle.

Out of nowhere,
Came a big whistle,
And the dog raced off,
Up the hill to a man
With a black coat on.

The dog faded away
In the distance
But didn't fade from my mind.

Adam Thompson (9)
Keyham Barton Catholic Primary School, Plymouth

The Tiger

On safari in the plains
Searching for new wildlife,
I saw a sturdy, two metre-long tiger.
It was bigger than the biggest
With its wet, slobbery nose.

As it prowled and halted,
Lurking suspiciously in the bushes,
It looked like a long standing beast.

Its fierce jaws opened
To reveal glistening, white teeth.
Its piercing, orange eyes,
Were as bright as the sun,
Were fixed on its prey.
Its thick, silky coat,
Was like an elephant's skin
And its sharp, rapid movement
Told me that it was a determined hunter.

When it pounced on its prey,
I was in shock
As it padded along the thin long grass,
Devouring the smooth skin
As it came.
Oh, how I wish
I could be that sturdy creature
The shocking, fierce tiger!

Oliver Swift (9)
Keyham Barton Catholic Primary School, Plymouth

Giraffe

High in the Savannahs
I saw a long leg pop out
Like a bamboo stick.
Then a little knee popped out
No bigger than a little ball,
A brownish, yellowish body was in sight,
Pineapple in colour,
Patches of dirty orange,
A long neck
Raced into sight,
Shaped like a drainpipe.
As the immense animal's
Head appeared
My heart beat with jealousy.

As I stared at the
Great
Nine-foot tall animal
A big *'errr'*
Came out of its mouth
Loud as a trumpet!
I wish
I could be that animal
Tall and free.

Declan O'Connell (9)
Keyham Barton Catholic Primary School, Plymouth

Harry The Budgie

Harry the budgie
Was very inquisitive
Every time he was let out
He looked at things with
His black eyes
Where he shouldn't.
The cat stopped Harry's pink feet from landing
On the surface of the low places.
The only places he would land
Were the high places.
Like on the picture frames.
No matter how the cat jumped
She couldn't get Harry.
To Harry
The cat was a big ugly monster
But on the other hand
Harry's brother, George
Was the loveliest thing
Harry had ever seen.

Alex Dupreez (9)
Keyham Barton Catholic Primary School, Plymouth

Snow
(In the style of Alfred Noyes)

The snow was as chilly as the ice building among the town,
The frost was as shiny as the big building plot,
The ice was as sharp as the huge big battle sword,
The ice spell came slowly, slowly, slowly,
The ice spell came up to the big ice rink.
The snow was as thick as the rocks,
The frost was as crunchy as an apple,
The ice was a skating rink,
The winter came slowly, slowly, slowly,
The snow spell came into the building,
The snow was as soft as the sponge,
The frost was as cold as the rink,
The ice was hard as metal,
The frost spell came into the outside.

Aron Finnimore (10)
Launceston CP School, Launceston

A Winter Walk
(In the style of Alfred Noyes)

The river was a rush of waves in a race to the pitch-black sea,
The leaves were raindrops dripping on my head,
The trees were wigs of hair being blown by a hairdryer
And we came marching, marching, marching,
We came marching through the dark and gloomy woods.

The wind was an everlasting fan blowing on my icy cheek,
The seagulls were a group of crying children in the dull sky,
The rain was the drip-drip dripping of a rusty tap,
And went climbing, climbing, climbing,
We went climbing over the rough rocks.

The ground was a massive rocky cliff overlooking the great blue sea,
The flowers were skeletons awakening from the dead,
The bridge was a slippery slide curving over the mad river,
And we came searching, searching, searching,
We came searching for the lost path.

And I was home, home, home,
I was home and never going out again.

Robyn Land (10)
Launceston CP School, Launceston

A Breakdown
(In the style of Alfred Noyes)

The radio was like a mumbling ghost upon a gloomy graveyard,
The rain was like water bombs plunging from the clouds,
The car was like an invisible plastic bag clung to an oak tree,
And the AA van came zooming, zooming, zooming,
The AA van came zooming up to the hard shoulder.

An aerosol can was like a TNT bomb unexploded in the moonlight,
The traffic was like a herd of stampeding elephants in the 100m race,
The temperature was like being in the middle of the arctic
And the raging vans kept beeping, beeping, beeping
And the raging vans kept beeping at the useless car.

The toe hitch was like a giant bulldozer attacking a defenceless cat,
The time we were in the car was like waiting for pigs to fly,
Our street was like a lifeless hall of dreams
And the night kept appearing, appearing, appearing
Until I realised it was a dream!

Tom Clogg (10)
Launceston CP School, Launceston

One Winter's Day
(In the style of Alfred Noyes)

The ice was a glistening jewel upon the white ground,
The snowman was a white ball beside red gloves and scarves,
The sky was a grey sheet over the cold earth,
And the air was bitter, bitter, bitter,
And the air was bitter around the bare trees.

I was joyful and restless riding on the toboggan,
I had a waterproof coat over me keeping me warm,
I was frozen and chilly in my warm boots,
And it was nippy, nippy, nippy,
And it was nippy among the houses.

The school was white upon other buildings,
The teachers were covered in snow upon the ground,
The grass was frozen upon the fields
And it was fun, fun, fun,
And it was fun when it snowed at the school.

Charlotte Duff (9)
Launceston CP School, Launceston

A Bad Day
(In the style of Alfred Noyes)

The glass was a gleaming crystal in the moonlight,
The house was a gloomy cave hiding upon misty moors,
The carpet was a ribbon of pure white snow freshly fallen from the deserted sky,
And the children came running, running, running,
And the children came running into the glass front door.

The dog was a muddy pig rolling in thick brown mud,
The paws were small brown pillows of lumpy mud on hairy feet,
The door was wide open to let us and the muddy dog in,
And the muddy dog came dashing, dashing, dashing
And the muddy dog came dashing onto the clean white sofas.

My sister was a clumsy waitress giving us drinks,
The chair was a ridiculous clown dressed in colourful coats,
The glass was a weak statue on the tableside,
And the sound of smashing, smashing, smashing,
And the sound of smashing that my sister broke a glass.

Natalie Stevenson (9)
Launceston CP School, Launceston

In The Winter
(In the style of Alfred Noyes)

The ice was like a glistening mirror, the ice was a glistening mirror on the bird table.
The fish down in the riverbank waiting for their food, until mother duckling came along,
The grass waving through the wind over the grassy hill.
The snowdrops fell down, snowdrops, snowdrops, snowdrops,
The snowdrops fell down into the icy riverbank.

The grit was a diamond on the rocks and somebody looked at it
And it glistened on their eyes,
The road was shining of happiness and a car was walking over it,
The sun was a torrent of a twinkling cloud and the clouds were as blue as ever,
The grit was a diamond, diamond, diamond,
The grit was a diamond.
The snow fell down lightly and it rustled down their back.
The snowdrops were a torrent of kindness and a meadow full of flowers and ice,
The snowdrops glistened over the hill,
The snowdrops glistened over the hill, glistened, glistened, glistened,
The snowdrops glistened over the hill.

Sophie Cameron (9)
Launceston CP School, Launceston

Canada
(In the style of Alfred Noyes)

The food was a burnt banana with sauce,
The air was a piece of burning toast on the seats,
The seat was as comfy as the bed in my house,
And the airplane came zooming, zooming, zooming,
And the aeroplane came zooming to the airport in Canada.

The aeroplane was a car going over bumpy rocks,
The aeroplane when it lifted up my legs felt like gravity had left off,
The windows were made of ice but even colder
And the aeroplane came banging, banging, banging,
And the aeroplane came banging to Canada.

My aunt sounded like a hyena screaming for food,
My cousin was as loud as a lion roaring,
The passengers were as quiet as a mouse
And the aeroplane landed, landed, landed,
The aeroplane landed at Canada airport.

Kayleigh Bickle (9)
Launceston CP School, Launceston

A Snowy Day
(In the style of Alfred Noyes)

The snow was a bag of flour tipped over the busy town below,
The frost was a swarm of angry ants viciously biting at your skin,
The houses were snow palaces in a beautiful snowy town,
And the children came running, running, running,
The children came running down the frosty path.

The ice was a trail of crystals glistening in the dimly lit sun,
The ground was a carpet of icing sugar sprinkled over the rooftops of the city,
The sun was a torch which had hardly any batteries left
And the children kept on yelling, yelling, yelling,
The children kept on yelling all the way out of school.

The clouds were cotton wool floating in the gentle breeze,
The sky was a chameleon which had lost its colour,
The air was filled with laughter like a tape recorder repeating itself again and again,
And the children came skipping, skipping, skipping,
The children came skipping along the icy road.

The trees were as though they were pulled out of a snow globe,
The snowmen were fluffy feather pillows stacked on top of each other,
The icicles were glass daggers which had been polished hundreds of times,
And the children kept laughing, laughing, laughing,
The children kept laughing all the way home.

Keziah Parnell (10)
Launceston CP School, Launceston

Summer's Day
(In the style of Alfred Noyes)

The grass was a sizzling scattered dessert among the burning trees.
The water was a burn of happiness upon the purple weeds.
The sky was a clearing of rubies beside the hard rocks.
And the sun came burning, burning, burning.
The sun came burning up to the old tired fox.

The view was an expedition to Florida beside the calm sea.
The motorway was a whizzing fly among the gusty moving key.
The tent was an icy cave upon the twenty sun machines,
And I came bouncing, bouncing, bouncing up to my old grampa.
I came bouncing up to my old grampa.
The wind was a gentle stroke beside the burning fire.
The sound was a bird song upon the sharp blood wire.
The field was a clearing among the noisy crows
And the dog barked, barked, barked.
The dog barked at the mowers.

Heather Davey (9)
Launceston CP School, Launceston

The Day We Got Our Puppy
(In the style of Alfred Noyes)

Her teeth were a row of pointy daggers among her clean pink gums,
Her coat of fur was a sheet of velvet over her pink smooth skin,
Her nose was a wet piece of black coal on her fluffy face,
And she came bounding, bounding, bounding,
She came bounding with her little tail wagging.

Her tail was a branch of an old tree swaying in the gusty wind,
Her ears were a pair of flags being fluttered about in a gentle breeze,
Her eyes are shiny brown diamonds glistening in the morning sun,
She was sniffing, sniffing, sniffing,
She was sniffing all around the house.

Her paws are as rough as sandpaper,
She is as playful as ducklings having their first swimming lesson,
She is as cheeky as a monkey swinging in the trees,
She is playing, playing, playing all day long.

When she grows up she will be as kind as me,
At the moment she is a young puppy but she will become an old lady,
When she is old she will still be my best friend,
She is young, young, young, she is a young puppy.

Laura Champ (9)
Launceston CP School, Launceston

Snow Day
(In the style of Alfred Noyes)

The snow was a white sheet of paper upon the snowballs,
The air was a freezer among the happy children,
The frost was a moon upon the snowy branch.
The snowflakes came falling, falling, falling,
The snowflakes came falling from the frosty sky.

The ground was as rough as sandpaper below the cold snow,
The leaves were as green as apples upon the misty trees,
The sky was as cold as snow above the foggy crowds
And the trees were blowing, blowing, blowing,
And the trees were blowing among the strong wind.

The icicles were hanging off a roof like a knife,
The ice was water upon the frosty ground,
The snowmen were skyscrapers among the houses,
The snow was melting, melting, melting upon the icy ground.

Liam Sloan (9)
Launceston CP School, Launceston

The Friday Snow
(In the style of Alfred Noyes)

The snow was blank sheets of white paper among the empty town,
My home was a hot bath as you walk in the door,
The garden was 1150 ice cubes upon the glistening snow,
My estate was getting busier, busier, busier,
My estate was getting busier as my neighbour came to my door.

My snowball was an ice ball as it hit me on the arm,
My snowman was a real person as I looked out of my window,
My cat Garfield was a pain upon the clogged up window ledge,
My snowball got smashed, smashed, smashed,
My snowball got smashed as my brother walked in the door.

The cars were slowly driving upon the snowy roads,
The people were rushing around the icy pavements.
The ice crackled as cars drove over them,
My brother walked, walked, walked,
My brother walked as my dad drove up the hill.

The wind was as windy as a flying aeroplane in front of me,
The cold was as if I were wearing an ice suit,
Lucky my cat was as cute as a princess,
The fence was covered in snow, snow, snow,
The fence was covered in snow as me and my mum walked past.

Claire Downing (10)
Launceston CP School, Launceston

When I Went For A Walk
(In the style of Alfred Noyes)

The sea was a shining jewel beside the rocky cliff,
The plants were a fresh smell of clothes coming out of the water upon the cliff side,
The mud was a mucky lake over the green grass,
And the sea was splashing, splashing, splashing,
The sea was splashing up to the high rocks.

The view was a person disappearing behind the other beaches,
The sand was a desert among the small tiny rocks,
The bush was a sharp pine around the rocky path,
And we just kept walking, walking, walking,
We just kept walking along the path.

The wind was a tree falling over around all the people,
The fields were a big fat pear among the fences,
The houses were a flower growing around the gardens,
And the wind kept blowing, blowing, blowing,
The wind kept blowing all day long.

Megan Jackson (9)
Launceston CP School, Launceston

Snow
(In the style of Alfred Noyes)

The garden was a frosty morning below the sky,
The snow was like a sheet of dotted paper along the road,
The trees were as bare as sticks above the ground,
And everyone was slipping, slipping, slipping,
And everyone was slipping like a cow on mud or a fish being handled.

My gloves were as warm as a heater that just got turned on a few minutes ago,
My scarf was like a snake around my neck,
My hat was like I had a cat curled up on my head,
And everyone was happy, happy, happy and the feeling was outside in the snow.

The icicles were as cold as a freezer,
The snowballs were as soft as melted ice cream,
The snowman was as big as a hippo,
And the grass was frosty, frosty, frosty below the sky.

Abby Bounsall (10)
Launceston CP School, Launceston

The Chainsaw Poem
(In the style of Alfred Noyes)

The garden was a pea among the flowers,
The chainsaw was a lion roaring in the dead of night,
The tree was a green mountain falling, falling, falling,
The tree was a green mountain falling out of the sky.

Dad's hat was as black as ebony on a piano,
His t-shirt was as dark as an inky sky,
His jeans were as muddy as a puppy playing in the park,
Dad came sawing, sawing, sawing,
Dad came sawing through the forest.

The sun was as bright as a fire but wind as cold as a frosty morning,
The mud was as soggy as porridge,
The tree came falling, falling, falling,
The tree came falling out of the sky.

Daniel Bradshaw (10)
Launceston CP School, Launceston

The Friday Snow
(In the style of Alfred Noyes)

The frost was a glistening jewel on the king's crown,
The snow was as soft as my mum's bed,
The crowd was as happy as me,
And the snow came tumbling, tumbling, tumbling,
And the snow came tumbling at half-past ten.
The snowballs were as hard as ice cubes,
The cars slid down as fast as a rocket,
The snowboards slid down the hill faster than I can run,
And snow came falling, falling, falling,
And the snow came falling as slow as a snail.
The snowmen were as high as a house,
The snow angels filled the garden,
The cars all abandoned,
And the people walking slowly, slowly, slowly,
And the people walked as slow as a snail.

Morgan Basford (9)
Launceston CP School, Launceston

Detention
(In the style of Alfred Noyes)

The sun was a phoenix curled in a ball hovering over the aqua sky,
The school was a fortress among the birds high,
The classroom was a dungeon upon the rough seas,
The teacher came running, running, running
The teacher came running up with her golden keys.

Maths was a very funny thing upon my rotten brain,
The teacher's hair was a golden mane upon the suffering and pain,
My laugh was a lion's roar over and out the door,
The teacher came marching, marching, marching,
The teacher came marching up with her cane dragging on the floor.

Detention was a very horrifying thing upon the scared children,
The headmistress was an evil witch over a boiling cauldron,
The clock was a horse's hoof among concrete slabs,
The teacher came smiling, smiling, smiling,
The teacher came smiling up with her pet crabs.

Adam Parnell (10)
Launceston CP School, Launceston

A Day In Spain
(In the style of Alfred Noyes)

The air was as breezy as a hot breath,
The games were as fun as a PlayStation,
The food was as hot as a frying pan on a hot stove,
The slides were slippery, slippery, slippery as scaly as a snake.

The floats were as squishy as a marshmallow,
The sun was as hot as lava,
The water was as fresh as the sea and ocean,
The towels were soft, soft, soft, as soft as a bunny rabbit.

The floor was a big pool of boiling water on my feet,
The shower was like rain tipping on top of my head,
The changing room was a cool ice cream with all the sprinkles on the top of it,
The children were laughing, laughing, laughing, as loud as a hyena.

Beth Chapman (9)
Launceston CP School, Launceston

The Cold Winter Night
(In the style of Alfred Noyes)

The breeze was howling like a wolf in the moonlight,
The trees had a sudden judder when the wind took a stroll past its feet,
The leaves were falling like a bird gliding peacefully from the branches in the moonlight,
I was sitting staring from the pale window.

The ice was sparkling like a diamond as bright as the sky,
The sky was as blue as a blue tit flying around in the morning,
I was walking, walking, walking, I was admiring the horrible weather.

The leaves were hanging like a sloth clinging onto the branches,
The fishes were swimming in circles like my brother to hurt me,
The birds singing like my horrible sister,
I was watching, watching, watching, I was watching the terrible morning.

Toby Knights (9)
Launceston CP School, Launceston

Skiing
(In the style of Alfred Noyes)

The skier came skiing, skiing, skiing off like a shot,
The people gathered around, around, around like a row of houses.

The people came down the mountain, the mountain, the mountain like a herd of sheep.
They kept falling, falling, falling like a man on a horse.

The skiers kept hurdling, hurdling, hurdling all over the fly jumps.
And as they came to the end, the end, the end they were all sweating like a sloth.

Thomas Davison (10)
Launceston CP School, Launceston

Ice Blocks
(In the style of Alfred Noyes)

The
Ice was an
Ice block
In the
Freezer.
The skater was like no other skater
Skating happily
The playground was like an ice rink
And the skater came skating, skating, skating,
The skater came skating
Up on the ice rink.

Jake Tozer (9)
Launceston CP School, Launceston

Sounds, Sounds, Sounds!

The roar of a jumbo jet,
The peaceful sound of a lull,
The bubble of custard nearly set,
The rustle of a book being turned,
The drip of a dog really wet,
The crackle of a bonfire being burned,
The ripple of a tangled fishing net,
The crash of a jug being dropped,
The scream of someone being cut,
The sob of someone being mocked,
The bang from the garden hut,
The chatter of the underground tube,
The whistle of the wind in the breeze,
The clap before the interlude,
The crackle of the feet in the leaves,
Sounds.

Harriet Brain (10)
Lydford Primary School, Okehampton

The ABC Of The Ocean

A quiet sandy beach waves lapping on the shore,
B arnacles cling to turtles and other sea creatures,
C oral sways gently under the greeny blue water,
D iving dolphins click and whistle to each other,
E eels swim, their body rippling,
F ish swim in and out of orange and yellow coral,
G iant waves come crashing onto the sandy beach
H uge whales rise to the surface of the water crashing down into murky brownness,
I nto the sea, white horses go, disappearing below the surface of the sea,
J ust the blue water and the smell of salt,
K ind-hearted turtles swim with the current
L apping waves come onto the yellow, sandy beach,
M anta rays swim slowly along the bottom of the sea,
N othing quiet, always the noise of waves crashing,
O ctopus stick to rocks and pebbles,
P urple-coloured fish swim gracefully through greeny-blue waters,
Q ueer fish live at the bottom of the sea,
R ed coral sways and clownfish swim between them,
S alt seawater rushes here and there,
T urtles lay the white eggs in silent coves,
U rchins stick to all the grey rocks they can find
V arious shells are found lying on the beach
W hales dive down, their tails flying up into the air and then down again,
eX hilarating dolphins and flying fish jump out of the water,
Y elling seagulls take people's lunch
Z est for life as you see coral fish.

Amy Marks (11)
Lydford Primary School, Okehampton

The Sea

Salty sea
Crashes up cliffs.
White horses galloping
Back and forth,
Jumping waves.
Waves getting bigger.
Slowly the waves get smaller
Elegant dolphins come up
And start playing.
Seagulls
Flying free.

Emily-Jayne Preen (10)
Lydford Primary School, Okehampton

The ABC Of Smells

A blossom tree smells of spring
B irds flying in the smell of fresh air
C hristmas trees smell of Christmas,
D elicious aromas of the teacher's coffee,
E xcellent whiffs for the fire,
F ish and chips, smells of the seaside,
G reat odours of my house
H orrific stench from flowers
I ncredible odours of people baking
J ammy smells fill the room
K itchens full of the smells of home
L ovely aromas swirl in my head
M agnificent whiffs of the cut grass
N asty smell of wet dogs
O dours of babies
P all of smoke fills our nostrils
Q ueasy feelings from greasy smells
R evolting smells of vinegar
S mells of hospitals
T errific odours of Mum's perfume
U nusual smells from Indian foods
V ery strong stenches of glue
W et rain smells
eX otic whiffs of fruit
Y ucky stench from farms
Z apping smells whirl around you.

April Stevens (10)
Lydford Primary School, Okehampton

Sunrise In Winter, Sunset In Autumn - Cinquains

Frostbite
Bites back, light breaks
The calm cold night. White flakes
Of snow start to melt when they fall,
Sunrise.

Sunset.
Red beads of light
Shattering the coming
Darkness, feeding the redness of
Autumn.

Thomas Rylands (10)
Lydford Primary School, Okehampton

Sounds

Loud
Sounds make
Me shake.

Quiet
Sounds make
Me feel quiet.

Pages
Of books
Flickering.

Doors
Squeaking.

Water
Dripping
From the tap

Waves
Crashing against
The rocks.

Chairs
Creaking when
People sit.

Birds
Twittering
In the trees.

Wind
Howling.

Lips
Moving.

Sound!

Emily Friend (10)
Lydford Primary School, Okehampton

Sea

Bobbing boats on the rough bumpy sea,
Gulls crying on lamp posts and rocks,
Yellow sand, sticky and bright,
Waves up, down, rolling and falling.
The fish all exotic and bright.
Elegant seahorses dance and twirl,
Crawling crabs red and fierce,
Pebbles bumpy, soft grey or brown,
Deckchairs all around,
Diving gannets swift and hungry.

Tom Green (10)
Lydford Primary School, Okehampton

Sound

Sound is quiet and loud and hard to hear,
Some sounds are nice, some are not,
Some are ear-bursting
Some are too quiet to hear,
Sound can be relaxing,
Sound can be shocking.

There are lots of sounds,
As quiet as a drop of water,
As loud as a group of bongo drummers,
Sound can have beats in musical sound.
Sounds come from music and instruments,
From animals and creatures.

Sounds come from machines,
Sound can be beautiful and relaxing,
Sound can be nice and loud.
Sound can be screeching,
Bad sounds, loud sounds
Beautiful and quiet sounds.

Paul Sieradzki (10)
Lydford Primary School, Okehampton

Silence Cinquains

Silence
Great lack of sound
Again complete silence
Muted people walking around
Quiet.

Quiet
Cold emptiness
Very dark, very cold
People are walking everywhere
Hushed.

Hushed
Sound is muffled
Cold emptiness inside
Quiet people stand everywhere
Nothing.

Kate Marks (9)
Lydford Primary School, Okehampton

Smells

Sometimes when you go in the bathroom
You can smell bathroom spray.

When you go to the petrol station
You smell diesel and petrol.

Smoke comes out of the exhaust pipe
Of your car.

When you wash your hair
You can smell your hair.

When you brush your teeth
Your teeth are clean and your breath is fresh.

When you go to see flowers and smell them
Sometimes they smell nice.

When you smell food it makes you hungry
And you want to eat.

Michael Marsh (8)
Lydford Primary School, Okehampton

Smells

Fire
Smells of burning wood.
Animals
Give off a certain smell.
Coal
Smells of smoke and heat.
Babies
Sometimes smell so grim!
Swimming pool
Smells nice to me.

Carter Davies (8)
Lydford Primary School, Okehampton

Silence

Everything's quiet
Emptiness is all around you,
Stillness can be seen,
Nothing can be heard,
Coldness is walking with you,
Faint sounds of breathing all around you,
Your body is silent, nothing but silent,
Connections can't be heard,
Nothing is there.

Lulu Friend (9)
Lydford Primary School, Okehampton

Seaside

Beautiful, blue, calm sea
Shiny pebbles.
I see seagulls flying free.
I feel crunchy shells beneath my feet.
Red crabs crawling along the smooth pebbles.
I smell sea salt.
I see dolphins jumping from the water.
I stand on green slippery seaweed.
Sea makes the pebbles shiny and smooth.
Rolling waves take the sand.

Rhiannon Sladen (8)
Lydford Primary School, Okehampton

Silence

Silence, the sound of nothing.
Silence, that nothing could be heard.
Silence, when it is in the middle of the night.
Silence, not a glimpse of noise.
Silence, people creeping through the night trying not to be heard.
Silence, when somebody is sad.
Silence, a pitch-black room with nothing in it.
Silence, where everything is quiet.
Silence, not a noise at all.

Edward Brain (8)
Lydford Primary School, Okehampton

The Ocean

The ocean is calm and freezing
When you get in the water.
Crabs pinch along the sand.
The sea is crashing together.
The seagulls are crying for food.
Dolphins are jumping quickly.
The sea quickly comes in.
The great white shark hunting for food to eat.
The ocean sea is now calm for tonight.

Caleb Stevens (8)
Lydford Primary School, Okehampton

Sunrise, Sunset - Cinquains

Sunrise
Into grey clouds
Getting lighter purple
Stars disappear into lightness
Morning

Moon comes
Hot sun shining
Purple colour sun through
Orange, dark yellow going gold
Birds nest.

Matthew Green (7)
Lydford Primary School, Okehampton

Laughter

People laugh at things that are silly
And funny.
Especially when they are tickled!
Some people laugh when they are nervous
And at jokes.
They think it is fun.
To make fun of people by laughing,
They laugh at people
When they don't believe them.
But if I were you
Don't laugh at people
In case it hurts their feelings.

Robert Heard (7)
Lydford Primary School, Okehampton

Winter

The winter fairy flies in the air,
With a tap of her wand
And a touch of magic,
Slowly but surely winter appears,
But after four months have gone,
She tapped her wand
And used a touch of magic,
And slowly but surely the cold snow disappears.

Clare Oliver (10)
Martock Primary School, Martock

New Year

New Year, New Year has come again
Last year has past,
Let's hope the new one's a blast.

Another year older,
It goes so quick,
Think I need a walking stick.

Won't see Santa for another year,
Oh dear.

Soon be summer I can ride my bike,
Because at the moment I get frostbite.

New Year, New Year will soon come again,
Then I'll be ten!

Jamie Craig (9)
Martock Primary School, Martock

Football

Football is my favourite sport
I think I'm quite good, but some people have a different thought.

I bought a player from a trade
And now he's wondering how much he's getting paid.

Football is great exercise
But then you go to McDonald's and supersize!

Christopher Dixon (10)
Martock Primary School, Martock

A Winter Wonderland

I walked into a winter wonderland
Everything was heavenly soft.
The ground was like a crystal palace
I was surrounded by snowy mountains and creamy rocks.
It looked like a dream come true.
It was as cold as a frozen river.

Shelby Norris (10)
Martock Primary School, Martock

The Hamster Poem

Neither a long neck or long legs,
Instead I have short golden hair,
And I am soft, soft, soft.

Neither a television or a computer,
Instead I love going on my wheel,
And I am soft, soft, soft.

For I remember every moment,
I climb, run and dig
And I am soft, soft, soft.

Jacqueline White (11)
Martock Primary School, Martock

The Rabbit Song

Neither wings nor scales have I,
But I can thump and scratch
And I am fluffy, fluffy, fluffy!

Neither wear clothes nor jet packs have I
But I have claws and ears
And I am fluffy, fluffy, fluffy!

I master every movement
For I hate swimming and sliding
And I am fluffy, fluffy, fluffy!

Naomi Slade (11)
Martock Primary School, Martock

Tigers

Tigers, tigers
I love them so,
I want one in my garden
But my mum says, 'No!'
'Can I have one?
Can I have one?'
'No, no and finally no!'

Katie Sealey (10)
Martock Primary School, Martock

New Year's Poem

The clock strikes twelve
A new year is finally here,
People think to themselves, what will this new year bring?

Will it bring luck?
Will it bring wealth?
Will it bring happiness together with good health?

I hope I will be happy and never sad,
I hope Chelsea win the league,
And so does my dad!

Dominik May (9)
Martock Primary School, Martock

Tigers

Tigers, tigers, big and small
Tigers, tigers, short and tall
Tigers, tigers, roaring loud
Tigers, tigers, standing proud
Tigers, tigers, have no fear
Tigers, tigers, like to eat deer
Tigers, tigers, they're so sweet
Tigers, tigers, like their meat
But tigers, tigers, don't eat me!

Gemma Baker (10)
Martock Primary School, Martock

Autumn

Patterned leaves of every colour,
Sky still getting grey and duller,
Oak, beach, conker trees.
Softly swaying in the breeze,
Cherries round and ruby-red,
Birds sweetly tweeting in their bed.

Charlotte Oliver (10)
Martock Primary School, Martock

Witches And Wizards

Witches and wizards they fly round the room,
Witches and wizards they zoom on a broom.
Witches and wizards they like rats and toads
Witches and wizards they are in wicked mode.
Witches and wizards they cook up great potions,
Witches and wizards don't have emotions.
Witches and wizards cast good spells,
Witches and wizards really smell.
Witches and wizards have big noses.
Witches and wizards hate chocolate roses.

Justine Taylor (9)
Martock Primary School, Martock

Around The World

Saw the Eiffel Tower last week,
Wish I wasn't scared of heights!

Went on the Great Wall of China last week,
Wish I'd brought my bike.

Went to the Sydney Opera House
Wish I'd brought a map.

Great! I went around the world last week,
I'm exhausted, time to sleep!

Emma Craig (10)
Martock Primary School, Martock

My New Year Poem

Welcome to the New Year
All the children sing
Welcome to the New Year
Let the bells ring
A year of hope for you and me
And a year of fun for everyone
So raise your voice and give a cheer
I wish you all a happy New Year.

Zoe Oliver (10)
Martock Primary School, Martock

Happiness

Happiness is like two blue and amazing teardrops
Quickly tiptoeing down your pale pink cheeks.
When you're cheerful,
When you fear dreadful things,
Just carefully listen out of the glass window
And you can hear people softly sing.
Just listen into the gentle breeze
And think when it's time for you to slowly freeze.
Go for a short walk,
But on the way don't talk.
Skip into the fields and admire the chocolate-coated cows
And then when you're down,
Go back home and have some fun.

Erin Morris (10)
Martock Primary School, Martock

I Saw An Angel

I saw an angel
With wings of gold.
I saw an angel
With eyes of deepest blue.
I saw an angel
With a halo shining like the sun.
I saw an angel.

Rosie Johnson (10)
Martock Primary School, Martock

School Poem

S chool we go to every day
C lass mates we laugh and play
H opping along and playing at break
O ff we go to a new lesson
O ff we go to our lunch
L aughing and telling jokes as we go home.

Curtis-Lee Moore (10)
Martock Primary School, Martock

The Moon

That night the moon gleamed bright,
On the cold shivering winter's night,
The stars came out gleaming,
The sky comes out black and dull,
The moon comes out white
And it is a very glamorous sight,
The bumps on its surface are very curved,
The moon is very round,
It looks like one enormous pond,
The ducks are sleeping,
The frogs have stopped leaping,
The fish start to swim deep,
Then I walked off to go to sleep.

Jessaimée Richardson (9)
Martock Primary School, Martock

My Frosty Poem

Smooth pillows in the pale blue sky
With puffy clouds like white candyfloss.
Crystal white banks.
Penguins waddle all around.
Look up high, what do you see?
Maybe snowy hills or a river that's frozen like an ice lolly.
It's winter not spring or summer or May
So enjoy every day,
Because winter wonderland has arrived.

Rosie Hadfield (10)
Martock Primary School, Martock

Sisterhood

Roses are red, violets are blue
There is no other sister as special as you.
You help me when I'm down,
You help me when I'm blue,
So thank you for being there when I'm not feeling as good as you.

Shannon Smith (9)
Martock Primary School, Martock

Cricket

Cricket is the greatest sport; I hope I catch him out,
Our bowler is the best of all; he has never missed the stumps.
There is no breeze at all.
This could be the perfect ball to end the batter's innings.
This could bring us the winnings.
There he goes . . .
The Ashes are just a finger length away, he bowls the ball!
The batsman has hit it into the air,
It is coming straight towards me, this is my chance!
I will be the best known cricketer in the world
I've caught it, go me!
The Ashes are ours!

Sebastian Kempf (11)
Martock Primary School, Martock

Cinda Rap

There was a girl called Cinderella,
Who wished her life could be much better,
She worked day and night,
It was not a pretty sight,
Until a letter from Prince Paul
Asking her to the royal ball.

Her wicked stepmother,
Was up to no good,
She made a great objection,
But Cinders must go to the ball
To meet this royal, Paul.

The sisters and the evil stepmother,
Set off to the ball,
And then a fairy godmother,
Came before her eyes,
And waved her magic wand.

Cinders and her footmen,
Went to the royal ball,
She danced with the prince,
Until the twelfth strike,
Where she left his sight,
The fairy godmother,
Waved her wand
And Cinders was a cleaner again.

Alice Bettison (9)
Menheniot Primary School, Liskeard

Magical Creatures

Mrs James said to me,
'We're all doing poetry,'
I don't know what to write,
Something about a magic kite
Or maybe trolls big and fat,
Cinderella and her cat,
A great wizard and his cloak,
Who can make a cloud of smoke,
Maybe an invisible man,
Or tall giants with a tan,
I don't know what to write,
What about a very brave knight,
But now I've written a big hit
And you've just finished reading it!

Emily Harris (10)
Menheniot Primary School, Liskeard

Sadness

Sadness is grey like a dead leaf.
Sadness tastes like saltwater.
Sadness smells like raw fish.
Sadness looks like someone chopping down a tree.
Sadness sounds like someone crying.
Sadness feels like being deserted.

Alex Moore (9)
Menheniot Primary School, Liskeard

Emotion Poem

Love is blue like a duck pond.
It tastes like burger and chips.
It smells like food.
It looks like chocolate.
It sounds like Pop Party 3 at full blast.
It feels like being in a tree house.

Luke Dryland (10)
Menheniot Primary School, Liskeard

Cinder-Linda

Good old Cinder.
Her name was Linda,
Was now married after all she had tarried.
She went with her prince,
To dine on fine mince,
Creamed potatoes too,
But there was something she would have to do.
For down in the cellar there was a broom,
Which was to bring Linda to her doom.
She knew that she would have to clean,
Linda was not very keen.
She'd been cleaning all her life,
But had had other ideas now she was a wife.
So as sneaky as a mouse,
Cinder-Linda left the house.
She ran out into the open air,
She was still in her rags,
But she didn't care,
She was going to try bungee-jumping off a cliff,
To help her she hired a man called Biff,
But back at the palace the prince was confused,
As Cinder-Linda came back battered and bruised!

Ellen Prisk (10)
Menheniot Primary School, Liskeard

I Swear My Pony Is A Unicorn

I was lying in bed one night,
Thinking of my pony in the moon so bright,
I crept down the stairs,
And stepped out into the cold fresh air,
I ran to her field,
Holding my coat sealed,
I called her name,
And over she came,
I said the spell very clearly,
And patted her mane very dearly,
And out of her ginger coat came a sharp horn,
For this was her power since she was born.
I climbed on her back
And gave her a soft smack
And off we went into the sky so high.

Rachel Compton (10)
Menheniot Primary School, Liskeard

The Man At The Windowpane

There is an old man at the end of our lane,
Who sits looking out of his windowpane.
He looks out on the street,
Where people meet
The man at the windowpane.

My friends and me were wondering,
About the man at the window pondering.
So we crept into the house,
As quiet as a mouse,
Like the man at the windowpane.

We ran up the stairs,
To find what was there.
We reached the door,
We crept along the floor,
To see the man at the windowpane.

But the chair was there,
On its own and bare.
It was still rocking gently,
The cushion was warm,
And he was gone,
The man at the windowpane.

Ellie Fruhauf (10)
Menheniot Primary School, Liskeard

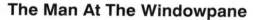

Rugby If You Try

When you're on the pitch, don't cry, just try,
Do your best tackling, kicking and passing,
It goes far if you try, you never know you might score
Sometimes I'm lucky.
Do your training, you'll get better,
Listen, never argue with the ref or you'll be sin-binned.

Steve Mears (10)
Menheniot Primary School, Liskeard

The Magical Sleepover

I really want a sleepover
One with ghouls and ghosts,
I'll send the invitations flying through the post.
I'll invite faithful Peter Pan
And a fat round invisible man.
Maybe even Cinderella
Or a spoilt girl named young Bella.
I'll have seven trolls
And eight dancing little moles.
Or maybe fairies with magic hands
Maybe two rocking bands.
I'll have the one and only Snow White
And send the seven dwarves an invite.
Finally, I'll have six friends
Who are the best and will always be my best friends.

Sophie Evans (10)
Menheniot Primary School, Liskeard

I Once Wondered If . . .

Mushrooms could fly
But would also die!
Unicorns could buy
And would also die!
Dragons know how to fly
And would also die!
But they would come back to fly!

I once wondered if . . .
Pigs could marry
And make their name Barry!
Fairies could marry
But wouldn't change their name to Barry!
Pixies could dance
But would also prance
But they are all lovely!

Lily Edwards (9)
Milton Abbot Primary School, Tavistock

Imaginary Fair

Whoa! Down the rainbow slide
Having lots of fun,
Towers high into the sky
But now the ride has gone.

Quick, get in the star ride
Before it goes into space,
It's very nice and worth the price
There is no time to waste.

Yes, it's the snowflake ride next
Twirling high in the sky,
Twirls round and round, you can't hear the crowd
Before coming gracefully down.

Now that's my day finished
My day at the imaginary fair,
There are no wolves or lions
Not even a single bear.

Stephanie Nolan (8)
Milton Abbot Primary School, Tavistock

Silly Creatures

M onsters munching messily,
O gres are an 'orrible lot,
N ature getting in their way,
S melly creatures annoying them
T ease them, squeeze them, you will just
E nd up wrong,
R ecklessly, so mean,
S eriously, they are just outside the door.

Bert Rodgers (8)
Milton Abbot Primary School, Tavistock

I Had This Dream That . . .

Fish could run,
Cats could fly
And dogs could eat really big pies!
The cheetah had a limp
So did the chimp
And the lion had a pimple!

But when I woke up . . .
Fish could run
Cats could fly
And dogs could eat really big pies!
The cheetah had a limp
So did the chimp
And the lion had a pimple!

That night I had a dream that . . .
Spiders could speak
Beetles really reeked
And butterflies could not fly!
Whales talked
Birds stalked
And antelopes could not lie!

But when I woke up . . .
Spiders could speak
Beetles really reeked
And butterflies could not fly!
Whales talked
Birds stalked
And antelopes could not lie!

So now you know
How my dreams sort of go
And I hope it lasts forever.

Lauren Dawe (9)
Milton Abbot Primary School, Tavistock

At Night, At Night

When an eagle cried and a wolf whined,
When a mushroom grew and a dewdrop fell,
At night, at night.
When the foxes barked and the moon came up,
When the sun went down and the stars came out,
At night, at night.
When the last stars out, the sun comes up and dawn is here.
When I wake up and an owl tucks in,
At night, at night,
Now the dawn is here.

Madeline Cullen (9)
Milton Abbot Primary School, Tavistock

The Hounds Of The Baskervilles!

Up high on the lonely Dartmoor hill
The mysterious Hounds of the Baskervilles
Waits for the pounce and thrill.

The snarling teeth and the dangerous jaws
Will soon be upon the victim,
For these boggy and lonely Dartmoor Hills
Are nothing but the hounds' kingdom.

The Hounds of the Baskervilles
Are really horrible creatures,
The claws, the teeth and eyes
Are the most terrifying features.

Hope Clarkson (9)
Milton Abbot Primary School, Tavistock

A Poem Of Love

The oily grass, the oil in my glove
These are the things that remind me of love.
Love, love, flutters around like a fairy when she is found.
Bound, bound, she is bound to be found.
Oh special, special, love is special.
Watch it flutter about the ground until it is found.

Emily Pearce (8)
Milton Abbot Primary School, Tavistock

My Fairies

My fairies say what I have to do
He's very bad but I am too!
I have a good fairy but I don't pay attention,
She always says, 'Do what I say!'
'I don't have to, I don't have to!' that's what I say.
So she takes me to another dimension.

Katie Stephens (8)
Milton Abbot Primary School, Tavistock

Robot

R obots run around this land
O cto is their king
B rot is his sidekick and he is very thin
O cto went to space and left the land to his son
T homas his younger son was jealous of him.

Thomas Barclay (9)
Milton Abbot Primary School, Tavistock

It's Going To Rain

The sea is glistening like glitter,
The trees are swaying in the breeze,
The sand is moving like autumn leaves,
The sky is getting darker, darker, darker.
The sky is getting darker,
It is raining now!

The sea is waving,
The sand is wet,
The trees are dancing,
The rain is crashing, crashing, crashing.
The rain is crashing,
Thunder and lightning, *argh!*

Zoë Walters (9)
Modbury CP School, Ivybridge

I am An Eeyore Fan

I am Little Miss Sunshine, bright and cheerful.
I am an Eeyore fan, cool and funky.
I am a Christmas angel, jolly and caring.
I am an artistic person, colourful and bright.
I am a freak, weird and wacky.
I am a cupcake, yum-yum.
I am an animal, wild and fun.

Holly Low (10)
Modbury CP School, Ivybridge

I Am A Shark

I am a shark, eating and killing.
I am a light bulb, bright and sparkly.
I am a bike, spinning and twirling.
I am the colour blue, icy and cold.
I am a blade of grass, sharp and wavy.

Steven Jones (9)
Modbury CP School, Ivybridge

The River Waves

The waves smashed against the water
As the trees swished in the wind
While people swam in the water
The clouds scurried in the sky.

Katrina Pettitt (10)
Modbury CP School, Ivybridge

The School Sound Collector
(Based on 'The Sound Collector' by Roger McGough)

'A stranger called this morning
Dressed all in black and grey,
Put every sound into a bag
And carried them away.'

The scribbling of my pencil,
The bouncing of the ball,
The slapping of the ruler,
The shouting in the hall.

The shrieking in the playground,
The splashing in the pool,
When I'm in the playground
The nattering of them all.

'A stranger called this morning
He didn't leave his name
Left us only in silence
Life will never be the same.'

Hannah Walters (9)
Modbury CP School, Ivybridge

I Am A Lumpy Orange

I am a lumpy orange, sweet and sour.
I am a zooming sports car, *brum-brum*.
I am a whining baby, annoying and irritating.
I am a seagull, never shutting up.
I am a Rubik's cube, hard to understand.
I am a blunt pencil, hard to use.
I am the colour red, fierce and evil.

Connor Twohig (9)
Modbury CP School, Ivybridge

245

The School Sounds Collector
(Based on 'The Sound Collector' by Roger McGough)

'A stranger called this morning
Dressed all in black and grey,
Put every sound into a bag
And carried them away.'

The arguing of the children,
The ringing of the bell,
The slapping of the footsteps as we run to tell,
The smell of the school dinners.

The banging of the doors,
The eating in the hall,
The splashing of the pool,
The talking of the teachers.

'A stranger called this morning
He didn't leave his name,
Left us only silence
Life will never be the same.'

Amala Williams (9)
Modbury CP School, Ivybridge

The School Sounds Collector
(Based on 'The Sound Collector' by Roger McGough)

'A stranger called this morning
Dressed all in black and grey,
Put every sound into a bag
And carried them away.'

The yapping of the children,
The banging of the doors,
The scratching of the sharpener,
The creaking of the floor.

The knocking at the door,
The donging of the bell,
The shouting of the teacher
As someone goes to tell.

'A stranger called this morning
He didn't leave his name,
Left us only silence
Life will never be the same.'

Thomas King (10)
Modbury CP School, Ivybridge

Mr Sound Man

(Based on 'The Sound Collector' by Roger McGough)

*'A stranger called this morning
Dressed all in black and grey,
Put every sound into a bag
And carried them away.'*

The clanking of the bell,
The bouncing of the ball,
The shouting of the children,
The whispering in the hall.

The scratching of the pencils,
The banging of the trays,
The ticking of the clock,
He carried them all away.

*'A stranger called this morning
He didn't leave his name,
Left us only silence
Life will never be the same.'*

Kelly Parry (10)
Modbury CP School, Ivybridge

Animals

From the ant that crawls furiously
To the pouncing tiger in the grass.
From the baby cub that steps
To the roaring lion.
From the swinging monkey
To the tall giraffe.
From the tiny fish that swim
To the great white shark that kills.

Thomas Scott (9)
Mount Street Primary School, Plymouth

The Marching Band

Lots of people gather around,
They can hear the marching band.
Bagpipes playing, people saying,
'Look at them, look at them they're doing a marching band like a sparkling gem.'
Colours flashing past my eyes
Why oh why do violins sound like they cry?

Kelli McArthur (10)
Mount Street Primary School, Plymouth

My Typical Family

My sister chucked a custard pie,
It hit my dad in the eye.
She said she didn't, when she did it
I said, 'You liar, stop being stupid.'
Then Dad threw a pancake roll at Mum
After that she looked so glum,
Mum chucked a tomato at the cat,
She did it with a tennis bat.
And it all started by my sister
No one threw anything at me.
Come to my house again next time
Then you will see me.

Maisie Perry (9)
Mount Street Primary School, Plymouth

Food Fight

A flying custard pie splattered in my eye,
I threw it back at my mum.
She threw a hot-cross bun at Dad.
Dad got mad and threw the cake and Baby covered him in milkshake.
Granny got into the habit and threw a rabbit at my sister.
Of course she had only one thing and that was to throw her cabbage stew.
My mum shouted, 'Stop it now, stop this very messy brawl.'
As you can see . . . we haven't got any tea!

Yasmin Egonu (9)
Mount Street Primary School, Plymouth

School Sounds

Here I stand in the school, everywhere I go I hear . . .
Clattering of plates in the dinner hall,
The scraping of the knives and forks,
The bouncing of the balls,
Clanging of doors,
The sneezing of ill people,
People play basketball but most of them are tall
The shouting of the noisy children,
And that's my school!

Fiona Lee (9)
Mount Street Primary School, Plymouth

At The Beach

Beach balls bouncing behind big buckets.
People chatting like pebbles clashing.
Spades scratching the pebbles like nails on a blackboard.
Shells echoing the sea like a person shouting into a cave.
Waves smashing against the shore like saucepans clanking.

Michelle Knight (11)
Musbury Primary School, Axminster

My Chickens

Crafty claw, scratching claws,
Flapping wings, flying feathers,
Pecking beaks, they are banging in the feeder,
Noisy squeaks and loud talks coming from the hen house,
Scrunching shovel against the feed.

Dominic Turner (10)
Musbury Primary School, Axminster

In France

The sound of . . .

Bees buzzing around the flowers,
Grasshoppers making croaking noises,
The dogs barking in the field,
The CD player growling loud music,
Birds echoing in the background,
The cat purring on the sofa,
The fire sizzling in the sitting room,
The sound of Jo picking flowers,
The geese honking at the dogs.

Jessica Rowden (10)
Musbury Primary School, Axminster

The Footballer

He is as fast as lightning,
He jumps as high as a kangaroo,
He has big hands like a giant,
He scores lots of goals,
He is always on target, like a dart.

Tom Aston (6)
Neroche Primary School, Ilminster

The Monster Truck

The monster truck has
Bright lights like the Milky Way.
The engine roars like thunder as it thunders over the grass,
With its giant, rough tyres, that look like rock faces as
It jumps over the tree trunks like a kangaroo in a field.

Nicholas Liggins (7)
Neroche Primary School, Ilminster

The Pink Bear

My bear is pink like some candyfloss that I buy at the fair.
She has black eyes and a nose like coal that you put in the fire.
She is pretty like me.

Katie Watts (6)
Neroche Primary School, Ilminster

Elephant

Her eyes as black as ebony,
They shine and glint in the sun,
Her thighs as robust as tree trunks,
They really help her run.

Her skin is as parched as a desert rock face,
So rough and coarse and dry.
Her shins as sturdy as a fence post,
That make her tower high in the sky.

Jessica Lawrence (10)
Neroche Primary School, Ilminster

The Kitten

The kitten is ginger like marmalade,
Her eyes twinkle like stars in the night,
Her fur is as soft as a feather,
She is cuddly like cotton wool,
She is as brambly as a bush,
She is as cute as a princess.

Eloise Poole (7)
Neroche Primary School, Ilminster

My Dad's Car

It is green like grass,
My dad can make it purr like a kitten,
He can also make it squeal like a pig,
And roar like a tiger.
It is fast like a leopard,
It drinks go-go juice like a fish,
When he drives it flat out it sticks to the road like glue,
When my mum drives it, she turns into Michael Shumacher.

Robert Andrews (10)
Neroche Primary School, Ilminster

The Ferrari

The Ferrari's engine roaring up the road,
The Ferrari's lovely, smooth leather interior.
The Ferrari's wheels shining in the sun,
The Ferrari's exhausts like flaring nostrils,
The Ferrari's big shiny badge on the bonnet,
The Ferrari's silver sleek body,
The Ferrari's headlights like cats' eyes.

Connor Gearty (11)
Neroche Primary School, Ilminster

My Puppy Banjo

My puppy Banjo
Can really go, go!
His tail is long,
He's very strong,
His teeth are sharp,
His nose is wet,
He's my best ever pet.

Aimee Dellow (10)
Neroche Primary School, Ilminster

The Tree

It grabs my coat with its arm,
Its skin falls on my head,
Its eyes watch me carefully,
Its feet are strapped to the floor.

Jenny Kerr (11)
Neroche Primary School, Ilminster

My Cat Is Like . . .

My cat is like a best friend,
Although she sometimes drives me around the bend.
Her coat shines so black like wet lumps of coal,
She waits for me in the kitchen to fill her bowl.
Her eyes glow so bright like the moonlight,
She jumps up on my bed like a cockerel
Waiting for me to lift my head.
Her tail so smooth like a whip, it moves as she sips creamy milk,
And rubs my leg like silk.
Always around, never goes too far,
I can hear her coming as she purrs like a motor car.
My best friend the cat, always listens when I want a chat.

Claire Johnson (10)
Neroche Primary School, Ilminster

My Dog Flora

Her eyes are like big brown beads,
Her fat belly grows like a balloon as she feeds,
On walks she's guided like a mole by her nose,
Her ears are like a bat's and pick up the call of crows,
Her chocolate fur like a woolly bear so soft to touch,
Her banded tail like a lemur which she wags so much,
Her playful spirit like a newborn puppy is such a joy,
She loves to play like a monkey with me and her toy.

Keri Oaten (10)
Neroche Primary School, Ilminster

Race Cars

Race cars have speed
Race cars are noisy
They are different colours
They have a lot of anger and frustration.
Race car drivers show their cars off
And make them look flashy.
Beautiful lines down the sides.
They attract crowds as they speed past.

Dominic Blackmore (10)
Neroche Primary School, Ilminster

My Kitten Sox

We have a young kitten
Who moved in with us,
She loves making trouble
And causing a fuss.

She is only little
Just more than a mouse,
She likes making trouble,
And breaks up the house.

She has a soft black coat
That feels like silk,
With four little footsies
The colour of milk.

She climbs like a monkey
With claws like pins,
And teeth more like razors
Fights she often wins.

She races around
Like a speeding car,
Loves to investigate
Near and afar.

She's ever so nosey
And sleeps in a box,
This is our wonderful
Kitten called Sox.

Peter Hansford (10)
Neroche Primary School, Ilminster

Rugby

A ball like an egg,
A big boy like a rhino,
The grass is like concrete,
The ball spinning like a propeller,
The fullback catches the ball like a dog,
Wingers go down the line like runner beans,
Players flattened like pancakes.

Ryan Deag (11)
Neroche Primary School, Ilminster

My Friend's Dog

My friend's dog's fur is as brown as oak,
My friend's dog has legs like four pillars,
My friend's dog's back is like an archway,
My friend's dog has shoulders like a square box,
My friend's dog has a tail like a snake,
My friend's dog's eyes are as blue as the sky,
My friend's dog has five pups as black as night.

Olivia Clark (11)
Neroche Primary School, Ilminster

Eating Peaches On The Beaches

I once went to the beach,
And there I ate a peach,
I mixed it up with sand,
And ate it from my hand.

Then feeling rather sick,
I went to Doctor Dick,
He said, 'Go for a walk,
And eat a pound of chalk,
And if you're still half dead,
You better go to bed.

And never eat canned peaches
When you're on sandy beaches.'

Sophie Cook (9)
Nether Stowey CE (VC) Primary School, Bridgwater

Tearing Your Hair Out!

Last night I had a nightmare,
And woke up feeling sick,
I went down to breakfast,
Then phoned Doctor Dick.

He said I had a illness,
That made me turn all blue,
Instead my hair fell out,
And I stuck it back with glue.

It fell back out,
When I got to school,
All the girls and boys,
Thought it was not cool!

Alice Horn (10)
Nether Stowey CE (VC) Primary School, Bridgwater

The Tortoise And The Hare

Said the hare to the tortoise, 'Would you like to race?'
Replied the tortoise to the hare, 'Of course I'd love to race.'
So they gathered at the starting line, the gun blew into space.
Hare left the starting line without a single trace.
Hare said halfway down, 'I shall win the race!'
Tortoise wasn't sure as he plodded on at a snail's pace.
Hare saw a tree, thought he was so ace, stopped for a rest from that great big race.
Tortoise plodded past, went over the finish, now he was the ace.
Hare galloped as fast as he could to find that tortoise had won the race.

Katie Mackenzie (10)
Nether Stowey CE (VC) Primary School, Bridgwater

You're Driving Me Up The Wall

You're driving me up the wall
You're driving me up the wall you are, you are
You're screaming your head off you are, you are
You're giving me a banging headache you are, you are.

You're following me around you are, you are
You've dropped your tea on the floor you have, you have
You're crying your eyes out you are, you are
Now I'm crying my eyes out I am, I am.

I'm walking to the door I am, I am.
I'm getting in the car I am, I am
I'm driving up the garage wall I am, I am.

Danielle Stead (9)
Nether Stowey CE (VC) Primary School, Bridgwater

Splash

I spy a dolphin in the shimmers of the sea,
Leaping in the air prepared for anything.
Swimming to the dark depths of the ocean,
Emerging for all to hear him sing.

He swims till his heart is filled with joy, across the scraped sun,
His graceful body plunges through the sea,
As he makes his way through the blowing waves.
Showing off some tricks for me.

Hark, the trawlers arrive, he's off in a flash
The speed of lightning,
In a disappearing splash.

Chloe Godden (9)
Nether Stowey CE (VC) Primary School, Bridgwater

What Has Happened To Buster?

What has happened to Buster, Mummy?
What has happened to Bust?
There's nothing left but his red bowl and cushion,
A place he liked to sit.

Why is his food untouched, Daddy?
His milk so stale and sour,
I've looked round the house, I've searched high and low,
I've looked at a picture on the wall Daddy,
Now I wait for him hour by hour.
I've looked outside Daddy, all I see is grass,
Where is Buster, Daddy?
Where is Bust?

Please tell me where he is,
I've looked upstairs, I've looked outside,
I've looked everywhere.

Jacob Pearson (9)
Nether Stowey CE (VC) Primary School, Bridgwater

The Bear

Happy in the forest playing with his cubs,
His golden coat shining in the sun,
Free as a bird he leaps and bounds,
Lolloping around, having great fun.

A man plodding, sees the bear in the forest.
He runs with the net in his hand
Gets closer to bear, chucks the net over the bear,
Pulls the bear to the lorry.

Pulls him out into the circus, on the stage,
Makes him dance and prance around,
Bruin the bear thinks that he is a fool,
Dancing and prancing around like a clown.

He gets all mad, starts to jump,
He runs and runs, he gets free.
People go mad, and the plodding man sets him free.

Louise Hall (9)
Nether Stowey CE (VC) Primary School, Bridgwater

Hector

Hector is the best.
He uses my bed as a nest.

One evening Hector ran away.
I remember it was a Wednesday.
We were all crying,
We thought he could be dying.
On the busy road, with a squashed toad!
We returned to our house.
I was as quiet as a mouse.
Suddenly we heard a thump!
My heart gave a jump!
There was Hector all safe and sound.
Curled up he had been found.

Rory Montague (9)
Nether Stowey CE (VC) Primary School, Bridgwater

Dragons

D ragons spit fire,
R un when you see one,
A ahh, Fire Dragon!
G reat daggers, lovely colours,
O ld dragons, shiny and bright,
N o one go near them
S o many dragons love to spit fire.

Chloe Gratton (10)
Newport Community School, Barnstaple

Winter's Wonders

W onders!
 I like playing in the snow,
N ever want to see it go!
T hrowing snowballs at my friends,
E arth is such a special place,
R ound the corner, a sunny day.

Josh Taylor (10)
Newport Community School, Barnstaple

Hallowe'en Is Coming

The date today is the 30th, tomorrow is Hallowe'en;
All the ghosts and ghoulies are going to turn mean,
It's going to be really scary,
Almost all the monsters are really, really hairy.

We're going to have a party with food and drink and games,
We'll dress up as monsters, with really scary names.
Mummies and ghoulies and monsters too,
Wizards and witches will be casting spells on you.

When we go on the streets at night,
We'll try to give someone an awful fright,
We'll be going trick-or-treating here and there;
People in their houses had better take care.

We'll have sweets in our bags, and we'll start to head home.
All the ghosts and ghoulies will leave us alone.
By then we'll be tired and we'll want to go to sleep,
We'll go off to bed to dream of the next trick-or-treat.

Shivon Burridge (9)
Newport Community School, Barnstaple

Stormy Night

Waves crashing,
Lightning flashing,
Rain splashing.
Wind howling!

Stormy night,
Stormy night!

Thunder clapping,
Sails flapping,
Shutters slapping.

Stormy night,
Stormy night!

Children waking,
Trees shaking,
Branches breaking.

Stormy night,
Stormy night!

Rebecca Browne (10)
Newport Community School, Barnstaple

Man U V Barcelona

Barcelona playing a 4-4-2,
On the ball is Eto'o.

Man Utd playing a 4-3-3,
In dives Rooney.

Oh wow, it's a foul,
The ref's gonna book Rooney now.

'Oh my, it's a red!'
The commentator said.

Free kick taken by Ronaldinho
Look at that it's a goal!

Here comes Paul Scholes
He's scored plenty of goals.

The whistle's gone,
It's over now,
Man U have won, we ask, but how?

There's Neville, lifting the cup
What a team, they had all the luck!

Don't worry; it's not what it seems
It was only a dream.

Sam Pincombe (10)
Newport Community School, Barnstaple

Either Way You Look Right

Small,
Tall,
Thin,
Obese,
Unhappy,
Depressed,
Lonely,
Confused,
You look right in all ways.
From our hearts
It says the truth.
Be proud of yourself
Because
Either way you look right.

Kelly Pert (10)
Newport Community School, Barnstaple

Stressed

I've started getting bullied at school,
They tease me about my hair,
My home,
My family.
I've started getting bullied at school,
They laugh at me about my skin,
My friends,
My work.
Why do I get so stressed?
Why am I so scared
To go to school today?
I have to get dressed, have hope, say 'Bye,' go to school,
I wonder if today it will be better or worse?

It was actually worse,
I can't believe my ears, it was my worst day ever,
I've started getting bullied at school,
I burst into tears today in class,
The bullies looked and laughed and laughed:
They thought I was a baby, they said,
Crying at home,
At school,
Crying in clubs.
Crying for help.
I've started getting bullied at school,
They tease me about my hair,
My home,
My family.
I've started getting bullied at school,
They laugh at me about my skin,
My friends,
My work.

Jasmine Moran (10)
Newport Community School, Barnstaple

Friends

Friends are there whenever you need them;
Friends can cheer you up when you are down;
Friends come in different shapes and sizes;
Friends look out for one another;
Friends are treasures to me,
And I wouldn't be without them.

Hannah Sutton (10)
Newport Community School, Barnstaple

My Rabbit

My rabbit's called Holly
She's got big floppy ears
Holly is big and Holly is fat
She sometimes likes wearing my hat.

Holly lives in a hutch
With only two rooms
Outside in the summer
Inside when it's cold.

She runs round the garden
At an incredible speed
She likes nibbling Mum's plants
And loves eating the leaves.

Holly loves carrots
And I hope she loves me
She twitches her nose
And she likes eating her tea.

Holly is my top dude
And I think she's really fab
I love my lopped eared rabbit
Holly's my pet and I'm glad.

Shane Prater (11)
Newport Community School, Barnstaple

Sister

My little sister, Eleanor
Is sometimes rather mad:
When I ask the question 'Why?'
I'm told, 'She gets if off our dad.'

She does some really wacky stuff
It makes me laugh out loud;
She could be a comedian
She'd get a great big crowd!

Some might say she's bonkers,
Some might say she's strange,
I love her the way she is,
I don't want her to change!

Jessica Smith (10)
Newport Community School, Barnstaple

Horses And Ponies

H acking out on horses,
O ver lots of jumps in courses
R ide up to a gymkhana show
S addle up and off you go
E verything you have to know to pass a test
S uper ponies are always delighted to have a guest

A ll the horses get excited
N ow they have returned from the ride they are very hot
D rummer, Thomas and all their gang.

P ony's saddle will slip if you let the girth hang
O ut in the field on a pony chase;
N ever leave the gate open, just in case
I finish the last jobs of the day
E very stable needs a hay net full of hay!
S eems all the ponies are my friends, never want the day to end.

Myah Field (10)
Newport Community School, Barnstaple

The Clattering Train

Clickety clack, it rolls down the track,
Its horn gives a great big sneeze.
Whilst it rumbles along its wheels sing their song,
And its pistons they whistle and wheeze.

The people on board, give a silent roar,
As they wave to farmers working in their fields.
Her colour's bright green, and her face drawn and mean,
As she clatters along at great speed.

At the station approach, the brakes give a squeal,
As the signal - it's calling a halt.
So the clattering train slows down once again,
And comes to a rest - with a yawn.

Charles Crutchley (10)
Newport Community School, Barnstaple

Swimming

S plashing sploshing in the swimming pool, gliding through the water
   it feels so cool.
W ater splashing on my face during a competitive race,
   people clapping and stamping their feet as I try my best not to get beat.
I love my swimming club on a Thursday night working on my strokes
   to get them just right.
M y dreams are to swim at the Olympics in London 2012 and hold up a
   medal in front of the crowd.
M y Dad's always diving in messing around but sometimes when he dives
   in his trunks fall down.
I love all the different strokes that you can do, breaststroke, backstroke,
   butterfly too, but front crawl is the best one I can do.
N ine years old and I've been swimming for a while, the furthest I
   have swam is one whole mile.
G alas are great and I have so much fun, people clapping and cheering
   us all the way along.

Alice Field (9)
Newport Community School, Barnstaple

The Beach

I love to watch the sea come in
While ice cream dribbles down my chin.

I love to watch the sea go out
While all the people scream and shout.

Sandcastles, sandcastles everywhere,
Salty seawater in my hair.

On the shore, jellyfish squirm and wiggle
Children just look, laugh and giggle.

Slap on the sun cream, slip on a hat;
To look like a lobster, I don't want that!

To spend every day at the beach is my wish;
To swim in the sea, alongside the fish!

Charlotte Rushton (10)
Newport Community School, Barnstaple

Pegasus

P egasus fly high in the sky
E clipsing the sun with his wings
G lides down to the ground hooves earthbound again
A ir rippling the grass as he lands
S py him cantering the plain, tossing his head shaking his mane
U nique in all ways, a legend far told
S uch a beautiful creature, many centuries old.

Gemma Wells (10)
Newport Community School, Barnstaple

Dolphins

D ancing through the seas
O cean water splashing around them as they jump
L eaping up and down day and night
P erhaps not everyone likes them
H ow could they not?
I certainly do
N othing but dolphins and fish in the sea
S wimming all the time.

Jessica Loder (9)
Newport Community School, Barnstaple

Photos

Who's that?
That's Auntie Sable;
And that's me
Under the table.

Who's that?
That's your nan, Lilly
Who's that?
Me being silly.

Who's that,
Licking a lolly?
I'm not sure
But I think it's Molly.

Who's that
Behind the tree?
I don't know,
I can't see.
It could be you,
It could be me.

Ysabel Thomas (10)
Newport Community School, Barnstaple

If I Had A Fluffy Kitten

If I had a fluffy kitten
I would wash up every day,
I would wash the car,
I would be really good
And never complain.

I would, on a Saturday, make the cooked breakfast,
And, on a Sunday, let Mum lie in,
But unfortunately for my mum
She's missing something special!

Charlotte Brend (11)
Newport Community School, Barnstaple

Kayaking With My Mates

K ayaks on the river
A nother boat bought
Y esterday I went on the surf
A fter a surf I have a hot chocolate
K ind, kind men to empty my boat
I ncredible rapids
N ever ever will I be scared of water
G onna always kayak with my mates.

Samuel Clarke (10)
Newport Community School, Barnstaple

My Cats

I love my cats,
My cats are bright;
They sleep all day
And play all night.

Blackie and Horlicks are their names,
Chasing mice are their games.

I love my cats
They are the best,
They make me happy;
They are better
Than all the rest.

Matthew Pearson (11)
Newport Community School, Barnstaple

Break A Leg

'Break a leg,' my coach said,
Not knowing it would come true;
Ten minutes passed - smack bang on the grass
The pain was carrying through.

I hobbled around, one foot on the ground,
I had to quit the match;
Put on the ice, visit A&E twice;
My bone, it wasn't attached.

I had to get crutches, so my foot now touches
Nothing but the air;
My friend thinks it's cool,
But he is a fool,
And I don't really care.

Justin Southam (11)
Newport Community School, Barnstaple

Jack And Spud

There was an old dog called Jack.
He would just sit on the mat.
There was a young dog called Spud,
He would roll in the mud.

Jack would bump himself on the wall
And would not care.
Spud would curl up in a ball
And had very short hair.

Spud held onto his lead
And never let go!
Jack pottered behind
And walked very slow.

Jack Richards (11)
Newport Community School, Barnstaple

A Rose

A rose, beautiful but quiet,
Its petals as red as blood,
Its thorns as sharp as daggers,
Its stem as graceful as a ballerina;
It only lives for a little while,
But until then,
I will keep it as a treasure.

Andrew Foster (10)
Newport Community School, Barnstaple

Fairies

Fairies, fairies, fluttering past
Fairies, fairies, going so fast
Fairies, fairies, look at their wings
Fairies, fairies, fascinating things
Fairies, fairies, glisten in the light,
Fairies, fairies, they're such a delight
Fairies, fairies, tooth fairies and all,
Fairies, fairies, beautiful as jewels.

Bethany White (9)
Newport Community School, Barnstaple

My PS2

To my PS2
I am stuck like glue:
It's the thing I love to do,
I can play both day and night,
But I don't always get it right.
Practise will make me
Better though,
Why don't you come
And have a go?

Oscar Milton (9)
Newport Community School, Barnstaple

The Sea

The sea is crashing,
The sea is choppy,
The sea is a deep green,
The sea is cold,
The sea is lifeless,
The sea is polluted.

The sea is smooth,
The sea is flat,
The sea is a bright blue,
The sea is warm,
The sea is full of life,
The sea is fresh,
The sea is incredible.

Miles Kingsley (10)
Newport Community School, Barnstaple

Football Cup

F ootball, football is so great,
O n the pitch run up and down,
O pen goal, shoot the ball,
T wo yellow cards equal a red
B all bouncing around and around,
A ll the players trying hard,
L ob the keeper and it's a goal,
L eague leaders have lost the game,

C elebrations, we have won the cup,
U nder a sunny sky we lift the trophy,
P layers and fans share the glory.

Thomas Roode (11)
Newport Community School, Barnstaple

When Will I Get Into The Garden?

The grass keeps on growing
My father keeps on mowing
I'm stuck in this house
With my pet mouse.
The rain keeps on falling,
My brother and sisters are bawling,
When will I get to play in the garden?

I'd like to go and play on my slide,
But Mum says we have to go out for a ride;
I'd like to go and splash in my pool,
But Dad says the water's too cool.
Oh when, oh when will I get to play in the garden?

Connor Smith (9)
Newport Community School, Barnstaple

Birthdays

B alloons are bursting
I love to have fun
R unning and slipping
T rifle is yummy
H appy birthday to you
D rinking party punch
A n adventure today
Y ou can jump and play
S o you can sing silly songs.

Jade Harris (10)
Newport Community School, Barnstaple

My Tropical Island

Crabs crawl sideways on the sandy beach,
Turtles swimming in the shallows,
Pineapples, papaya, mangoes and coconuts;
Crystal clear ocean and white frothy waves.
Palm trees swaying in the tropical breeze
Sandy beaches, baking hot,
Blazing sun shining down on me.

Bethany Westcott (10)
Newport Community School, Barnstaple

My Beautiful Country Walks

In the summer
I did long walks
I walked up country lanes.
All I could hear was the wind blowing
Through the trees.
The sun gradually creeping down the hills.
The wind a perfect temperature.
Apple rosy-red on the trees perfect to eat.
Big oak trees with loads of pine cones hanging
From the very top.
Not knowing where you are going
People in cars would not see what I see
At the end of the day feeling healthily tired
When the sun goes down and the moon comes out
I go to bed
I could still feel and hear the beautiful atmosphere
Of the countryside.

Alice Leaman (9)
Newport Community School, Barnstaple

Fudge The Hamster

F at and furry,
U nusual but cute,
D ocile and lazy,
G reedy little animal,
E xceptional beauty.

Lauren Bawden (10)
Newport Community School, Barnstaple

Biscuit

My kitten is called Biscuit.
He has a cute button nose,
And bold black eyes.
His fur is coloured like a ginger nut.
He plays like an acrobat,
But eats like an elephant;
He jumps up high, and tries to eat soil;
He sleeps like a baby
And purrs like a growly bear.
But most of all, I love him
And he loves me!

Gemma White (9)
Newport Community School, Barnstaple

Seasons

Spring plants grow
Summer rivers flow
Autumn leaves fall
Winter birds call
Spring leaves falling
Summer birds calling
Autumn fall down low
Winter trees start to grow.

Imogen Tarran (8)
Newton Ferrers CE Primary School, Newton Ferrers

Chembakolli

Forest humid,
Sunset finished,
All blue,
Birds chattering
Mice scattering,
Streams flowing,
Mist thick,
Ground wet,
Can't see,
Monkeys screaming,
Streams flowing,
Eagles hovering, diving and swooping.

Emily Vyain (9)
Newton Ferrers CE Primary School, Newton Ferrers

Chembakolli

Elephant working
No rain
Crackling, dead bush
No trees
Dead trees
Large, slow, wrinkled elephant
Dry, cracked ground.

Jenny Willis (9)
Newton Ferrers CE Primary School, Newton Ferrers

Chembakolli

Beneath the wires
In the village
Lots of people walk.

Yellow taxis driving along
The busy, dirty road.

Colourful buildings in the shelter.

Sweetcorn sold in bags.

Anna Barnett (7)
Newton Ferrers CE Primary School, Newton Ferrers

Chembakolli Poem

Flickering fire,
Coconut cracked,
Battered pots and pans,
Smiling faces throughout the darkness.

Marina Carrick (9)
Newton Ferrers CE Primary School, Newton Ferrers

Seasons

Spring leaves grow on trees.
Summer sun beams hotness.
Autumn leaves fall from trees.
Winter cold and snowy.

James Willis (8)
Newton Ferrers CE Primary School, Newton Ferrers

Green

On a hot summer's day the grass was still,
The trees were swerving side to side.
Children wearing bright green scrunchies.
Children eating bright green apples.
Children cheating on every test not trying to do their best.
The light between the green trees makes them wheeze.
The monkey in the trees have fleas.

Issie Hartley & Jessica Peel (10)
Newton Ferrers CE Primary School, Newton Ferrers

Tsunami

Water rushing by the gallon
Shaking the floors of houses
Animals scurrying to shelters
Trees being uprooted by an aqua monster.

Sam Dowling (10) & Fergus Shaw (11)
Newton Ferrers CE Primary School, Newton Ferrers

Earthquake

Earth splitting
People running
Glass smashing
Terrifying, collapsing
Animals crying
It stopped
Dead bodies everywhere.

Michael Crow (10)
Newton Ferrers CE Primary School, Newton Ferrers

Seasons

Spring birds tweeting,
Summer animals eating,
Autumn leaves turn yellow,
Winter we meet a huge old fellow.

Tanya Pearson (8)
Newton Ferrers CE Primary School, Newton Ferrers

Seasons

Spring bunnies hopping fast
Summer days always last
Autumn leaves falling
Winter robins calling.

Fergus Carruthers (7)
Newton Ferrers CE Primary School, Newton Ferrers

Seasons

Spring flowers with lots of buzzing bees,
Summer trees with spring leaves,
Autumn leaves blowing in the breeze,
Winter winds blow through the trees.

Benjamin King (9)
Newton Ferrers CE Primary School, Newton Ferrers

The Prince And The Princess

The princess combed her hair,
And the prince put on his suit.
The princess ate her pear,
While the butler played the flute.

Naomi Sweeny (9)
Okehampton Primary School, Okehampton

The Fox And The Rabbit
(Inspired by 'The Owl and the Pussycat' by Edward Lear)

The fox and the rabbit went for a walk
And grumbled about the laundry shed.
The people are nutters, they spread all their butters
And dine when they are dead.
Fox said to rabbit, 'How fondly I ache to chase you to bake.
So I can crunch your bones,
Your bones,
Your bones,
Your bones,
So I can crunch your bones.'

There is some ice
And some white mice
Eating ham
That turned to lamb.

 William Armstrong (8)
Okehampton Primary School, Okehampton

The Penguin And The Husky
(Inspired by 'The Owl and the Pussycat' by Edward Lear)

The penguin and the husky went to the pools
In a silver glittering sledge,
They took some fish and plenty of tools,
Hidden behind a shimmering hedge.
The penguin looked to the moon above
And sang to Vasaline.
'O lovely husky! O husky my dove,
What a beautiful husky you are,
You are,
You are!
What a beautiful husky you are!'

Emily Franco (8)
Okehampton Primary School, Okehampton

The Elf And The Polar Bear
(Inspired by 'The Owl and the Pussycat' by Edward Lear)

The elf and the polar bear went to the North Pole
On a block of ice.
They took some ice and plenty of mice,
Wrapped up in some rice.
The elf looked up to the stars above and sang
To a small trumpet,
'O lovely polar bear, O polar bear my love,
You are,
You are!
What a beautiful polar bear you are.'

Aaron Dearing (8)
Okehampton Primary School, Okehampton

The Parsnip And The Goat
(Inspired by 'The Owl and the Pussycat' by Edward Lear)

The parsnip and the goat were born in a field,
Raised up by a wrinkled carrot.
They met a fishy and ate it on a dishy
When they met its mother the shark.
The goat said to the shark towering above,
'O ugly shark, o shark you're ugly
What an ugly shark you are!
You are
You are!
What an ugly shark you are!'

Kate Bailey (9)
Okehampton Primary School, Okehampton

The Witch And The Wizard
(Inspired by 'The Owl and the Pussycat' by Edward Lear)

The witch and the wizard went to France
In a beautiful shiny car.
They had sweets and plenty of treats
Wrapped up in a big glass jar.
The wizard looked up to the moon above,
And sang to a small recorder,
'O lovely witch! O witchy's my love,
What a beautiful witch you are,
You are,
You are!
What a beautiful witch you are!'

Sasha Lerch (9)
Okehampton Primary School, Okehampton

The Lamb And The Pop Star
(Inspired by 'The Owl and the Pussycat' by Edward Lear)

The lamb and the pop star went to see a boxer
In a beautiful dazzling car,
They took some clothes and plenty of toads,
Wrapped up in loads of purses.
The pop star looked up at the stars,
And the lamb said, 'What a beautiful pop star you are,
You are,
You are!
What a beautiful pop star you are!'

Holly Yelland (9)
Okehampton Primary School, Okehampton

Tom And Jerry
(Inspired by 'The Owl and the Pussycat' by Edward Lear)

Tom and Jerry went to the shops,
On an ugly, slimy, slug,
They took some books and plenty of hooks,
Placed in an old black plug,
Tom looked up at the clouds above,
And sang, 'Oh what an ugly mouse you are,
You are,
You are,
Oh what an ugly mouse you are!'

Miranda Jewell (8)
Okehampton Primary School, Okehampton

The Dragon And The Teacher
(Inspired by 'The Owl and the Pussycat' by Edward Lear)

The dragon and the teacher went to sea
In a beautiful, racing car,
They took some fruit, and a pink leather boot,
Wrapped up in an old sweetie jar.
The dragon looked up to the sun above
And sang to a small guitar
'O lovely teacher! O teacher my love,
What a beautiful teacher you are,
You are,
You are!
What a beautiful teacher you are!'

Brandon Francis (9)
Okehampton Primary School, Okehampton

The Lion And The Leopard
(Inspired by 'The Owl and the Pussycat' by Edward Lear)

The lion and the leopard chased a bee
Until they came to the sea.
They saw a goat and jumped into a boat,
But they knocked their knee and couldn't go to sea,
When the boat couldn't float,
Away went the goat!
'Oh jump dear leopard, jump for your life!
I am too injured to go,
To go,
To go!
I am injured so go!'

Sophie Compton (9)
Okehampton Primary School, Okehampton

My Friend

My friend is beautiful,
She's like a super star
With fashion.
If she was a butterfly
She would be
As elegant as a rose.
She makes everyone else
Look different.
She's the only one I know
Who could win a fashion show.

Cara Leahy (8)
Okehampton Primary School, Okehampton

The Stars And The Sun
(Inspired by 'The Owl and the Pussycat' by Edward Lear)

The stars and the sun had a fight,
On a beautiful, dark black night.
They finished their fight,
At the dead of light,
The sun looked up to space above,
And sang to the twinkling of stars.
'O lovely stars, O stars, my love,
What beautiful stars you are,
You are,
You are!
What beautiful stars you are!'

Anna Neale (9)
Okehampton Primary School, Okehampton

As Pretty As . . .

As pretty as . . .
An ice palace,
A rose,
A snow glow,
A baby,
An opal,
A primrose dress,
A fairy queen,
A summer's day,
Spring,
New York at night,
Everything!

Andree de La Fontaine (8)
Okehampton Primary School, Okehampton

My Cat

My cat is fast.
He pounces round the house
Like a leopard.
If he was in the Olympic races
He would win every time.
He makes everyone seem slow.
He's the only cat I know
Who is as fast as a Ferrari.

Beau Donovan (9)
Okehampton Primary School, Okehampton

Nanny's Garden

Nanny's garden is a beautiful sight
With all the flowers left and right.
There's a tree I can climb
You'll find me there all the time.
The sandpit there that Nanny made
Where I play with my bucket and spade.
Nanny's garden is the place to be
With lots of things to do and see.

Ashleigh Sandford (8)
Okehampton Primary School, Okehampton

My Mum

My mum is kind,
She cooks really good,
Just like a chef.
If she was a professional cook,
Her food would be delicious,
She makes everybody look like they can't cook,
She's the only person I know,
Who can cook delicious food.

Declan Coyle (8)
Okehampton Primary School, Okehampton

Polar Bears

Polar bears slip and slide
But never glide.
Some are big, some are small,
And some are very tall.
They like fish but not on a dish,
Even if it's big or small.
They run and always have fun,
They slip and grip even if they trip.
They have white and bright fur.

Scott Bending (9)
Okehampton Primary School, Okehampton

Cats

Smooth and soft
Lovingly, happily, hungrily,
Creeping, snoozing, scratching, cleaning!

Lucy Dean (8)
Okehampton Primary School, Okehampton

My Gran

My gran is sneaky,
She shuffles from room to room like a mouse.
If my gran was an animal she would be a shrivelled up tortoise.
She makes everybody else seem normal!
She's the only person I know who can eat a giant bar of chocolate
In only a few minutes!

Ellsie Hutt (8)
Okehampton Primary School, Okehampton

My Uncle

My uncle is stupid
He walks into fences
And bounces around in a million circles.
If he was an animal
He would be a dopey dog.
He makes my grandad look grumpy,
He's the only person I know who
Says that he rides on dinosaurs.

Ailsa Gibb (9)
Okehampton Primary School, Okehampton

Monsters

'Mam,' said Ben, 'there are monsters,
Monsters up the stairs,
I'm kind of scared of them,
As they are always, but never there!'

'First,' he said, 'there's the monster under me bed,
His eyes are a glowing red,
He's got dagger-sharp teeth,
Plus he fancies me teddy bear who fell on the floor!'

'Then,' continued Ben, 'there is the one down the toilet,
He's a blob of green slime, but he doesn't mind,
He is the kindest of all the monsters,
But he keeps on sneezing, *yuck!*'

'How could I forget the one in the closet,
She is so scary, (and she can get quite lairy),
And when she's in a fine spirit,
She does a disappearing act with the food!'

'See Mum, I'm telling the truth, honest,
What else could explain all the damage to the house?'
'The dog Ben,' said Mum,
'The dog.'

Harriet Walsh (10)
Parkfield Primary School, Taunton

My Mirror's Words

I see me, I see hair.
I see here, I see there.
I see colour, I see light,
I see fear, I see fright.

I see curtains, I see floor.
I see wardrobe, I see drawer.
I see freckles, I see lips.
I see moon, plus one eclipse.

I see even, I see fair.
I see love, I see care.
I see interest, I see bore.
I see boxes, broken laws.

I see brown, I see black.
I see hard work, I see slack.
I see music, I see fun,
I see people, everyone.

I see trophy, I see muck.
I see wisdom, I see luck.
I see feeling, I see trust.
I see things to do and lust.

I see people, it's what I see
I see you, I see me.

Sophie Knutt (11)
Parkfield Primary School, Taunton

Dream Unicorn

Her golden silky mane,
Shining like the stars.

Her beautiful creamy head,
With its razor-sharp horn!

Her friendly beady eyes,
Watching carefully.

Her calm and gentle trot,
So much like a horse.

Her lively, swishing tail,
Moving joyfully.

That's my snowy unicorn,
That no one else can see.

Susannah Slack (10)
Parkfield Primary School, Taunton

The Fairy

The fairy runs through the fields,
Her body twisting and turning and doing cartwheels,
Her hair is as yellow as butter,
She doesn't want to go and get her mum's gingerbread cutter.

Her dress pink, purple, orange and green,
How does she keep everything so clean,
The weeds tickling her legs amongst the grass,
She is thinking of good times in the past.

All of a sudden
She falls down dead, a person doesn't believe,
There she is lying on the grass, where she was happily playing, unable to breathe,
That is what happens when you say you don't believe.

Alexandra Stapleton (10)
Parkfield Primary School, Taunton

Run Away, It's Coming

Mum, it's coming downstairs,
I can hear it behind me.
Mum hide, it's after me and you,
It's scary and as big as a house.
Run away, it's coming!

It's scary, it looks like this,
Eyes like footballs,
Claws like razor-sharp swords,
Teeth like snake fangs,
Run away it's coming!
I'll tell you more,
Its body's like a tree trunk,
Head like the moon,
Arms like a chimney,
Run away, it's coming!
Run Mum it's going to kill me and you,
Quick we have to hide,
It's going faster and faster,
It's going to kill us,
Run away, it's coming!

We're trapped!
We're trapped!
We're trapped!
It's my brother in fancy dress!

Ryan Marsden (11)
Parkfield Primary School, Taunton

The Troll

He's got great, big, fat, hairy feet.
He's actually quite nice to meet.
His name is Bill,
And he just wants to chill.

I go to sleep with him every night,
Our dreams are soaring like a kite.
When I wake him up, he's always mad,
But he's never, ever, ever bad.

He's really, very, very big,
Nearly as big as a big, big pig.
He's actually a small little doll,
But compared to my others he's a great big troll.

But I think he's big, as big as his heart,
And he had to come in a great big cart.
Suddenly it dawned on me,
He's not that big, he's 0 foot, 3"!

Rosie Dunkley (11)
Parkfield Primary School, Taunton

I Believe In Fairies

I believe in fairies,
Oh yes I do!
Even when I'm angry,
Or with you.

I believe in fairies,
I visit their garden.
I think they've got tiny voices,
'Uh pardon.'

I believe in fairies,
I love the dresses they wear,
Pinks, purples and even grey!
But are they really there?

I believe in fairies,
I begin to shout,
I think the neighbours hear,
At least they don't know what
It's about!

I believe in fairies,
I begin to cry,
But why don't they visit me?
Was it all a lie?

Jessica Bennett (10)
Parkfield Primary School, Taunton

Gazing Up To Heaven

Last night I gazed to light and heard the angels sing,
They sounded as if a glorious choir to be sung along the clouds of the world,
I saw many spirits to clang the carrying notes of the air,
They glided wonderfully as if a winding gust struck down from Heaven.

My compassion of heart is to glide along with them one day,
When I've gone and swallowed the earth I will sink upon,
That's why I pray to Lord to open the gates,
And let me walk upon the clouds.

But I praise that time will not be rung,
Until it is truly meant to be,
And for now it's just a dream,
But later on in life it will be reality.

Finn Bowdrey (11)
Parkfield Primary School, Taunton

The Devil

The Devil sleeps right under me,
It always hums like a bumblebee,
Why won't it go to sleep at night?
Whenever I look it's always in sight.

The Devil's horns are as sharp as knives,
Its body is like a long red balloon,
Its feet are like dragon's teeth,
Its hair is as red-hot as the sun.

My sister sleeps right under me,
She always chats like a chatter bee
Why won't she go to sleep at night?
Whenever I look she's always in sight.

My sister's bunches are as pointy as knives
Her body is like a long greasy sausage,
Her feet are like little lollipops,
Her hair is as brown as the bark on a tree.

My sister is a devil, a devil as can be,
But . . . what about me?

Jasmine Broom (10)
Parkfield Primary School, Taunton

Killer Bunny

Once I found a killer bunny eating in a hole,
I went to have a closer look,
And found a ripped up mole.

Then I let out one killer sneeze which wasn't all my fault,
He turned around and bared his fangs,
And politely asked for salt.

His coat was stained crimson red,
So much for the just washed white,
He also was rather pleased that he killed it in one bite.

He also had good table manners, which shook me quite a lot,
But then he sighed and said to me,
That he preferred it hot.

Then he said, 'Goodbye old chum,'
And then before going,
He wriggled his bum.

Henry Giles (10)
Parkfield Primary School, Taunton

My Strange Teacher

My strange teacher is sometimes tall,
But sometimes tiny.

My strange teacher is sometimes lively,
But sometimes dull.

My strange teacher is sometimes boring,
But sometimes fun.

My strange teacher is sometimes sane,
But sometimes loses her head.

My strange teacher is sometimes confusing,
But sometimes explains herself well.

My strange teacher . . . I think is human
But I can' t be sure!

Harriet Kelly (10)
Parkfield Primary School, Taunton

Is Yours As Bad As Mine?

He's really quite disgusting
He loves his tiny ted
He is mean and he is fierce
But he still wets the bed.

In his room you'll find pimples
And pickings from his nose
You'll find rosy-red boils
And cuttings from his toes.

He throws people across the room
When he doesn't get his way
He's more interested in his girlfriend
Than Mum's seven meal buffet.

He's rude to Mum and Dad
He doesn't do what they say,
He likes to slouch on the couch,
When he does work he always wants good pay.

He's the stinkiest around
But always more tougher
Guess who he is?
He's my six pack brother.

Harriet Wiltshire (10)
Parkfield Primary School, Taunton

My Teacher

My teacher, she's very old,
Thirty or forty, I've been told.
Her emerald green eyes, pierce you down,
And her forehead forms a wrinkled frown.

My teacher's hair, is short and brown
She wears a long, crimson gown.
Her fingernails are painted pink,
And her new perfume, *really stinks!*

My teacher, she sets homework every day,
And if you don't do it, you'll have to pay!
Miss your break, lunch too,
And even worse, clean the *loo!*

My teacher, she's really not that bad,
If she goes, I'd be pretty sad.
She's always having fun, and playing the fool,
I suppose, my teacher is pretty cool.

Chloe Griffiths (11)
Parkfield Primary School, Taunton

The Monster In My Bedroom

'Mum! There's a monster in my bedroom!
It's got a square head,
That's green and fluffy,
And is eating my TV!
Mum! Help!'

'Mum! There's a monster in my bedroom!
It's pink and blue striped,
And is shaped like a giant prune!
It's really, really scary Mum!
So please, please help me!'

'Mum! There's a monster in my bedroom!
Its hands are like spades!
They are like steel plates, Mum!
They look really, really menacing!
So help, please!'

'Mum! There's a monster in my bedroom!
Its teeth are like sharp razors,
And . . . oh no, they're green!
I don't think this monster brushes his teeth Mum!
So why do you tell off me?'

Sam Underwood (10)
Parkfield Primary School, Taunton

Dogs

Lots of dogs
Are just like frogs.
They bounce around,
Without making a sound.

They beg for food,
When they're in the mood.
They'll just want more,
But that's a bore.

They chase the cats,
And scare the bats.
In the barn,
Storing the yarn.

Around the house,
Sniffing for a mouse,
Chasing a cow
Who knows quite how.

But that's just dogs isn't it!

Amy Howes (10)
Parkfield Primary School, Taunton

My Sister Is Annoying

My sister is annoying,
I'm not quite sure, why.
Maybe I was mean,
Although I'm not sure how.

My sister is annoying,
Always changing channels,
Then nowhere to be found,
There she is mad as a *hatter!*

My sister is annoying,
Always watching me,
When I turn around,
Her eyes are fixed to the telly.

My sister is annoying,
I'm never alone,
Like a stalker,
Hunting me down.

My sister is annoying,
Always making noises,
In some rude places,
But somehow never moves.

My sister is annoying,
Never any fun,
Always endless shouting,
I never get anything done.

My sister is annoying,
But sometimes my sister,
Just has to have time out,
But only when *Tracey Beaker's on!*

Nathan Wilson (10)
Parkfield Primary School, Taunton

Ten Things Found In An Elf's Pocket

A book of toys
A book of how to make more toys
A toadstool to sit on
A 'how to mend things' book
A bit of wood
An elf's help book
A book to make a doll's house
An elf's hat as big as an elf
An elfy chocolate bar.

Jack Bedford (8)
Polruan Community Primary School, Fowey

Ten Things I Found In A Mermaid's Pocket

The rarest shell brought back from the ocean's finest hotel.
A bag of ancient rocks
A piece of a bow off a boat found in the docks
A pinch of golden sand
A precious photo of land
A scrunched up page from a book called 'Swimming is Fun'
Rippling water with the captured reflection of the sun
A lucky charm of which there's only one
All the sea creatures from Amazon Piranhas and worse!
A mermaid's purse.

Isabelle Bean (11)
Polruan Community Primary School, Fowey

Ten Things Found In Henry VIII's Pocket

A bag of used gold wedding rings
Crumbs from last week's between meal snacks
An instruction manual on how to get rid of unwanted wives
A gigantic heavy chain for his neck
A picture of his most loyal executioner
A letter to the Pope retiring from being a Catholic
A red and white rose
A bag of strength pills for his horse
An extra large belt for his tunic
A pearl choker for his next wife!

Stephanie Dobson (11)
Polruan Community Primary School, Fowey

Ten Things From A Spaceman's Pocket

A bag full of blue cheese from the moon
A picture of his alien friend
A book on 'how to fight gravity'
A piece of a satellite
A fish bowl, for his head
An instruction sheet on 'how to catch an alien'
A file on 'how to live on the moon'
Instructions of 'how to land a rocket'
A letter from his wife
An anchor, to keep the ship down.

Louis Gough (10)
Polruan Community Primary School, Fowey

Ten Things Found In A Giant's Pocket

An information leaflet on how to climb down a choppable beanstalk
A photo of his wife - which grows bigger when he looks at it
An advertisement saying 'Where has Jack gone?'
Two golden coins awarded for his laziness
A book on 'how to make food bigger'
A goose which lays terrific golden eggs
A replacement for the world for when he destroys it!
An admirable axe - stolen from Jack
A cloud of candyfloss which is replaced when he's having a walk
A nail trimmer for when his yellow nails grow too long.

Chelsea Newton (11)
Polruan Community Primary School, Fowey

Ten Things Found In An Angel's Pocket

A fluffy piece of cloud from the far east of Heaven
A self-playing harp
A bird's-eye view of glittering galaxies
A gold glistening halo
An instruction manual to brighten the sun
A jewel-encrusted collar and lead for her pet eagle
A bulging packet of goodness
A feather preening kit
A moving photograph of the Earth encircling the sun
A list of 'jobs to do' from God.

Fiona Norman (10)
Polruan Community Primary School, Fowey

Ten Things In Santa's Pocket

The third page of 'How to look after your sleigh'
A half chewed carrot - going a bit brown
Two cups of white wine - he was too full to drink
An extra red jacket (in case the last one pops with too many mince pies)
An instruction leaflet 'How to fit down the smallest chimneys'
Rudolph's 'red' collar and lead
A spare nose for Rudolph (just in case)
A couple of mince pies - half eaten
A photograph of Mother Claus with a tint of snow on it
A beard trimmer.

Tamara Collin (10)
Polruan Community Primary School, Fowey

Ten Things Found In Santa's Pocket

A naughty or nice list of boys and girls
A spare woolly red hat
A photograph of Mrs Claus
Two Christmas bells
A half eaten mince pie saved for later
A glass of milk full of stars and Saturn's rings
Carrots for Comet
A book called 'How To Control Your Reindeer'
Wrapping paper from last year's boots
A golden ring for Mrs Claus still waiting to be delivered.

Melissa Ross (10)
Polruan Community Primary School, Fowey

Ten Things Found In An Artist's Pocket

A pot of every colour mixed with stars and moons
A rubber made from a magic money tree
A magic pencil which turns into a paintbrush
A shiny hill in every shade of green
An art studio on Mount Olympus
A book of painted pictures from every century
A drawing pad the size of a car park
All the paints in the world
Every yellow of the sun
A water pot the size of an ocean.

Ben Palmer (9)
Polruan Community Primary School, Fowey

Ten Things Found In A Spaceman's Pocket

A piece of rare blue cheese from Pluto
A photograph of a little alien
A beautiful gleaming star
A slice of the Equator
A thermometer to check his temperature
A set of jump leads for his rocket
An everlasting view of space
A bottle of Jupiter's air
An extremely lucky pendant
A 'moon walk' step by step book.

Callum McCarthy (9)
Polruan Community Primary School, Fowey

Ten Things Found In A Spaceman's Pocket

A bit of a spaceship
A piece of a cloud flying by
Milky Way bar
A twinkling star
A map to get him back to Earth
A piece of Jupiter
A bucket of weights to keep him down
A map to get him home easily
A bit of his daughter's dress
A picture of Pen Ven Alien from Mars.

Bradley Pearce (8)
Polruan Community Primary School, Fowey

Ten Things Found In A Witch's Pocket

A poison to turn people into frogs
A hypnotising necklace
A small pet bat
A disguise stone
A spell book
An old hat which grows bigger when worn
A spell that gives her a bigger nose
An extra pair of witch boots
A new grey wig
A broom that grants wishes.

Abigail Newton (9)
Polruan Community Primary School, Fowey

Ten Things Found In A Spaceman's Pocket

A jar of wind from Saturn
A burning coal from Mars
A flame from the sun
A photo of his family
A Galaxy bar from an alien
A heavyweight to keep him down
A ticket to the moon
A slice of moon cheese
A piece of his spaceship
A small star.

Joe Wakeham (9)
Polruan Community Primary School, Fowey

Ten Things Found In A Spaceman's Pocket

A CD called 'Good Moon Music'
A book about how to drive a rocket
A bit of very hot sun
Blue cheese cut from the moon
A letter from his green penfriend
A photograph of Mars
A phone book for alien emergencies
A spare spacesuit in case of splits
A bucket of heavy stones to weigh him down
Moon sweets that taste heavenly.

Ruby Mitchell (9)
Polruan Community Primary School, Fowey

Ten Things Found In Santa's Pocket

A wrapper from a mince pie
A photograph of his favourite reindeer
A book called 'How To Feed Your Reindeer'
A diet sheet for overweight men
A spare nose for Rudolph
A list of children that are good and bad
A spare hat
A picture of his favourite chimney pot
A book called 'Flying A Sleigh Is Easy'
A list to tell him what his elves have to make.

Kim Carcas (8)
Polruan Community Primary School, Fowey

Ten Things Found In An Elf's Pocket

A pile of fluff
Magic glitter
A book of good and bad girls and boys
A button from a hat
A toadstool to sit on
Potion for growing round ears
A fishing rod
A photograph of Santa
A letter from the fairy queen
A jar of early morning dew.

Alice Bate (7)
Polruan Community Primary School, Fowey

Ten Things Found In Henry VIII's Pocket

A get slim quick cook book
A perfume to attract wives
A CD on how to start wars!
A bottle of armour oil
A full bag of wedding rings
A bill from a divorce lawyer
A photograph of his favourite horse
A spare ruff
A new executioner's axe
A bunch of roses - red and white.

Maria Norman (7)
Polruan Community Primary School, Fowey

Ten Things Found In A Spaceman's Pocket

An alien pet from Mars
A book on how to drive a spaceship
Milky cheese from the moon
Space dust
A plan to create atmosphere
Weights to keep him on the ground
A meteor
Space chocolate
A space mouse
A space map.

Kyle Fajht-Taylor (8)
Polruan Community Primary School, Fowey

My Dad

My dad is the best dad ever!
He helps me with my really hard homework,
My dad is more than fantastic!

My dad helps me all the time,
My dad talks to me if I feel really upset,
My dad is more than fantastic!

My dad takes me out all the time,
He buys me lots of lovely things,
My dad is more than fantastic!

My dad is really kind and caring,
My dad is the best dad ever,
I love my dad, lots!

Abbie Squire (9)
Portishead Primary School, Bristol

My Dog

My dog is called Cully,
She wags her tail when she is happy,
Cully likes running fast,
When we go for walks she pulls hard.

She is black and white,
Her coat is soft and shiny,
Cully is very furry
And loves being brushed.

She chases small cats
And is very strong,
I always give her big cuddles
And she is the very best!

We throw her jingling ball
And she goes charging after it,
She loves her walks
And I love her!

Georgia Humphreys (9)
Portishead Primary School, Bristol

Amazing Dark

Dark is amazing
And fun
Also the moon comes out,
That sparkles in the light
And don't forget the stars that peep out too.

Sometimes dark is quiet,
Sometimes dark is noisy,
Even owls peep their heads out
And bats hang upside down,
Also the dark is peaceful too.

Sometimes stars twinkle in the dark
And shine brightly,
There are no clouds at night,
Just a moon and stars,
The dark is great!

Bethan Berry (7)
Portishead Primary School, Bristol

Down Under The Sea

Deep down under the sea,
It's really dark down there,
Really, really cold,
Under the sea.

Very funny fish down there,
Very, very strange,
Everything looks so, so dark,
Under the sea.

Go up to the top part now,
Lots and lots of fish,
Seaweed growing up so tall,
Under the sea.

It's clear and warmer up there
And much more colourful,
Loads of fish swimming about,
Under the sea.

Hungry sharks come snapping up
Small fishes, for their tea
And I really like it,
Under the sea.

Cameron Tarrant (9)
Portishead Primary School, Bristol

Under The Sea

The sea is very cold,
There are fat fish,
A very silly shark,
There are beautiful dolphins,
There is a beautiful castle,
There is a pretty mermaid called Grace.

There is a very grumpy fish,
The sand is very slippery,
The dolphins slide alone in the waves,
The castle is cold,
There is a very evil sea witch,
I love being in the sea!

Lucy Minall (7)
Portishead Primary School, Bristol

My Family

My mum is smiley
My dad is cool
My sisters are annoying

My gran is pretty
My grandad is grumpy
My auntie is lovely

My uncle is great
My cousins are fun
That's my family

My mum does the cleaning
My dad does the cooking
My sisters do the shouting

My gran does the ironing
My grandad reads the paper
My auntie buys the toys

My uncle does the laughing
My cousins do the playing
I love my family.

Rachel Roberts (9)
Portishead Primary School, Bristol

My Great Dad

My dad's great,
He brings me fantastic things,
My dad is mechanical,
I love my great dad,
I love my great dad.

My dad is kind,
He is wicked,
My dad is lovely,
I love my fabulous dad,
I love my fabulous dad.

My faithful dad,
He is a fine dad,
My great dad,
My only great dad,
My only great dad!

Benjamin Keen (9)
Portishead Primary School, Bristol

Great Water

Water is in waterfalls as blue as blue can be,
It crashes down the waterfall as fast as fast could be
Into the blue, blue pool under the waterfall!

Water is in showers, taps and in the sea,
In taps it drips, *drip-drop* as warm as warm could be,
It could be as cold and as frozen as could be!

Water is also in the sea,
It is the deep blue sea,
Fish live in the sea, it's wild, as wild as could be!

Harry Gill (9)
Portishead Primary School, Bristol

Down The Stream

Water flowing down the stream,
Transparent, clean and fresh,
Flowing calmly and slowly,
Lovely, cool and wet.

Getting near the waterfall now,
It's just about to fly,
Over the edge it goes,
Whizzing through the sky.

The water is near the bottom now,
It's just about to fall,
It's just about to splash,
In the great big water pool!

Connie-May Rawlings (8)
Portishead Primary School, Bristol

Water Runs

Water splashes in the sea,
Water runs down the drainpipe,
Water's cold in the bath,
Water drips from the taps,
Water's deep in the sea,
Water's clear blue in the sea,
Water's see-through in the bath,
Water's salty in the sea,
Water's polluted sometimes,
Water keeps us alive!

James Bowell (7)
Portishead Primary School, Bristol

The Playground

The playground can be noisy,
The playground can be quiet,
There are people crunching crisps,
We're all having a lot of fun.

There are children running rapidly all around,
Footballs flying everywhere,
Children are playing tag,
We're all having a lot of fun.

Girls sitting on benches giggling all the time,
People connecting to tamagotchis
People playing on Game Boys,
We're all having a lot of fun.

The whistle blows - time to line up,
Children are all unhappy,
All the children go back into class,
Now the playground is big and empty,
No noise or rapid running,
We all love the playground!

Oliver Hubbard (9)
Portishead Primary School, Bristol

Kind Night

The night is very dark blue,
It is sparkling and quiet.
Gold stars peep out to twinkle all night long,
As they help the moon shine bright.

The night is so peaceful
And very, very graceful.
Night is so soothing
And quite delightful.

The night is so amazing,
It can be quite cold or very hot.
You fall asleep so quickly,
Because the night is so kind.

Rebecca Wilson (8)
Portishead Primary School, Bristol

Flowers

Flowers are lovely
Flowers are beautiful
Flowers are fantastic
Flowers are interesting

Flowers are single
Flowers are spiked
Flowers are tall
Flowers are short

Flowers are different colours
Flowers have single colours
Flowers have bright colours
Flowers have dull colours

Flowers love shimmering
Flowers are shining
Flowers have petals
Flowers can grow

Flowers can fall
People staring at flowers
Flowers are dying
And that's all.

Sophie Olver (7)
Portishead Primary School, Bristol

My Friends

My friends are kind
They are playful
My friends are good at games
My friends are great.

My friends are tidy
They have a good laugh
They help me when I fall over
My friends are great.

My friends give me presents
They like to explore
My friends are special,
My friends are great!

Rebecca Fletcher (8)
Portishead Primary School, Bristol

Chairs

Rocky, round chairs,
Big and small,
Round and unusual chairs,
Some are plastic and some are wooden,
Some are big and small and some are shaped like a bird,
Some even have wooden backs.

Some are metal chairs with holes in,
Bendy chairs,
There are even glass and round chairs,
Some are soft and cosy,
Some you can even sink in,
Some have beaks on,
They are shaped like bumblebees too.

I love chairs!

Nicholas Freemantle (8)
Portishead Primary School, Bristol

Dragons

Fiery dinosaurs in the sky,
Leaping around,
Fairies fleeing the shadowy figure,
Fire is dancing around the street,
His deafening roar echoes all around,
As dark magic covers the town.

Lily Wildgoose (8)
Portishead Primary School, Bristol

Water Heaven

Dripping water from the tap,
Going down the pipe,
Leading into a bumpy river,
Now going down a waterfall.

Running down some rapids,
Now leading into a stream
And beginning to get into bumpy waves,
The waves get really massive.

Now into the calm blue sea,
Water is now going further out,
The water's getting very deep,
Now it starts to rise for the water cycle.

Theo Howarth (8)
Portishead Primary School, Bristol

Playtime

In the huge playground,
Where noisy children play,
There are children eating fruit
And children playing games.

In the huge playground,
Where noisy children play,
There are children in tears
And children having a good day.

In the huge playground,
Where noisy children play,
There are children eating crisps,
They all love to play.

Playtime is great!

Meg Owen (8)
Portishead Primary School, Bristol

My Sister

My sister is pretty and annoying
But I've always wanted one
So I have to live with it
When I change her nappy
She always pees on me
Apart from that
I love her very much.

Joshua Baker (8)
Portishead Primary School, Bristol

The Scary Room

The dark, cold, creepy room,
Just stands there looking scary,
Spiders crawling up the wall,
They are very large and hairy!

The different cold, strange, room
Oh! it is pitch-black,
I warn you don't go in that room,
Or you might never come back!

The room has creaky floorboards,
So please don't trap your foot,
It is very messy,
For there is lots and lots of soot!

Grace Martinson (9)
Portishead Primary School, Bristol

Moon

The moon is out,
The moon comes out at night,
When the trees are whistling.

The moon is glittering,
The moon comes out at night,
When the fox is on the prowl.

The moon is bright,
The moon comes out at night,
When the stars are shining in the dark.

The moon is a bright yellow ball,
The moon comes out at night,
Night, night, sleepyhead!

Abby Milnes (7)
Portishead Primary School, Bristol

Rhinos

Rhinos rushing dangerously fast
Breaking trees tumbling down
Stamping trees with weighty power
Kneeling down to charge
Charging quickly into cars
Dashing quickly for shady trees
Stamping bravely into water
Cooling himself in mud
Bang! Rhino's dead
Spirit is awakened
Runs to Heaven
And lives again.

Matthew Spensley (8)
Portishead Primary School, Bristol

Pond Fish

Swishing silently exploring the water,
In winter they are invisible in the murky water
And catching the passing flies
Underwater they eat algae
But there are dangers all around
In the weed they hide when the heron comes down.

James Boardman (8)
Portishead Primary School, Bristol

Balloons

Balloons are colourful
Balloons are small
Balloons are big
Balloons can pop into little bits

People's faces going red
Balloons as big as heads
Pop, pop everywhere
Balloons floating

Balloons for babies
Balloons for children
Balloons for everyone
Everyone loves balloons!

Oliver O'Hare (7)
Portishead Primary School, Bristol

The Beach

People screaming,
Sun's gleaming,
Children soaking,
Adults smoking,
Swimmers swimming,
Locals skimming,
Ice cream selling,
Adults yelling,
Jellyfish stinging,
Climbers clinging,
Sea swishing,
Fishermen fishing,
Babies crying,
Seagulls flying.

Connor Williams (9)
Portishead Primary School, Bristol

Dolphins

Dolphins spin as they jump up
All together they play in the deep blue sea
Gliding and as swirling as can be
The dolphins zoom past the shore
Flying up towards the sky.

Erika Mason (8)
Portishead Primary School, Bristol

Summer Has Been Found

Sun dazzling on the grass,
Children merrily playing in the playground.
Mothers walking, barking dogs,
Summer has been found.

People swimming fast in the pool,
A lovely splashing sound.
Flowers blooming colourful petals,
Summer has been found.

Small insects darting on the stones,
Children joyfully skipping on a mound.
Artists sketching the lovely gardens,
Summer has been found!

Jessica Pointon (8)
Portishead Primary School, Bristol

In The Air

In the air there are moons spinning in the dark
Black sky at night, blazing sun by day
Rain gently falling from dark clouds
Stars shining light years from the Earth

Rockets *zooming* into space
Daring astronauts floating in mid-air
Birds having a bird's-eye view of me and you
Planets swooping around the peering sun!

Amy Francis (8)
Portishead Primary School, Bristol

Fairies

All of the fairies,
Of Glitter Rain Wood,
Loving and caring,
Like good fairies should.

Their tingling magic,
Makes you want to shiver,
Their dainty wings sparkle,
Like golden, glowing glitter.

The happy fairies,
The colourful treasure,
A pool of shining gems,
Fairies are here forever.

Alex Gilborson (9)
Portishead Primary School, Bristol

The World

The sea glistens in the sun,
Sea creatures dancing under the waves,
Birds soaring in the sky,
Singing on branches, with the summer song,
But up the cold north, rivers flow,
Colourful rainbows match the pretty flowers,
Round the world, sparkling moonlight shines,
The hot sun has set,
Darkness reigns,
But the world is still alive!

Rachel Howard (9)
Portishead Primary School, Bristol

Animals

Animals hunt in the night
While we are all asleep
They pounce onto their prey
They're strong and quick and they can bite

They are very brave
You must be careful or they will bite
Some of them sneak into a cave
Some of them are very light
Most of the young are very active
Quite a lot of them are poisonous.

Caleb Stride (8)
Portishead Primary School, Bristol

Animals

I have a dog, his name is Lucky
I have a frog, her name is Lilly
I have a cat, her name is Tabby
I have a bat, his name is Black
I have a rabbit, he has a bad habit
I have a horse, she is good at jumping, of course
I have a lovely monkey, she is very funky
I have a tiny guinea pig, he is very cheeky
I have a small mouse, she has a little house
I have a snake, he could eat a drake
All these animals live with me, around a very big lake.

Charlotte Hubbard (7)
Portishead Primary School, Bristol

The Nightmare

Every night, after dark, when you fall asleep,
Something's coming,
Treading softly, slowly through the day.
But when it comes to night,
It gallops, like a whirlwind,
Travelling through your dreams -
The nightmare.

The nightmare looks like a dark, black shadow from a distance,
But it never gets close enough for man to see it.
It has a silky, black mane,
Lavender-blue eyes
And pearl-white hooves.

It tears your hopes to pieces
And ruins your best dreams,
It gets your fears roaring,
It's nothing what it seems.
It has an evil glint of fiery-red in its left eye,
It never, ever stops,
It can never die.

But when the light streams through the window,
The nightmare's gone, *phew!*
But you hear the nightmare whisper,
'I'll be back again for you!'

Daisy Newth (7)
Portishead Primary School, Bristol

Seaside

S eagulls swooping in the air
E agles building their nests high in the cliffs
A nd the jellyfish and the fishes in the sea
S harks snapping at your feet
I ce cream oozing into your hot mouth
D olphins flipping back and forth
E ager mothers proud of their babies

I wish I could go to the bottom of the sea some day.

Nancy Williams (7)
Portishead Primary School, Bristol

Brothers And Sisters

My brother is annoying
My sisters are very cool
They sometimes let me use their make-up
I think this rules!
My brother normally fights with me
But he still keeps me company
I use him as a punch bag
When I get huffy
We fight over the telly
We fight over the computer
We fight over everything
Even our own mother!

Aimèe Schools (8)
Portishead Primary School, Bristol

My Plum Tree

I have a little plum tree,
I think it's good for me,
The plums are wonderful,
I think they taste like truffle.

I love it a lot,
It cooks in a pot,
Oh! My little plum tree,
You will stay with me.

Julian Stephens (9)
Portishead Primary School, Bristol

Parrots

Parrots squawk
They are really noisy
They fly everywhere
They are multicoloured
And they flutter everywhere
And they cost thousands of pounds
But when it's night
They're as quiet as a mouse
Then a whole new day starts again.

Mitchell James Woolley (7)
Portishead Primary School, Bristol

People

People are kind,
People are mean,
People are naughty
And some are fine.

Babies cry,
Babies drink,
Babies sleep
And some fight.

Adults are happy,
Adults are sad,
Adults are grumpy
And some are mad!

Phoebe Horton (8)
Portishead Primary School, Bristol

Surprise

S urpised
U tterly amazed
P ractically blown away
R eally fantastic
I rritatingly impressive
S urprisingly good and
E xtremely *extreme!*

Elizabeth Callaghan (8)
Portishead Primary School, Bristol

My Birthday

You can have anything for your birthday!
I want a sleepover
I want all my friends over
I want them over today

We will eat chocolate and crisps
Drink lots of orange juice
Go and play in the garden
And have lots of fun.

Maddy Stubbs (7)
Portishead Primary School, Bristol

My Brothers

My baby brother is cheeky all the time
He makes me laugh
He sucks my thumb every day
My little brother is silly
I kick him out of my room
He is annoying
Both of my brothers are monkeys.

Rachael Randall (8)
Portishead Primary School, Bristol

Dolphin

Diving through the shiny ocean
Feeling joyful and free
Splashing through the mighty waves
Hunting through the sea

Swirling like the sand
Dashing like the wind

Mouth open, as wide as can be
The fish pop in, yum-yum, I've had my tea
I'm glad I'm a dolphin
Because I eat fish and laugh with glee.

Fairy dust on my back
Goldfish staring at me
Me looking happy
Sniffing rocks and seaweed.

Oh, dolphin, dolphin, you shine like the sun.

Chloe Nicholas (9)
St Mary's (VC) Primary School, Bridgwater

Elegant Dog

Cute
Fluffy
Lovely
Dog
Running to the food
Elegantly
Fast
Like a baby sea lion swimming to its mum
I would cry if you ran away, dog
Elegant dog.

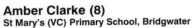

Amber Clarke (8)
St Mary's (VC) Primary School, Bridgwater

A Poem For My Two Best Cousins

Grace and Romy are so cute,
Romy wears a lovely suit,
Grace loves Romy like no other,
Even though she wanted a brother.

My cousins are so special to me,
I only wish that I could be,
Nearer by them, down by the sea,
Just Grace, Romy and me.

We could play on the sand,
Holding one another's hand,
We'll have fish and chips on the pier,
I can't wait till you are here!

Shannon Briffett (8)
St Mary's (VC) Primary School, Bridgwater

The Door

(Based on 'The Door' by Miroslav Holub)

Go and open the door
Maybe there'll be a flying unicorn,
Or a multicoloured ogre that's jazzy.

Go and open the door
Maybe there'll be a bee, crossed with a bull
Or a golden staff
Or an edible land.

Go and open the door
If there's a sea it will clear.

Go and open the door
Maybe there'll be a singing swimming pool,
At least there'll be a frog!

James Nash (8)
St Mary's (VC) Primary School, Bridgwater

Truth

Truth is yellow
It smells sweet and mellow
It tastes of fresh mints
It sounds peaceful and quiet
It feels comfortable inside
It lives in everyone's heart and soul.

Paige Langdon (11)
St Mary's (VC) Primary School, Bridgwater

The Door
(Based on 'The Door' by Miroslav Holub)

Go and open the door
Maybe there's
A magical garden
Or a chocolate city

Go and open the door
Maybe there's
A dolphin jumping
Or maybe there's
A star glistening

Go and open the door
Maybe Narnia's waiting

Go and open the door
Maybe there's a storm gushing
Or maybe the sun's shining

Go and open the door
Even if there's nothing there
At least they'll be a draught.

Rosie Gibbs (9)
St Mary's (VC) Primary School, Bridgwater

Pain

Pain is orange
It smells like burning blood
It tastes like the devastation of the Earth
It sounds like children crying and screaming for help
It feels like a thousand tigers jumping and slashing with their claws
It lives in a deep labyrinth.

Ashley Gaylor (10)
St Mary's (VC) Primary School, Bridgwater

Peace

Peace is pale blue
It smells like a garden of flowers
It tastes sweet and fresh
It sounds like birds singing
It feels like cool, pure water
It lives in Heaven
And spreads down to Earth.

David Sims (10)
St Mary's (VC) Primary School, Bridgwater

Rage

Rage is a stampede, look out!
It can be anywhere in the air
And it is everywhere
It can be even in your hair
You can try to calm it down
But it is very hard
It is almost impossible.

Christopher Bell (11)
St Mary's (VC) Primary School, Bridgwater

Happiness

Happiness is all the colours of the rainbow
It smells of roses blooming in the summer's air
It tastes like nothing you have ever tasted before
It sounds like children playing in the park
It feels like a brilliant sensation worth keeping forever
And it lives in the hearts of you and me.

Rebekah Rich (11)
St Mary's (VC) Primary School, Bridgwater

War

The colour of war is red
It smells like bullets zooming in the air
It tastes of blood and pain
It sounds like men, crying in shame
War feels like a dagger stabbing your heart
War lives in the deepest, darkest soul.

Lauren Parr (10)
St Mary's (VC) Primary School, Bridgwater

Gold And Silver

Gold is
A ring, sparkling on a lady's finger
Or a star, shining down on Earth from the night sky
It's a pound coin sitting in a pocket with nothing to do
And a golden trophy, an award for a job well done.

Silver is . . .
A doorknob shining brightly on my front door
Or a sharpener cutting through a pencil
It is a silver plate twinkling on the dinner table
And the moon shining on a frosty night.

Harry Michelmore (8)
St Peter's School, Exmouth

Silver

Silver is . . .
Delicate cobwebs dancing in the morning breeze
A sparkling ring, flashing proudly, showing off its expensive diamond.
It's a slimy snail making a glistening trail along the garden path.
A dazzling sword with its sharp edges shining wickedly.
And stiff armour creaking slightly in a ruined castle.

Silver is . . .
A pointed icicle hanging dangerously, like a sword form a snow cave.
It's bright sparks spluttering in the hearth like a volcano erupting.
It's a gleaming trophy polished brightly on my shelf
And dull fillings making a smile of decayed teeth.
It's a sleek sliver of moonlight tiptoeing into dark alleys.
It's an aged beech tree all gnarled and wrinkled,
And dazzling stars winking knowingly through the night.

Silver is breathtaking!

Megan Haward (8)
St Peter's School, Exmouth

Silver Is . . .

Silver is . . .
Stars shining so brightly in the gloomy darkness
And a beautiful statue glinting in the bright sunlight.
It's a sharp candle with flickering, multicoloured flames,
A beautiful dress worn by a rich lady,
A colourful sparkler flashing in the silent night,
It's a glinting coin hidden in your secret, sparkling purse,
A church bell resting in the gentle breeze,
A silver fountain with the water gently running down it like a stream trickling by
It's a glowing crown, when you put it on your head it lights up your house
A colourful sports car going so fast that it shines like the sun reflecting.

Jade Broadhurst (8)
St Peter's School, Exmouth

Silver

Silvery glitter shimmering around the moon
Bright stars twinkling in the night sky
Slowly, silently the spider spins his silvery web
Glistening frost clings onto branches of trees
A can glowing as it falls around the floor
The flashing of armour and swords as the Romans fight the Celts
A unicorn's reflection in a crystal pool.

Amelia Mason (8)
St Peter's School, Exmouth

Silver Is . . .

Silver is . . .
A metal tin with amazing reflections of yourself
It's a shining screw, like a sharp treasure in a wooden bench
And a five pence coin to put in a delicate piggy bank
It's a heavy earring that hangs like a precious square jewel on your ear
Or a sharp cheese grater that cuts like a skin-cutting dagger.

Silver is . . .
A silver spoon that will not bend or stain
And a shining car that is hypnotised by your beauty
It's a polished kettle that whistles like a bird trying to sing
Or a beautiful necklace constantly glinting in the bright sunlight
It's a beer mug, unbreakable, unusable, but extremely precious
Silver is a gift of love.

Max Savage (9)
St Peter's School, Exmouth

Gold

Gold is . . .
The resplendent crown glistening with precious jewels
Like a sword blade shining in the blazing sun
It's a beautiful smile from a first-born child
Like a shining star lighting up the murky moonlight
Or a flaxen phoenix weaving through the trees.

Gold is . . .
A bald eagle circling his dead prey
Like a car driving round a roundabout
And a shining statue hidden in an echoing cave
It's a joyful car driving on the flat motorway
Or the strong rays shining through the sacred church window
Gold is a bright angel hovering over Jesus.

Harri Lai (8)
St Peter's School, Exmouth

Gold

Gold is a padlock, locking a castle door,
Gold is a Christmas candle shining in the night,
Gold is a flask full of special golden dust,
Gold is a Christmas watch wrapped in special paper,
Gold is a crown for a king.

Megan Dalrymple-Hay (6)
St Peter's School, Exmouth

Dragon

There once was a dragon that burned down the school,
All the kids thought it was cool,
It killed the teacher in the staffroom
And brought him to his doom.

It smashed the window and the glass,
It even whacked the teacher, who flew so fast,
Then she hit the door
And ended up being extremely poor.

He laughed and laughed but being daft,
He tipped and landed in a shaft,
Poor dragon, he didn't notice the bin
And so I'm sorry, but that was the end of him!

Dominic Thorne (9)
Sandford Primary School, Sandford

Magic

A black cat flying across the land,
Witches cackling, a monster band.

Ogres groaning, in the night,
Vampires moaning, hate the light.

Magic medicines cover the ground,
Wands making an eerie sound.

Darkness gathers across the sky,
Kissing the sunlight a wicked goodbye.

Children cosy, warm and asleep,
Safe from the evilness they will keep.

Lightning flashes like a ghostly chain,
Memories of a horrendous pain.

Bats swooping and soaring high,
Mysterious and dark as they fly.

Shadows lurk beneath your bed,
Monsters hiding in the shed.

Night-time might be black and tragic,
But don't forget, there's always magic!

Amaya Salisbury (9)
Sandford Primary School, Sandford

Amazing Scrapman

Scrapman, Scrapman, stretching his legs,
Made of worn-out cars and pegs.

He could terrify you and me too,
His rusty body looks different from me and you.

He is so kind,
Even though he's got a rusty old mind.

''Ello,' he'd say, to whoever he meets,
When he moves, you would hear some creaks.

He came out at night,
When everyone was snuggled up tight.

He is so large,
Made from a phone that had no charge.

Scrapman, Scrapman, I know you arn't funky,
Full of rubbish and very junky.

Isaac Heather (8)
Sandford Primary School, Sandford

Night

Night can be such a fright
When you can't find light
Dark, evil and eerie
It can make you all teary.

Black bats hunt sky high
Swooping round as they fly
Nocturnal badgers dig for prey
Sleeping, snoring in the day.

Zombies climbing out of their graves
In the darkness they are bathed
Dumb, moaning and heavily groaning
They really need some combing.

Monsters coming out from holes
Peeping from the dark like moles
Spreading evil around the sky
Making all the goodness die.

Adam Jones (9)
Sandford Primary School, Sandford

A Poem About Scrapman

He runs happily and jumps slowly,
He stretches further than any man
And his head is as big as a TV,
His heart is a rusty thing,
From a car that's pink and green,
He smells like a dustbin,
Lying on the street,
He's made out of junk
And he's such a punk,
Scrapman, Scrapman,
What can you do?
I can lie in bed just like you,
Arms going out,
Legs all about,
He's made out of iron, steel
And metal with a hard feel,
''Lo,' he says to whoever he meets,
When he moves you would hear some creaks
Scrapman, I know you are so junky,
I bet your junk is so old you can't be funky,
Scrapman, Scrapman,
What can you do?
I can run faster than you.

Jacob Bell (8)
Sandford Primary School, Sandford

Fright

I dodge a body flying through the air,
Mines blow at my feet,
Men scream and take flight,
I fire my pistol, but it misses,
It hisses through a monster's body
And it drops down dead.

Then I roar at a man, who was attacking my best mate
And what thanks do I get? Nothing, not even a bye-bye,
He runs, screaming like a girl
And I drift off to sleep
And get gangrene,
The doctors help, but can't do a lot
And I die in hospital, feeling betrayed and sick.

Robert Fletcher (9)
Sandford Primary School, Sandford

How To Make A Mad School

1 teaspoon of detention duties
4oz of underpaid teachers
2oz of agitated teaching assistants
4oz of chaotic kids

Now I have my ingredient, make like this:
Add 4oz of chaotic kids to the bowl
Mix in a teaspoon of detention duties with 2oz of agitated teaching assistants
Stir quickly while adding 4oz of underpaid teachers
Spread your mix evenly over a tray of baking paper
Cook at gas mark 6 for 40 minutes
Serve while hot.

Leia Senington (10)
Sandy Hill Primary School, St Austell

Kittens

Kittens are so cute,
They are often sleeping,
Tigger is really tiny,
Tig is quite big,
Every time they're on my lap
They *purr*,
Never fight with each other,
Stop! I say,
When the dogs come out to play.

Emily Cocking (9)
Sandy Hill Primary School, St Austell

Forever

F amily and the best of friends
O r they can be worst enemies
R ichard and Tim are brothers right to the end
E ven when they fight
V ery often gives you a fright
E very single day
R ichard and Tim go out to play.

Ross McGall (11)
Sandy Hill Primary School, St Austell

Midnight

M agical fairies come out to play
I n the day they go away
D ead and quiet, lightens up
N ight has come and they wake up
I ndigo lights, magical colours
G o to dance rain or dusk
H ippy ones, posh ones
T ime to go, oh no! They've gone!

Clarissa Minns (10)
Sandy Hill Primary School, St Austell

My Best Friend

My best friend is really cool,
She does very well in school.
She will help you wherever you are,
When you thank her, you'll call her a star.

My best friend gives me presents for my birthday,
If you ask to borrow something, she always says OK.
When she comes to visit me,
She often stays for some tea.

I think she's really great,
That's why she's my *best mate!*

Jessica Bettridge (10)
Sandy Hill Primary School, St Austell

My Tiger

My tiger is enormous,
My tiger is the fastest in the world,
My tiger is the cutest on the planet,
My tiger is light and bright,
My tiger is always searching for food
My tiger is sometimes in a funny mood!

Ryan Cornelius (9)
Sandy Hill Primary School, St Austell

Bedtime Rows

Who said the dreaded bedtime shall suffer and lie in pain.
Who said the dreaded bedtime shall feel the awful shame.
Who said the dreaded bedtime shall be lower than the floor.
Who said the dreaded bedtime shall be scratched by a tiger's paw.
Who said the dreaded bedtime shall fear me for evermore.

Be quiet, my mum is coming,
I must not let her know.
Oh no, she's seen me.
All hope is lost.
Well, it's time for me to go.

Molly Meikle (10)
Stoke St Gregory CE Primary School, Taunton

Fashion And Friends

Holly and I are having a blast,
Imogen's trends are never the last!
Abbey and Molly are retro cool,
Alice, Kathy and Jess like hanging around the pool.
Fenella and Molly are Year 5 friends,
On non-uniform day they've got the trends.
They'll all come to my house for a party night,
All our clothes shining bright!
Holly arrives in her red 'n' pink threads,
She shouts, 'Hey gals!' - we all turn our heads.
In the morning we'll go shopping for fun,
And buy new fashions for everyone!

Jade Elliott (10)
Stoke St Gregory CE Primary School, Taunton

Some Teachers

Some teachers . . .
play nice games.
Some teachers forget our names.

Some teachers . . .
are happy.
Some teachers are a little snappy.

Some teachers . . .
are artistic.
Some teachers go ballistic!

Some teachers . . .
smell of last night's curry.
Some teachers make you work in a hurry.

Some teachers . . .
are nicely dressed.
Some teachers are very stressed!

Some teachers . . .
look nice,
but you'd better think twice.

Abbey Boobyer (10)
Stoke St Gregory CE Primary School, Taunton

My Rabbits

My rabbit 'Special' is speckly brown,
She is cuddly and fluffy and loves hopping around.
She waits for her fuss, when I get off the bus,
And leaps into my arms with a bound.

My rabbit 'Jessie' is quiet and shy,
If you didn't know her you would pass her right by.
Hay is her favourite food, the more she eats, the better her mood.
Special and Jessie, though different in many ways,
Are my much loved pet rabbits, and will be every day.

Fenella Chedham (9)
Stoke St Gregory CE Primary School, Taunton

When Roses Red Brought The Dead

Under the hedgerow roses grew,
Scarlet was their colour, one and two.
Then one morning
As light was dawning,
Down by pond not far beyond,
A hand of bone rose upon the marsh,
Looking odd and rather harsh.

Pearl-white were the tips of its fingers
And yet the roses did still linger.
Up and up the corpses came,
Not weak, nor strong, nor lame,
Their glowing eyes of garish red
Spinning round in each skull head.
And to this day
That's where they'll stay.
If you should ever go
To where the roses grow,
What you reap is what you sow.

And that's when roses red
Brought the dead.

Holly Wilson (9)
Stoke St Gregory CE Primary School, Taunton

On The Farm

O n the farm is great,
N othing better,

T han being on the farm.
H edgecutters are cutting away,
E ngines go *roar* on the tractor.

F armers are working
A s hard as they can,
R eady for all the crops to grow.
M y favourite place is on the farm.

Thomas Merritt (10)
Stoke St Gregory CE Primary School, Taunton

School At Night

School is over
The classrooms are deserted
There's no one about
No voices to shout
No people to scream
No teachers to teach
No students to listen
No pupils to work
All alone in the school

The abandoned swing set
The lonely slide
The silent play area
The empty playground
The quiet classrooms

The cry of the wind
The creak of the swings
The hoot of the owl
Outside the moonlit school.

Eleanor Newton (9)
Taunton Preparatory School, Taunton

Grumpy Old Men

'Bah humbug,' is all they say
If a child asked one, 'Do you want to play?'
They'd say:
'Shut up and go away!'

They are reluctant to everything
And transparent right through
They are so lonely
And smell like old shoes!

'Back in my day!' they also say
The kids get fed up and walk away
They use these walking sticks for no reason at all
I think that's their way of being cool!

They abominate Christmas
And despise kids too
Their food is all mouldy
And they don't flush the loo!

Henry Havercroft (11)
Taunton Preparatory School, Taunton

The Big One

All the training is done
No more soft bags to tackle
Time to be counted
No place to hide, it's all about pride.

The whistle blows with a sharp screech
We wade through the mud to our foe
We twist and turn, push and shunt
Our parents shout orders of battle.
The game is coming to a close
No time to doze.

One minute to go
We see a weakness in our foe
A penalty is awarded
My large size and weight is
At last to be rewarded
1, 2, 3 I grip the ball
I hit the human wall
I remain tall with a fall and a reach
I breach the line
The game is won by the big one.

William Mileham (11)
Taunton Preparatory School, Taunton

The Time Machine

If I had a great big time machine
I would not know where to be
I would probably go to the future
But they are very much smarter
I might have gone back to the past
But their technology is not very advanced.

If you had a great big time machine
Where would you like to be?
Would you go to the past or the future?
Be a man and see some monsters
The choice is yours, but be quick
Or someone might come and nick it.

If they nicked it what would you do?
Go to the cops or find some clues?
If they nicked it were would they go?
The past or the future, nobody knows
So come and listen to good advice
Use it quick and at night.

Rory Harrison (11)
Taunton Preparatory School, Taunton

Through My Window I Can See . . .

A robin flying in the tree
Snowy weather and slippery floor
Sliding snowflakes
And strong skating on the ice
Dazzling frosty weather
People covered with powdery snow
Trees are covered
Coats of soft winter and sparkly bits all around
Dazzling into the gloomy weather
Sparkling icy snowflakes dropping
Out of the sky
And ice rinks for people to skate on
Horses galloping in the wind
Dropping through the snow as I go
People wrapped in the slippery, slidy snow.

Natalie Brown (8)
Taunton Preparatory School, Taunton

Dead Or Alive

The dead souls go up in the sky
While their skeletons go down in the ground
Alive people walk miles around
And newborn babies cry.

They float away the dead souls do
Skeletons have many bones not few!
People every day walk to the zoo
While babies just cry.

While floating dead souls disappear
Skeletons are now rotting away!
People are still alive today
Babies now don't cry, they sneer.

Max Jeffs (11)
Taunton Preparatory School, Taunton

Through My Winter Window I Can See . . .

Snowflakes as cold as ice floating down
Birds hopping in the crispy snow
Chilly people skating on a thin, frozen lake
Snow angels on the ground
Birds hopping in frosty snow
There are pretty spider webs.

Michael Styles (8)
Taunton Preparatory School, Taunton

Through My Window I Can See . . .

A powdery white carpet covering my garden
With snow-laden trees and clear white roofs
The chilly air comes in so I put on my cardigan
And I hear the clips and the clops of the horse's hoofs
The rider all snowy
And riding quite slowly
Because of the chilly air outside
The village is quiet and breezy
And the ducks are searching for food
The lake is frozen and freezing
And there's people skating, having fun, in a good mood
I can see the fresh white snow
Some powdery, some crunchy though
People wade and wallow, through the deep winter-wonder surprise (the snow)
They look so cold but they're having fun, I don't think they will ever want to go
Some swans I notice are sliding so gracefully
I bet their feet are cold as they skid across the ice
Even though their feathers are warm and woolly
I love swans, they're so nice
Oh! Some skiers are here!
I thought they might come, because there's snowy hills near
Oh! It's getting nippy!
I feel very cold
A snowflake lands on top of my head
I can see some icicles hanging down the windowpanes
And some wrapped up warm people walking down a dotty white lane
There are bare brown trees, sprinkled with floury white snow
Resting on tree branches
And around the tree trunks so low
An eagle is flying way up past our heads
It's probably flying to nest
The snowflakes are falling from the afternoon sky
Until they tumble down and lie
The ground is all slushy in some parts near trees
Which are not evergreens, so they have no leaves.

Georgia Blackwell (9)
Taunton Preparatory School, Taunton

Through My Winter Window

Through my winter window I can see . . .
A red squirrel jumping tree to tree
A prickly hedgehog snorting through the snowy grass
A white rabbit hopping about
A mouse scurrying across the path
Freezing ducks plodding slowly.

James Cowling (8)
Taunton Preparatory School, Taunton

Dad, Just Go Away!

I sometimes want to bring friends home
And show you off at school
But then you'll do something to make me cringe
And feel like such a fool

It could be those hideous trousers
Or the paint-spattered overalls
It could be the family holiday snaps
That make me want to climb the walls

You just don't get it sometimes
When Ellie or Josie come to stay
You poke your head around the door
And I just have to say, 'Go away!'

Oh and I'll never forget that drunken dance
You performed at Christmas before last
I swear you'd had more than two or three
I just wanted it to end, and fast

My first trip away from home I know
Was very hard for you
You rang me every night of the week
To check I'd been to the loo!

And when the coach pulled up the drive
You were chatting to parents you'd wanted to meet
I was the last to leave with all my bags
And then you swept me off my feet

So now you know just how I feel
Please can you calm down?
You'll always be my dad; of course
But try not to act the clown!

Lara Rodgers (11)
Taunton Preparatory School, Taunton

Through My Winter Window I Can See . . .

Through my winter window I can see . . .
The cold winter creeping up the frothy snow all so white and cold
The birds are singing, the children are playing, horses are trotting
And people are chatting
Lights are going on in all houses and
The trees are swaying, the wind is blowing so hard that the bushes are blowing
There's no stopping the footsteps that the children leave behind
While playing a game of hide-and-seek
They also wonder why
People keep finding them
They just give up!

Emma Davey (8)
Taunton Preparatory School, Taunton

Through My Winter Window I Can See . . .

Through my window
I can see . . .
Animal paw prints
In the crispy white snow
I wonder what they could be
Badgers, foxes or dogs they could be.

Through my winter window
I can see . . .
A giant snowball aiming for me
Flying in the freezing sky
An eagle having a snowball fight
With an excited beaver at night.

Through my winter window
I can see . . .
Some rabbits hopping near me
Jumping high right in the sky
Trying to find some food nearby.

Through my winter window
I can see . . .
Animals getting tired at tea
They yawn, they stretch and rub eyes
And find their bed under the sky.

Matt Pearce (9)
Taunton Preparatory School, Taunton

Through My Winter Window I Can See . . .

. . . A cold, icy pond
Horses galloping across the frosty grass
People ice skating on shiny sheets of ice
Sheep on the Jack Frost grass in their warm coats
The wind is chilly and freezing
The ground is carpeted with snow
The trees are bare with ice and snow
In the snow you nearly sink in it
On the ice you can glide, skate, skim and slip
Birds fighting over a long wriggly worm
Dogs running for bendy sticks
Children throwing snowballs at each other
And that is all I can see through my winter window!

Imogen Henry (9)
Taunton Preparatory School, Taunton

What's Behind The Splintered Door?
(Inspired by 'The Door' by Miroslav Holub)

What's behind the splintered door?
Will it be a blood-covered graveyard with
Dead trees lurking behind the depths of darkness?
Will it be the buzzing of the phone call that
Was never meant to happen?

What's behind the splintered door?
Will it be the tenth tear dripping from your
Eyes as you watch your friend being shot ten
Times in the back?
Will it be the faint scream of your mum and
Sister as they get dragged away?

What's behind the splintered door?
Will it be a mad scientist crouching down
To saw a dead skeleton's bones in half?
Will it be a great warrior with a thousand
Spears in his head trying not to let out a
Cry of weakness?

What's behind the splintered door?
Maybe it is nothing like that
Maybe it is just memories
At least you will have good ones.

Sebastian Ralph (10)
Taunton Preparatory School, Taunton

Through My Winter Window I Can See . . .

A thick layer of powdery snow
A swirl of snowflakes falling
Glistening icicles in a rainbow.

Giant fur trees sprinkled with a thin layer of snow
Squirrels squabbling over acorns and birds eating berries and bugs
Snowmen being made.

Children ice skating and playing ice hockey
Adults collecting wood and walking dogs
People singing carols.

People wrapped up warm and cosy
Children running against the fresh air
And fires being lit and mugs of hot chocolate being drunk.

Abi McHardy (9)
Taunton Preparatory School, Taunton

A Recipe For The Countryside

Take a mixing bowl and add 100 grams of hay
Add two teaspoons of fresh air
Mix in well with 2½ cups of tractors
Marinade with a farmer-assured sauce for forty minutes
Then add a pint of combine harvesters
Oo-ar, oo-ar, that smells good!
Add 30 grams of cows
Knead well, whilst slowly adding 1 teaspoon of pigs
Add 300 grams of flowers
Then take 1½ cups of honey and mix in well
Then add the secret ingredient . . . a beautiful farmer's daughter!
Bake for half an hour then leave in overnight in 40 acres of land
The next day put in some animal feed
Now that you have your very own countryside, tuck in!

Drew Boorman (11)
Taunton Preparatory School, Taunton

Through My Winter Window I Can See . . .

In the thick snow, hailstones fall to the ground
Turning into slush
Frosty glassy icicles
That sparkle and glitter
Gleaming, soft, powdery
Crunchy, dazzling, deep, fresh, chilly snow.

The skating, skiddy, slippery ice
Snowflakes, snowstorms crashing
To the floor
Glitter-like frost.

Connor Coventry (9)
Taunton Preparatory School, Taunton

The Quangle Wangle's Hat

The Quangle Wangle danced to the tune of the flute
Mr Quangle Wangle asked the squash for a song and a dance
Then the Blue Baboon said, 'I'm going to the land of Tute,'
And the Attery Squash said, 'I'm going back to France,'
The Quangle Wangle waved goodbye to the Blue Baboon
He turned around and noticed the Dong had gone to the moon
The Quangle Wangle ate a burger and went to fetch a towel
When he got back his plate was empty, greedy Fimble Fowl
Mr Quangle Wangle Quee.

Alex Hill (9)
Taunton Preparatory School, Taunton

Through My Winter Window I Can See . . .

Through my winter window I can see
Snowflakes falling from the sky and floor is blanketed with snow
And I see my dog in the snow trying to find his toy
The trees are encrusted with ice and sprinkled with snow
The air feels chilly, crisp and fresh
Oh what a delightful morning!
The village looks arctic
It looks just like a winter wonderland!
I can hear happy voices playing in the snow and
See all the snowmen in the village and snowball fights all around
The cars slipping on the road, people trying to go to work and
Oh! I see a little robin singing in the snow
That's what I can see through my winter window.

Imogen Allen (9)
Taunton Preparatory School, Taunton

Monsters

I'm the monster hiding under your bed
Razor-sharp teeth and eyes glowing red
I'm the monster hiding under your stairs
Blood-thrilling screams and spiders in my hair
I'm the monster who will never ever miss you
If I do you will be the next meal or two
Tell spooky stories to your friends all night
But it won't stop me coming to give you a fright
If you don't believe in me or my friends
You'll be sorry 'til your life comes to an end
Come outside in the jet-black night
Don't be such a scaredy-cat
I'm sure you won't die!

Carly Brown (9)
Taunton Preparatory School, Taunton

Through My Winter Window

Through my winter window I can see . . .
A sly fox scrambling through the snowy bushes
Black cats prowling on the frosty wall
A brown duck waddling through the thick snow
A nimble rabbit digging under the big wall
An owl tooting through the dark night
A singing robin by my snowy window
Some fast fish swimming under the frozen lake
A frozen lake on the sprinkling grass.

Oliver Jones (9)
Taunton Preparatory School, Taunton

The Premature Funeral Of Jonathan Wilde

When Jonathan woke
He just saw black
And he felt a jolt down in his back
He couldn't feel anything
Thought he was dead
But there was something soft
Under his head
A pillow!
Was he sleeping?
But he heard someone weeping
For him?
Surely not . . . he felt something hot
Near his feet, they were about to melt!
The wood was burning
Jonathan was yearning
Just to get out
He tried to shout!
He bashed through the lid
With wood in his hair
And gave all the guests
A pretty good scare
When Jonathan said,
'Wait! I'm not dead!'

Sarah Parfitt (11)
Taunton Preparatory School, Taunton

Through My Winter Window I Can See . . .

Through my winter window I can see . . .
A frozen lake with people ice skating
And crows scavenging in the snow

Through my winter window I can see . . .
Frosty icicles hanging from the trees
And orangey red foxes hunting for food

Through my winter window I can see . . .
Snow-covered hills shining in the sunlight
And horses huddled together keeping warm

Through my winter window I can see . . .
Rabbits hopping in the snow hoping to find some food
And the birds' heads under their wings

Through my winter window I can see . . .
Icy, crispy and frozen bridges
And ducks flying and waddling.

Mey Haines (8)
Taunton Preparatory School, Taunton

When The Earth Rumbled

The earth rumbled
The dragons were coming
Breathing fire with intense heat
Cooking people alive
Their wings creating winds
Their clawed feet
Causing destruction wherever they went
Dragons everywhere
In the sky
And firm below
Blinding light with their fiery eyes
Smoke destroying crops
With intense heat
Their stone-like tails
Destroying buildings with one blow
Their job was done
Our town was burnt to debris
Their work was done
The village and its surroundings destroyed
When the dragons came
It was hell.

Chris James (11)
Taunton Preparatory School, Taunton

In The Forest

Deep in the ancient, deserted forest
Everything changes when the last walker trudges back to his car
Then the gloomy forest becomes an enchanted wood

Mist gleams on the grass like fairy dust
Fairies ring their tiny windflower bells that human ears can't hear
Sheltering under the soft beeches from the glistening rain

The trees tell magnificent stories
How they survived tremendous wars
Wood elves dance in soggy leaves

But when a traveller passes there
The misty magic drifts away
And it's just a dull forest again
On a damp, dark day.

Caitlin Williams (9)
Taunton Preparatory School, Taunton

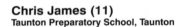

Through My Winter Window I Can See . . .

Through my winter window I can see . . .
Beds of snow, crisp and fresh
Layers of ice, splitting under children's heavy feet
Robins chirping merrily in the golden sunset sky

The breezy air, nippy and cold
Beautiful, white, slushy, crunchy snowflakes fluttering around
And settling on children's heads

Frozen squirrels squabbling over solid nuts
Rabbits burrowing deep into their holes to get away from the cold
Jack Frost, leaping in the air sprinkling the earth with snow

People skating on frozen ground
Blue tits, robins, goldfinch and crow
Circling the fresh and crispy air

Snowballs flinging from door to door
Flying over little children's heads, landing on
The frozen oak tree

The trees bare and stiff, glistening and glittering
With beds of snow settling on the bendy branches
The sky grey and crisp.

Morwenna Harnett (9)
Taunton Preparatory School, Taunton

Out Of My Winter Window I Can See . . .

Out of my window I can see . . .
A big red robin dancing in the tree
His feathers are fluffy to keep out the cold
Looking for seeds to eat, quite old

Out of the winter window I see . . .
A deer's bright eyes looking at me
His antlers are red, he's ready to run
If he moves now we'll see some fun

Out of the winter window I see . . .
An owl gliding past as quiet as can be
He's looking for food deep in the grass
I can see his shadow swooping past

Out of the winter window I see . . .
A big dark storm cloud blowing to me
It's full of snow to drop on the hill
I'll put on my coat and run to the mill.

Charlie Upton (9)
Taunton Preparatory School, Taunton

Easter

Easter is nice
Easter is cool
I like the eggs
We all hunt for

On Easter day
We have people around
The bunny has come
All look for eggs

End of the day
It has gone so fast
What happens now?
Summer of course!

Summer is nice
But do you know what I like?
Not Christmas, not New Year
But Easter!

Rachel Nuttall (11)
Taunton Preparatory School, Taunton

Over The Hills

Over the hills we wander
Over the hills we roam
Searching for our country
Trying to get home

Off go the sirens, wailing in the night
Running, running faster now
In our blind, diverted flight

Over the hills we're running
Sprinting for our lives
The enemy is right behind us
We can even see their knives

We've finally reached our homeland
Let's all give a cheer
They were no match for me and you
They cannot harm us here.

Alexander Hall (10)
Taunton Preparatory School, Taunton

Dragon's Den

The dragon stared at me
I felt a cold shiver
From my head to my toes
It stared at me menacingly
It was going to pounce

Its nostrils flared, it blew fire
I ran to a bush
I dived under it
The dragon flew out
After circling me, it flew up

It flew towards my village
When I arrived I saw
People screaming and running
The huts were on fire
And there was the dragon
Looking for more villages

I took a bow and arrow
And aimed for the rider
I shot the arrow
It flew through the air as if guided
And found the target

The rider fell from the dragon
And the dragon fell too
Falling, disappearing
As it hit the ground
Nothing was there
The dragon had gone.

Matt Haines (11)
Taunton Preparatory School, Taunton

Who Am I?

English teacher
Science preacher
Story teller
Church beller
Taunton School
Not too cruel
Science lab
Absolutely fab!

A: Mrs Tucker

Imogen Gray (10)
Taunton Preparatory School, Taunton

An Elephant Thinks What He Thinks He Thinks He Does

An elephant creature is a bad, bad thing
Which mingles with the crowd
And muffles all the buffles
Hidden somewhere in the crowd

An elephant lives in a dark, warm place
And thinks what he thinks
But what he doesn't know
What he thinks he thinks

An elephant is scared of a tiny little thing
It's a mouse which is eating all the leaves
And the rats are the worst
Which attack all the mice!

Edward McBride (11)
Taunton Preparatory School, Taunton

In The Dance Of The Moon

In the cool of the afternoon
I met a lady under a big white moon
There was an orchestra with a banjo
Playing for us to dance the tango
And the people all clapped as we danced
And then we ended it with a little prance!

After we danced and pranced
I got out my 'lance'
And there at the end was a ring
She saw the ring and started to sing
By the light of the glorious moon
I put it on her finger and we're getting married soon.

Jessica Weeks (10)
Taunton Preparatory School, Taunton

Kittens

My kittens run like headless chickens
They run into the door . . . *crash!*
They fight on the floor . . . *bash!*
They run down the gutter like nutters
They bite my brother
They're from a small litter
They like the look of glitter.
Ooo shiny.

Callum Fiske (10)
Taunton Preparatory School, Taunton

Holiday In The Sun!

For Christmas dinner it's a barbeque
While you're at it get a tan too!
You'll find a dove
And fall in love
It's holiday in the sun!

Open your presents on the beach
In your stocking you'll find a peach!
No need to pay attention
No need for detention
It's holiday in the sun!

It's time to go home, but it's not over yet
We're going home in a brand new jet!
As we fly high
We'll be touching the sky
It's holiday . . . back home again!

Evangeline Caroll (9)
Taunton Preparatory School, Taunton

Who Ate All The Carrots?

B rought to the show by Herr Hans
I n his arms, what a struggle was he
G erman giant, too large you see

H erman the German a rabbit is he, he ate all the carrots, so there were none for me!
E ars floppy and long to hear many a sound
R eliable and calm, he just flopped around
M assive in size and cuddly too
A continental gent bigger than you
N ow he's just a toy isn't he?

Heather Poulter (11)
Taunton Preparatory School, Taunton

Crazy Christmas

P eople having fun
R ampaging around the house
E veryone round the tree
S nowing in the garden
E ating Christmas pud
N eeding to open presents
T insel on the tree
S anta has come! Finally.

Tom Chandler (10)
Taunton Preparatory School, Taunton

What Am I?

Shaky-wakey
Children break me
I give you flavour
I'm your saviour

I sometimes moult
But that's not my fault
I am cool
I make people drool
I come from seas
I can make people sneeze,
What am I?

A: Salt and pepper.

Harriet Armstrong (10)
Taunton Preparatory School, Taunton

My Silly Dog

My little white dog
She likes to play in the fog
Her name is Lilly
She is very silly (no really)
Most people call her a bog brush
And she's always in a rush
She gets very scuffed
She's made out of fluff
She is very funny and makes me eat loads of honey
When she's asleep at the end of the day
You can't hear a peep
But she's very crazy and is not very lazy!

Charles Solanki (10)
Taunton Preparatory School, Taunton

Trafalgar

To this day 200 years ago
Men were working down below
Loading the guns, carrying the casualties
And running around like mad doggies
While outside ships were sinking
Men with one eye still hoping
That the day would come when all was still
But many of their friends were still ill
That day came, that day went
But the world must live on as I am now dead.

Toby Butters (11)
Taunton Preparatory School, Taunton

It's All Happening

Witches on their broomsticks fly
Moons and planets slowly pass by
I'll stay here till the morning's nigh
It's all happening in the night

Fish of every colour swim
Eels over the ocean floor skim
The things in the distance are oh so dim
It's all happening in the sea

Going slowly on its way a snail
Leaving behind it a sticky trail
Upstairs no one's there cos there's a gale
It's all happening underground

Up here there's not a sound
Just me and the soft green ground
I can see for miles on top of this mound
It's all happening above the Earth

Things like this happen everywhere
We don't have time to stop and stare
We have to be here and there
It's all happening in the world.

Samuel Newton (11)
Taunton Preparatory School, Taunton

I Know A Dilly Dancer

I know a dilly dancer who dances all night
Her terrible singing gives the neighbours a fright
She dances down the alley
And the people think she is doolally
If the people try to complain
She'll go dancing in the rain

She is a nutter, because she dances with butter
When she dances not even the butterflies flutter
One day she went dancing with a pike fish
The other day she danced in a dish
She surprised the king
When she had a buffalo wing

I don't know my friend the dilly dancer
She really is a nutter
But somehow . . . somehow
She has got *me* to go and dance with her
And when I do fancy tricks guess what she says?
'Oh don't be such a show-off William!'

Fraser Crawford (11)
Taunton Preparatory School, Taunton

Hooray Today!

Finding, finding, finding them all
Hockey and tennis and football galore
It's time for cricket and rugby too
What's going to happen and what are we going to do?
It's time for boring lessons and no fun
It's like I'm going to shoot myself with a gun
It's time for PE and we're having a swim
And I'm really good and I've got a fin
I'm going home and I'm going to play
No school on the next day, *hooray!*

It's the next day and I've just woken up
And I've made breakfast and a cup
It's 12 o'clock and time for lunch
We're having fish and chips and I've got a bunch
Now I'm watching 'Match of the Day'
And Liverpool win two-nil, *hooray!*

It is Sunday and I'm having roast lunch
I've eaten so much that my mouth goes crunch
I've played on my DS with my sister Holly
This time luckily she didn't bring her dolly
I'm going to bed and it's school next day
First lesson is science, *not hooray!*

Jordan Dunbar (11)
Taunton Preparatory School, Taunton

My Sports

The rain is falling and the time is ticking
We're five-nil down and it's half-time
We are puffing and Mr Ward is bluffing
The second half's beginning and we're thinking of winning!

Ohh so close
Matt's had a shot and hit the post!
We're playing Clifton and we feel like toast
Damn! Full time
Two oranges each. *Urgh!*, they taste like lime!

Three to win and I'm in batting
If I miss I'll get the sacking!
Well here goes . . .
Yes, I hit it and it's going for a four, and the fielder's slacking
The pressure's on and the players are cracking.

Benson Pocock (11)
Taunton Preparatory School, Taunton

The Beach

Before everyone arrives
The sand looks golden and sparkly
Smooth and untouched
Waves gently lapping the shore
Wind fluttering the flags

Suddenly . . .
People shouting
Children racing to the sea's edge
Ladies trying to find a space for sunbathing
Dogs barking and yapping
Surfers trying to catch a wave

The sea glistens
Splashes and swishes
Children jumping over waves
Sailors out at sea
Billowing sails and gusts of wind
The taste of salt and the rushing air

The sun drifts down
The sea drifts in
Washing away the footsteps
Clearing the sand
For another summer's day.

Rebecca Kinnear (11)
Taunton Preparatory School, Taunton

My House

Up the driveway and through the door
Into the hall and onto the hard, hard floor!

Into the playroom and onto the sofa
Turn on the tele and on it a loafer!

See the kitchen with an open door
Smell the scent of cakes galore!

Out to the garden where you'll find the zip wire
By the time you're at the end you'll be on fire!

Up to the football pitch and have a couple of games
Play with me and my dad and also my friend James!

Back into the house and up the stairs
Into my bedroom where I cuddle my bears!

So there's your tour of my beautiful home
Come again and we'll have a bash in my *home!*

Josh Kelly (11)
Taunton Preparatory School, Taunton

The Port

Walking through the gates
Past a world of tombs
The port arose before us
The buildings bleak with gloom

The Roman world erupted
Imagination racing
Life bustled all around us
With fat old Roman's pacing

A lot of buildings remain
For one thousand years or more
Guarding most mosaics
On the ancient floor

With seating halfway round
The theatre hosts a play
The stone theatrical masks
Look down on a fun-packed day

Walking down the main street
Behind a colonnade
The mercantile offices
Lie hidden by the shade

Through the clearing steam
Of the calidarium
Purified souls arose
To greet Emperor Valerian

Flights of fancy racing
But I must be on my way
Reluctantly I leave this town
After a most enlightening stay
Till next time
Ostia Antica.

Elysia Upton (11)
Taunton Preparatory School, Taunton

The Quangle Wangle's Hat

On the early morning of that day
The Golden Grouse felt dreadfully ill
And they found it had flown away
To stay with a very good friend called Phil
He lived in Spain where it was hot
Loved the sun and sunbathed a lot
The Golden Grouse just had to go back
But he was stuck in a muddy track
Explained the Quangle Wangle Quee!

Samuel Popham (10)
Taunton Preparatory School, Taunton

Dreaming!

I'm ready for my mission
Jetting off to space
We are starting the ignition
The rocket is rushing to its pace

I hear the final countdown
10, 9, 8
Oh no, we've got a failure
On this very important date!

The failure has been fixed now
We are soaring way up high
The Earth looks like a golf ball
Engulfed by rich blue sky

The sun is shining brightly
The moon cannot be seen
Our destination is the planet Jupiter
This is the furthest I have been!

The rocket is turning around now
We have finished our explore
The Earth is enlarging quickly
As we speed towards the floor

I hear this kind of buzzing
I am feeling quite wet
I open up my eyes now
To see that I'm in bed!

Elly Chandler (11)
Taunton Preparatory School, Taunton

Winter

Winter is cold, dark and gloomy
Perfect for playing in snow
Deep footprints follow me
Winter is fun ya know

A bitter wind bites my face
Turning it red and raw
Inside my house a fire burns
My mother opens the door

When I enter the sitting room
I find the Sunday roast
Here and now in wintertime
I enjoy hot food the most.

Vivien Keech (11)
Taunton Preparatory School, Taunton

What Would The World Be Like?

What would the world be like without racism?
No segregation
The world would be one nation

What would the world be like without water?
The world would be dry
Life would die

What would the world be without schools?
The world would be dumb
Boring and glum

What would the world be like if everyone was happy?
Friendships stronger
Marriages longer

What would the world be like without money?
People would share
The world would be fair

What would the world be like with peace?
The people calm
The world a charm

What would the world be like without fun?
The world would be a bore
It would feel like a chore

What would the world be like without anger?
The world would be nice
Even the mice

What would the world be like without food?
The world would be thin
The size of a pin

What would the world be like without war?
No devastation
The world would be one nation.

Oliver Large (11)
Taunton Preparatory School, Taunton

Through My Winter Window

Fir trees covered in snow
Frost patterns criss-cross the windows
Through my winter window

People ice-skating on ice
People drinking hot chocolate
Through my winter window.

George Whitburn (8)
Taunton Preparatory School, Taunton

My Hamster Peeka

In the middle of the night
Where there was no light
I went down to peek
I went down to sneak
At my hamster Peeka

I opened the lid with a squeak
I thought he would be asleep
He is usually in his wheel
Which makes an awful squeal
Something was wrong, all was quiet

But I did not realise this at first
So I went to the kitchen to quench my thirst
When I was satisfied I came back again
To see Peeka snuggled in his den
But he was not there!

It was very worrying
But then I heard some scurrying
It came from the chair
This was an awful scare
What if it was my hamster?

I started shaking
My knees were quaking
It was Peeka running free
I could not leave him be
I must have left the cage door up
When I went to fill my cup

Now he is back in his bed
Dreaming dreams in his sleepy head.

Sarah Theobald (11)
Taunton Preparatory School, Taunton

Through My Winter Window

Through my winter window I can see . . .
Prickly hedgehogs rolled up in a ball in the frosty snow
Dripping icicles sparkling in the sun
Sliding ducks quacking on the icy pond
Bare branches outlined against the white sky
Snowflakes swirling softly around
Shivering birds searching for crumbs
A red squirrel darting across the crunchy grass
A tiny robin with bright eyes looking at me
A freezing wind pushing against my window
The bright blue sky blinding my eyes.

Alexander Raikes (8)
Taunton Preparatory School, Taunton

The Ticking Clock

Now I go tick tock, tick tock
Now it's seven o'clock
And off they go to eat
And they sit on their seat
So they leave me and wait for the chime

Now I go tick tock, tick tock
Now it's eleven o'clock
I will chime myself silly
With my banging on and rhythm
They leave me and wait for the chime

Now I go tick tock, tick tock
Now it's twelve o'clock
They go to eat their lunch
And/or just maybe a brunch
So they leave me and wait for the chime

Now I go tick tock, tick tock
Now it's six o'clock
They go for their tea
And so all completely forgetting about me
So they leave me and wait for the chime

Now I go tick tock, tick tock
Now it's nine o'clock
And they all go to sleep
Now very deep I go:
Ding, dong, ding, dong.

Robin Evans (11)
Taunton Preparatory School, Taunton

Through My Winter Window

Through my winter window I can see . . .
Black cats prowling on icy roads
Icicles on trees falling in the snow
Brown deer running on the snow
Happy children ice skating
Snowdrops poking out of the snow
A wet dog rolling in the white snow
A big rabbit bouncing in the snow
A red fox looking for food on a white bank
A pure white lake frozen in ice
Bare trees swaying in the breeze
Sheep invisible in the snow.

Mathew Morgan (8)
Taunton Preparatory School, Taunton

A Visit To The Farm

'Up there!' he says and shows me a field,
'So many crops each year they yield.'
Suddenly I see the ass
In the corner eating grass.

After looking at the hens
I see the sheep in their pens.
I see a flash, must be a cat
I hear squeals, it's caught a rat.

Then I walk to the river:
It looks so cold it makes me shiver.
In the rushes I spot a mole
Maybe it's a water vole.

Then I walk back to the house;
They say they have a pesky mouse.
On my way I spy a fox
Sneaking around, licking its chops.

What great things today I've seen
And no one knows where I've been!

Tom Odgers (11)
Taunton Preparatory School, Taunton

Everest

My heart is pounding
My ears are thumping
There's no turning back
I have to climb it

Slowly I start to lift my chin
I stare at the mountain
It stares back at me
Towering over the tiny person

Icy snow caps
Tumbling rock faces
Jagged rocks
And 50 foot drops

It's easy to climb it
It's coming back that's hard
Your oxygen's low
You wobble to and fro
This is the part where I die.

Callum Deakin (11)
Taunton Preparatory School, Taunton

The Chao Garden

Open a gate to find creatures
Don't worry, they don't have scary features
They are so cute, they're called Chao
They're so cute, no need to bow
Take them to the kindergarten to learn
But don't set them alight or they will burn
They are so cool
Give them a ball
If you hurt them say pardon
So I'll see you there at the Chao garden
Give them a hat
But not a bat
Teach them to race and play karate
And if they win, have a party
You can adopt a Chao
But we don't see cows
You can give them a name
And they won't go lame
The Chao professor will give you hints
And he might even like some mints
Go to the doctor to have a check-up
But don't worry, it won't turn into a pup
Feed Chao fruit for lots of good health
So come to the Chao garden to save your wealth.

Thomas Hayes (10)
Taunton Preparatory School, Taunton

Large Pepperoni Pizza

Oh pepperoni pizza
You're exactly what I need
You're spicy yet so saucy
You make my tastebuds bleed

You're welcoming and needed
You're hot and you're so sweet
You're squidgy on the fingers
I love your sizzling cheese

Oh what a magic moment
When I touch you on the crust
I want more, more and even more
I'll eat you, yes I must

You're obviously edible
I'll make you last forever
Your runny sauce is beautiful
When I eat you I'm in Heaven.

Daniel Rodgers (11)
Taunton Preparatory School, Taunton

Through My Winter Window I Can See

Through my winter window I can see . . .
Small black birds pecking snow for worms
Fit grey squirrels jumping from tree to tree
Active golden retriever eating icy snow
Skinny white cat sitting on an icy shed
Bare tall trees swaying from side to side
Tiny prickly hedgehogs curling up in the frost
Red-breasted robins flying from fence to fence
Happy children having snow fights
Big chestnut ponies galloping from each field
Parents staying in having hot chocolate.

Luciana Metherall (8)
Taunton Preparatory School, Taunton

Through My Winter Window

Through my winter window I can see . . .
Ginger cats jumping onto the sparkling wall
Bare trees swishing in the snow
Stripy badgers sniffing through the snow for food
A wise owl swooping down for prey
Scared mice hiding in the leaves
Green leaves covered in frosty snow
Brown ponies sniffing with cold noses
A sly fox preying on chicks for his cubs
A golden dog rolling in the snow
At last the snow falling from the sky.

Holly Conquer (9)
Taunton Preparatory School, Taunton

Through My Winter Window

Through my winter window I can see . . .
Starving squirrels scuffling through the frosty leaves
Spiky brown hedgehog scuffling through the earth
Tiny rabbits hopping through the scary woods
Big brown barn owl hooting in the night air
Icy pond cracking under chilly children's weight
Frosty bushes swishing silently through the breeze
Delicate snowdrops swaying in the frosty wind
Scurrying and hurrying mice looking for food
Tiny blue tit finding food on the wall.

Elizabeth Merson (8)
Taunton Preparatory School, Taunton

Through My Winter Window

Through my winter window I can see . . .
Big hungry foxes smelling out for food
Walking through the freezing snowy bushes
Large, big, heavy blankets of snow on the icy rivers
Icicles dropping from trees onto lakes cracking the ice
Lots of happy children ice skating on very thick ice
Snowy leaves steadily dropping into the snow
Dogs running trying to catch some blackbirds in the snowy grass
Fast little squirrels scurrying across the ice
Trying to dodge the falling icicles when trying to find nuts
Happy children building funny snowmen
Lots of children in a village having toboggan races down a very steep icy hill
Excitable children having mega snowball fights in a big snowy field.

Henri Cooney (9)
Taunton Preparatory School, Taunton

Through My Winter Window

Through my winter window I can see . . .
Freezing cold squirrels climbing up a swaying tree
Prickly brown hedgehogs trying to find their way
Skinny black cats standing on the icy road
Swooping, spooky barn owls looking for their prey
Sparkling snowdrops getting the pretty flowers to grow
Bare, icy trees standing in the cold, thick snow
Soft fluffy rabbits digging in the frosty snow
Galloping ponies going around the big paddock
Sad, dirty badgers in the dark frosty night
Mad dogs rolling around in the wet snow.

Kate Drew (8)
Taunton Preparatory School, Taunton

Through My Winter Window

Through my winter window I can see . . .
Red and white foxes running in the frosty air
Tortoiseshell cat catching a tiny snowflake
Ginger ponies running in the snow
Red-breasted robin flying in the cold air
White-breasted ducks quacking in the frosty pond
Black dogs barking in the air getting snowflakes in their mouths
Goldfish splashing in the water
Fluffy bunnies bouncing around throwing snowballs at each other with their feet.

Emma Read (9)
Taunton Preparatory School, Taunton

Through My Winter Window

Through my winter window I can see . . .
A small black dog sniffing the cold air
A sly red fox prowling in the snow
Ginger cats bounding through the bare trees
Children sliding on coloured toboggans
Prickly brown hedgehogs plodding along the icy road
A soft, silent owl gliding through the night air
A small grey mouse scurrying in the snowy grass
Red-breasted robins pecking in the frosty grass
A fast little squirrels scurrying across the deep, thick snow
A small brown rabbit hopping quickly across the thick ice.

Max Popham (8)
Taunton Preparatory School, Taunton

Through My Winter Window

Through my winter window I can see . . .
Cold, fluffy robins flying through the softly falling snow
Small grey squirrels sleeping in the bare trees
Snow-covered ponies eating frosty grass
Confused ducks pecking at the icy pond
Pond fish swimming under frosty weed
Chilly children ice skating in the town ice rink
Shivering rabbits hiding in the dewy grass
Woolly sheep plotting to escape!
Wise old owl swooping through the dark sky
Dogs sheltering in snowy bushes.

Mollie Stallard (8)
Taunton Preparatory School, Taunton

Through My Winter Window

Through my winter window I can see . . .
A cunning fox rustling in the frosty field
Sweet, silent hedgehogs curled up hibernating
A little blue tit feeding from the bird table
A tiny, red-breasted robin searching for food in the snowy air
Tabby cats rolling in a blanket of snow
Young children riding on their toboggans
Small puppies jumping on the thin ice
Bare trees swaying in the light breeze
White horse's owner's softly grooming her on the sparkling white grass.

Emily Vickery (8)
Taunton Preparatory School, Taunton

Through My Winter Window

Snowflakes spinning through the air, landing on the trees and houses
Ponds sparkle in the light, glistening and shining in the night
Leaves flutter down from the trees, the last one left alone
Through my winter window

The ground looks like a huge white blanket
I can hear people falling in the crunchy snow
And dogs sliding on the ice
Through my winter window

White trees outside my window
I can see a sugar-covered lake
I can hear children laughing
Through my winter window.

Hannah Jolley (9)
Taunton Preparatory School, Taunton

Through My Winter Window

Fir trees covered in fresh white snow
Sharp pointed icicles pointing to the frost-bound ground
Frosty patterns on the frozen windowpane
Through my winter window

The winter weather is calling us
Snow angels in the crisp white snow
With woolly hats and long scarves
Through my winter window

Skiers skiing down steep slippery hills
Jack Frost has been and left some frost
Cold and chilly are these winter days
Through my winter window.

Emma Stacey (8)
Taunton Preparatory School, Taunton

Through My Winter Window

Snowflakes spinning and twirling to the ground
Sparkling icicles as sharp as daggers hang from gutters
Red-cheeked children playing in the crisp snow
Through my winter window

Jolly snowmen being built by laughing and happy children
Dogs are slipping and sliding on the gleaming ice
Slushy snowballs flying through the numbing air
Through my winter window.

Harriet Turner (9)
Taunton Preparatory School, Taunton

Through My Winter Window

I open my window to a winter wonderland
I see dazzling white snow on rooftops
I feel the bitter air on my bare arms
Through my winter window

I taste light, slushy snow on my tongue
I hear the wind whistle in and out the hoary trees
I look to the church camouflaged in powdery fresh snow
Through my winter window

I smell fresh bread coming out of the Aga in the bakery
I see children from the village building a snowman
In the distance, trees covered in glistening white, sparkling snow
Through my winter window.

Alicia Mileham (9)
Taunton Preparatory School, Taunton

Through My Winter Window

Trees swinging in the blustery winter wind
Hot chocolate being stirred with jolly, smiley faces
Jack Frost has stopped off on his way, painting frost patterns on the windowpanes
Through my winter window

Children wearing woolly hats and gloves
Snowmen being jolly men, being built by screaming children
Robins tweeting merry tunes on tree branches
Through my winter window.

Luke Townsend (8)
Taunton Preparatory School, Taunton

Through My Winter Window

Snow drifts to the ground
Rocks, grass, leaves and trees are buried deep
Squirrel, rabbit and fox tracks criss-cross the garden
Through my winter window

Icicles are pointed clear and sharp as they hang from gutters high above my head
Jack Frost has been and gone leaving patterns behind him
With a carrot for a nose, rock eyes and smiles, snowmen stand tall and stern
From my winter window.

James Dancey (8)
Taunton Preparatory School, Taunton

Through My Winter Window

People skating on the icy lake
Snowballs flying through the air
Skiers fly down the slopes
Through my winter window

Dogs playing in the deep snow
Snowmen being built
Children laughing and running around
Through my winter window

Lots of trees outside my room
Horse riders going past
Tawny fox running fast
Through my winter window.

William Haughton (8)
Taunton Preparatory School, Taunton

Through My Winter Window

Long pointing icicles curling to the ground
Skiers skiing down steep mountains crashing into fir trees!
Ice skaters jumping and dancing merrily on icy ponds
Through my winter window

Snowflakes twirling down to the ground
Fox tracks on the snowy forest floor
Snow covers trees
Through my winter window.

James Spackman (9)
Taunton Preparatory School, Taunton

Through My Winter Window

Snowflakes swirl and tumble to the icy ground
The snowflakes are really white
The snow is so very white
Through my winter window

The snow is crunchy and deep
The snow is lots of fun to play in
Trees covered in snow
Through my winter window.

Natalie Boulton (9)
Taunton Preparatory School, Taunton

Through My Winter Window

Snowflakes dancing to the ground
Fir trees splattered with icy snow
Horses trotting through covered woods
Through my winter window

Robin tracks in the snow
Patterns and shapes on my icy windowpane
Snowballs flying through the air
Through my winter window

Ponds freezing up like big pieces of glass
Untouched snow is clear and white
Children racing slip on the icy snow
Through my winter window.

Marcus Worrall (9)
Taunton Preparatory School, Taunton

Through My Winter Window

Snowflakes fluttering to the ground
Snowballs shooting through the air
People skating and over they go!
Through my winter window

Dogs playing and barking
Happy children laughing and shouting
People dancing all around
Through my winter window

Frosty patterns on my window
Children making snowmen
Carrying coal, carrots and twigs
Through my winter window.

Milly Butters (8)
Taunton Preparatory School, Taunton

Through My Winter Window

Horses playing in deep, deep snow
Ice ponds covered with a dusting of frost
I hear children laughing and playing throwing snowballs
Through my winter window

Snow swirls and settles on the ground
Robins and blackbirds peck crumbs from the bird table
A snowman with a carrot nose and coal eyes, he smiles at me
Through my winter window.

Olympia Martin-Pope (9)
Taunton Preparatory School, Taunton

The Panther And The Tiger

A panther creeps over a mound of dirt
A tiger prowls through the long grass
Their eyes meet . . .
Bam!
They attack!
They spring at each other
They toss and they turn
Grapple and scratch
Bite and kick
Clouds of dust can be seen for miles
Snarls and growls
Scrapes and dents
Suddenly it stops
The panther stalks off its head held high
The tiger crawls off beaten and ashamed.

William Baldwin (10)
Taunton Preparatory School, Taunton

A Bird Sitting In A Tree

A bird sitting in a tree
Cat as eager as can be
Climbs to the top
Forgets to stop
Fire brigade comes
The cat is chewing his gums
He is so scared
He begins to run
Bird singing having fun
Cat got very stuck
And ends up in muck!

James Poole (10)
Taunton Preparatory School, Taunton

Wishing Washing Water

Coming down the exciting falls
It hits a sharp pointed rock like glass
Shattering and glistening
Then it becomes a peaceful pool

It forms a shimmering stream
And it becomes full of multicoloured fish
Then it tips into the stormy sea and everything becomes rough again
As it was in the beginning.

William Jolley (10)
Taunton Preparatory School, Taunton

The Buzzy Bee

There was a busy buzzy bee
And he was a celebrity
He sang and sang until one day
He dropped dead on the pathway
The yellow flower drooped her head
To see poor buzzy bee now dead.

Chloe Coleman (11)
Taunton Preparatory School, Taunton

Spider

Under the staircase there is
A spider's web
Under the stairs it lies
Free and silver in the moonlit cupboard

For the house spiders cast
And the trap itself
Was frightening me
And the silver scout

I was curled up inside the cupboard
I screamed for help
But no help would come
It was creeping and crawling all around
So *help, help* get me out!

I try to let the flies out
But they were already dead
They died upon my little feet
I was crying so loud
My mum and dad heard
And took the spider away for me.

Holly Nicholson (8)
Temple Guiting CE Primary School, Cheltenham

Spider

In the corner of my dad's shed
The spider's home
The sticky web
All the flies caught in the lacy trap
The silvery web strung from strap to strap
Glowing in the darkness
Spider prancing and dancing and trapping the flies.

Pete Andrews (8)
Temple Guiting CE Primary School, Cheltenham

Spider

Spider's web under the stairs
Flies stuck, spider's land
Spider dancing his dance of death
Left, right he goes
Left and right
Up and down he goes
Up and down
Leaving his web
He will return
And dance his dance of death.

Ross Holland (7)
Temple Guiting CE Primary School, Cheltenham

Spider

In the corner of my room,
sits a spider in the slivery gloom.
Spinning its web it sits there now,
I think it likes it in our house.
Eating flies all night,
it gives them quite a fright.
Its web is thin,
big and sticky,
the flies think it's quite icky!

Eloise Henson (7)
Temple Guiting CE Primary School, Cheltenham

Dragon

Big fierce dragon
Dark, dark cave
He comes to visit the town
We're all afraid
He goes back to his cave
Gets a little rest
And in the morning
He flies to terrorise
With his terrible breath.

Poppy Bridgwater (7)
Temple Guiting CE Primary School, Cheltenham

Spider

In the corner
The dark, dark corner
Hexagonal web
Sticky, icky web
Pouncing, catching trapping
Flies trapped
Trying to get free
Spider's tea.

Bethany Swallow (7)
Temple Guiting CE Primary School, Cheltenham

Spider

In the cupboard
Under the stairs
Web dangling
Flies hanging
Spider's house of death.

Benjamin Bowen-Jones (7)
Temple Guiting CE Primary School, Cheltenham

Five Little Puppies

Five little puppies
Sitting on the shore
One got stranded
Then there were four

Four little puppies
Sitting near the sea
One got wet
Then there were three

Three little puppies
Went to the zoo
One got eaten
Then there were two

Two little puppies
Found a loaded gun
One got shot
Then there was one

One little puppy
Went to a fort
He got put in jail
Then there was nought.

Gabriella Ball (7)
The Park School, Yeovil

Animals

I once saw a baby troll
And it was riding on a full-size foal
I once saw a big fat pig
And it was wearing a big fat wig
It went down to the ocean and saw a shark
But the shark was silly and it turned to bark
I once saw a little cow
It did a trick but I don't know how
I once saw a big fat sheep
And it was driving a black and white jeep
I once saw a tiny cat
And it was wearing a bright yellow hat
I once saw a little duck
But it didn't have much tuck
I once saw a bumblebee
And it ate a giant flea
I once saw a crocodile
And it said, 'See you in a while'
I once saw a little dog
And when it went running it got lost in fog
I once saw a little rabbit
And it had a very big habit.

Alexander Maggs (9)
The Park School, Yeovil

Over The Garden Wall

Over the garden
Through the hedge
All I can see is a little blue ledge
I look and I look for things to see
But all I can see is a reflection of me

There is a lake
The size of a sea
Or at least that's how it looks to me

I see a duck
It's out of bounds
Having a quack
Swimming around

Then I see my garden bare
Not a leaf
It isn't fair
I look around me start to cry
Why do flowers have to die?

Caroline Craig (11)
The Park School, Yeovil

Five Spotty Cows

Five spotty cows
Sitting on the floor
One went out to eat
And then there were four

Four spotty cows
Finding a big bee
One got stung
And then there were three

Three spotty cows
Trying to say boo
One got scared
And then there were two

Two spotty cows
Sitting in the sun
One got burnt
And then there was one

One spotty cow
Eating a bun
The cow ran away
And then there were none!

Amelia Walker (8)
The Park School, Yeovil

Just Imagine!

I am in the classroom doing French
But I can just imagine being in a faraway land on a bench
I would be surrounded by wild creatures and flowers
And people with magical powers

I can imagine a river
Vast and wide, that won't make you catch a cold or shiver
I can see an enormous fountain
Surrounded by huge towering mountains

I can imagine a forest so full of growth and life
You couldn't slash a tree with a knife
I can see a sea of green and blue
It would reflect in my shiny shoe.

Sian Rufus (10)
The Park School, Yeovil

Five Fat Cows

Five fat cows
Walking through a door
One got stuck
Then there were four

Four fat cows
Saw a bumblebee
One got stung
Then there were three

Three fat cows
Were going moo
One got a sore throat
Then there were two

Two fat cows
Were going for a run
One fell over
Then there was one

One fat cow
Gave a loud snort
Oh no he's got a cold
Now there are nought.

Toby Finch-Hatton (7)
The Park School, Yeovil

Bananas

Bananas are so
lovely, bananas
are so nice, bananas
are the best thing
a boy would want
for life. I love them
when they squelch
and squirm beneath
my teeth, they are the
best! They beat the rest!
That's why bananas are
so lovely, bananas are
so nice, bananas are the
best thing a boy would
want for life. *Yeah!*

Edward Pratt (10)
The Park School, Yeovil

Five Little Aliens

Five little aliens
Going through a door
One got stuck
Then there were four

Four little aliens
Sitting in a tree
One fell down
Then there were three

Three little aliens
Covered in goo
One needed a bath
Then there were two

Two little aliens
Lying in the sun
One got burnt
Then there was one

One little alien
Felt like a hero
He flew away
Then there were zero!

Gabriel Airey (8)
The Park School, Yeovil

Little Leaping Lizards

Little leaping lizards love leaping like leopards
Lizards like lettuce leaving leftovers
Little lizards love lizard legend like leaky lizard laws
Little leaping lizards leap low
Lizards live like llamas
Lizards love lazing in lakes
Little lizards like lying to lazy llamas
Lizards love lurking like leopards for llamas.

Matthew Lingard (9)
The Park School, Yeovil

Five Grumpy Baboons

Five grumpy baboons
Came to a door
One got knocked out
Then there were four

Four grumpy baboons
Found a golden key
One got locked outside
Then there were three

Three grumpy baboons
Went to the loo
One fell in
Then there were two

Two grumpy baboons
Got a job as a nun
Her friend said goodbye
Then there was one

One grumpy baboon
Lost her son
She went to find him
Then there were none.

Jemma Gane (8)
The Park School, Yeovil

Leaping Dolphins Jumping Mermaids

Dolphins leaping through the sea
Happy as can ever be
Mermaids ride them through the air
Showing off their golden hair

'Come on now, it's time for bed.'
That is what the mermaid said
Both of them are fast asleep
On the highest seaweed heap.

Kirby Mullis (10)
The Park School, Yeovil

My Life

My life is like an oyster
In the sea -
Hard to get to the best part
But worth it in the end

If God is on your side
You cannot fail
In times that are hard
You must keep on trying

I hate my life
I love it too
Sometimes I don't know
What to do

I turn to God
Read the Bible
In some way
God helps me
To understand

My life
Is a book
Got a start
Middle
But no end.

Dominic Stephens (9)
The Park School, Yeovil

Magic

Fairies are my favourite, fairies are the best
They have loads of magic
They have wonderful dresses and a beautiful style
Unlike pixies who go wild with style

I still like pixies though sometimes they are mean and cruel
Green and ugly clothes made of chestnut shells
Some are beautiful, pretty and soft, but others are ghastly and horrible
Wild and frizzy their hair is!

Fairies have magic. Beautiful wonderful magic
But in a day or two the pixies come
To steal their magic, they do, they do
But once they steal the magic, they get more powerful too!

The fairies are pretty, very pretty
But don't be fooled, they are powerful
Their queen is anyway
So beware! they are not as dainty as you think.

Isabelle Zanelli (10)
The Park School, Yeovil

Snowdrop

I once had a hamster
Very small and white
With whiskers that twitched
And eyes very bright

She would sit in my hand
Then run up my arm
I always made sure
She would come to no harm

Her wheel would go round
Then she would run through her tube
Hoping to find her dish of food

But then she grew old
And her wheel went quiet
She became very thin
As if on a diet

We put her in a box and went to the vet
She was put to sleep
I was very upset
Poor little Snowdrop

My only pet!

Yasmin Andrews-Urvoy (10)
The Park School, Yeovil

Pretty Ponies

Muddy ponies come out of the field
Meant to be grey, but actually bay
'Get that pony in the stable, clean it
Groom it, do whatever you can do!
Just clean that pony so it can go to a show!'

Into the horse box all shiny and gleaming
Now grey, but not bay, tail all washed
As shiny as can be!

At the show in the 'best turned out category'
Win all the prizes, next show ahead
'Number 137!'
'Now it's my turn!'
'The jumping competition!'
'Clear round!'
'Number 137 - 1st!'

Hannah Rees (9)
The Park School, Yeovil

Five Small Unicorns

Five small unicorns
Sitting near a door
One ate a carrot
And then there were four

Four small unicorns
Sitting by the sea
One fell in
Then there were three

Three small unicorns
Sitting by a shoe
One fell in
Then there were two

Two small unicorns
Found a jam bun
One started to eat it
And then there was one

One small unicorn
Thought she was a hero
Went to join Superman
Now there are zero!

Olivia Gregory (7)
The Park School, Yeovil

Five Army Men

Five army men
In the war
One got shot
Then there were four

Four army men
Standing by a tree
One climbed it
Then there were three

Three army men
One lost his shoe
Who knows where it went
Then there were two

Two army men
Found a gun
One went and stole it
Then there was one

One army man
Had a bun
Then he ran away
Now there are none.

Robert Paterson (7)
The Park School, Yeovil

Five Strong Soldiers

Five strong soldiers
Going in to war
One gets shot
Then there were four

Four strong soldiers
Headed out to sea
One had a fight
Then there were three

Three strong soldiers
Heard a loud moo
One went to have a look
Then there were two

Two strong soldiers
Thought they were done
One went to have a rest
Then there was one

One strong soldier
Drove to his port
Had a fun time
Then there was nought.

Kyle Bishop (7)
The Park School, Yeovil

Unicorn Tail (Tale)

The whispering wind that gently
Caresses my curtains
Slips into the darkened room
It's warm and soft and slick
Due to this warm month, June

I pull my covers around me
Lit by a mystical light
As a curious creature approaches me
Coming from the depths of the night!

Its sad eyes gaze into mine
Pools as dark as the sky
It snorts and snickers and whinnies
And floats to the place I lie

Its muzzle pushes deep into my duvet
Its warm breath tickles my feet
If only I had a pet like this
So gentle and so sweet

If people would only realise
How beautiful they were
With manes as soft as candyfloss
And a coat as smooth as fur!

The creature gives me a promising wink
She flicks her pure white tail
And with a quick whinny of deep delight
She decides to set sail

So when you're lonely and all forlorn
And unhappy and all shy
Just remember one important thing
The creature that lives in the sky.

Jessica Whittick (9)
The Park School, Yeovil

Tanks

Like a slug slow and green, like a monster
That is hard to see
Tracks that go, round and round and green armour
That looks like ground

Rumbling, tumbling walls go crumbling
When the tank crosses no-man's-land
Bullets firing, missiles whining and mines deep underground

Its armour like a shell
A shell of a tortoise its
Gun like the spit, the spit of a snake

It rumbles on as loud as a bomb
Churning up ground like a rake
Crushing buildings, mining up earth
And firing at planes from a distance

All different sizes all different shapes
Different colours, there's a tank
Like a snake Challengers, Abrams, Centurions and more
There's thousands of tanks and the T34

Rumbling, tumbling walls go crumbling
When the tank crosses no-man's-land.

Philip Bridge (9)
The Park School, Yeovil

Football

Football, football round not thin
What if it lands on a pin?
The ball goes off the field and gets thrown back in
Round not thin!

Harry Grinter (10)
The Park School, Yeovil

I Wish

I wish I were a dragon breathing fire all the time
I wish people swam to school
I wish I were a scarecrow scaring everyone
I wish I were a fish swimming in the pond
I wish I were a dog barking at the postman.

Samuel Hawkins (9)
The Tynings School, Staple Hill

I Wish I Were A . . .

I wish I were a huge tree
Blowing in the wind
I wish I were a zooming cheetah
Zooming through the wild
I wish I were a bouncing, boxing kangaroo
Hitting its enemy
I wish I were a charging rhino
Charging through the boiling jungle
I wish I were a swimming shark
Eating everything around and in the misty sea
I wish I were a swinging monkey swinging from tree to tree
I wish I were a storming elephant
Storming through the jungle.

Ryan Becker (10)
The Tynings School, Staple Hill

For My Birthday I Would Like . . .

A greedy, blood-sucking vampire so it can make
all of my worst enemies jump out of their skin.
Also I'd like a massive, gigantic lollipop that never loses its flavour
and every time I lick it, it turns to a different taste.
And I want that pen that can write everything that pops into my head
But to everyone else it looks like a normal pen.
Plus I would like a magic wand with a pointy star at the end of it
and it did everything that I wished for
and a fairy that shines bright pink and sings a tune
and twirls around on my hand.

Hollie Eyers (10)
The Tynings School, Staple Hill

I Wish I Were . . .

I wish I were fluffy black cat lying on a back garden wall creeping up quietly to get
the small grey mouse
I wish I were a huge, blue, pretty dolphin splashing up and down, side to side
through the huge icy sea
I wish I were a massive elephant stomping into the sunny colourful forest
I wish I were a long white snake slithering through the long powerful grass hissing all day
I wish I were a pink fat pig rolling in the mud chomping loads of smelly food all the time
I wish I were a small monkey swinging from a green tree to get some bananas.

Mollie Staff (9)
The Tynings School, Staple Hill

Dark Red Fox

The dark red fox is on the prowl
Baring teeth, snarling growl
In the moving bushes, the beastly eyes stare
At a tiny rabbit leaping there to there
Peering round the corner, walking forward
It leaps! bashing the poor brown rabbit to the ground
A screeching noise came from behind, a golden eagle so clever and kind
The prowling fox went off with a gallop
No tea for him and his family for hours.

Joshua McCarthy (9)
The Tynings School, Staple Hill

Fireworks

Up high in the misty, moonlit sky a sharp-eyed rocket goes *boom*
And a screaming screamer goes *screech*

Down low a spraying fountain goes *fizz* and a spinning Catherine wheel
Goes *whoosh, swirl* and *zoom*

But no matter how high in the gloomy sky or how low on the damp grass
Fireworks are always special!

Jack Withers (9)
The Tynings School, Staple Hill

I Wish I Were . . .

I wish I were a snake winding in and out of the green pointed grass
I wish I were a rhino charging as fast as the speed of light
I wish I were a leopard on the prowl ready to pounce on my prey
I wish I were a shark swimming in the open misty water
I wish I were an elephant stomping in the forbidden jungle.

Curtis Drew (9)
The Tynings School, Staple Hill

I Wish I Were A Snake

I wish I were a snake gliding through the grass
I wish I were a snake hissing in a tree
I wish I were a snake hunting in a desert
I wish I were a snake hanging from a tree
I wish I were a snake!

Jack Wilkins (9)
The Tynings School, Staple Hill

I Wish I Were A . . .

I wish I were a
Monkey swinging
In a tree, eating
A banana like a
Buzzing bee

I wish I were a
Bear, scratching my
Hair

I wish I were a
Kangaroo bouncing
Round a chair
Like a hare

I wish I were a
Firework crackling
In the sky

I wish I were a
Cheetah sprinting
In the grass

I wish I were a
Dog barking at the
Window

I wish I were a . . . ?

Michael Bramley (10)
The Tynings School, Staple Hill

My Baby Brother

My baby brother Morgan
He likes to eat all the time
Biscuits and he drinks all his milk
He even eats his wet wipe!
Morgan screams all day and night
And sometimes he is quiet when he is eating
He sleeps long when he is tired
He lets us know because
He puts his dummy in his mouth
And cuddles up on his dog Pug
And his Pooh Bear
Then he is fast asleep.

Shelbie Brown (10)
The Tynings School, Staple Hill

The Freezing Cold

I feel the wind beating against my small wide back
I feel bitten by the frost
The wind is forcefully beating against me, enough
For my arms and legs to fall off
My hands are covered in frost
My hands were as white as a polar bear
My legs are as thin as a frosty pole with snow beating on them
My head is a freezer being defrosted
My fingers are icicles melting in my gloves
My goosebumps are tall mountains in the Himalayas.

Cameron Lippiatt (9)
The Tynings School, Staple Hill

I Wish I Were . . .

I wish I were a seagull which could soar through the bright sky
I wish I were a tree which could sway with the wind
I wish I were a dolphin which could cut through the turquoise water
I wish I were a kangaroo which could jump into space
I wish I were a giraffe which could reach the white fluffy clouds
How I wish
How I wish
How I wish.

Rosie Emma Say (9)
The Tynings School, Staple Hill

I Wish

I wish I were a beautiful dolphin swimming in the River Thames
I wish I were a dolphin swimming gently through the lonely water
I wish I were a dolphin jumping in the River Thames
I wish I were a dolphin rushing quickly in the river
I wish I were a dolphin rushing slowly, jumping in the air
I wish I were a dolphin to sing to you.

Grace Spence (10)
The Tynings School, Staple Hill

It's A Secret

It's a secret but I take a dog for a walk and no one knows
It's a secret but I've met a giraffe in Africa
It's a secret but my horrible teacher is a monster
It's a secret but I've swam with dolphins and other sea creatures
It's a secret but I've scored a hat-trick in a football match.

Daisy Merrifield (9)
The Tynings School, Staple Hill

I Wish I Were . . .

I wish I were a chocolate horse trotting warmly
I wish I were a butterfly flapping my wings in the crystal sky
I wish I were a sun, gleaming in the day, hiding at night
I wish I were a blue sky making people happy
I wish I were a dolphin whizzing in the air
I wish I were a happy bear sitting by the fire
I wish I were an aeroplane flying everywhere
I wish I were . . .
What could I wish for next?

Ellie-Maye Taylor (10)
The Tynings School, Staple Hill

I Wish I Were A . . .

I wish I were a dolphin that could soar the water
I wish I were a book that never stopped
I wish I were a video that never finished
I wish I were a millionaire that could never stop being one
I wish I were a giraffe that could reach the sky
I wish I were an eagle that could shoot through the sky!

Carsten Herbert (10)
The Tynings School, Staple Hill

I Wish I Were A . . .

I wish I were a roaring lion showing off my mane
I wish I were a prowling tiger chomping my white teeth
I wish I were a galloping horse swaying through the breeze
I wish I were a tweeting guinea pig looking cute and sweet
I wish I were a cute little puppy playing with my toys
I wish I were a pouncing kitten pouncing and rolling everywhere
But most of all I love being me!

Jodie Rudd (9)
The Tynings School, Staple Hill

I Would Love To Be . . .

I would love to be a red, shiny, fast sports car speeding down the motorway
I would love to be a delicate, gliding bird gracefully flying high over the town
I would love to be a tender, juicy strawberry covered with delicious cream
I would love to be a shiny, bulky skyscraper towering over the gleaming city.

Jack Stephens (9)
The Tynings School, Staple Hill

What I Want For Christmas

For Christmas I would like a duck with pointy teeth that could bite a strong tree
For Christmas I would like a green slimy frog with five eyes that could see all around the world
For Christmas I would like a large yellow alien with ten brains that could do all my homework
For Christmas I would like a small rhino with six horns that could charge through large walls
For Christmas I would like a great white shark that could walk on land and not swim
For Christmas I would like a cheetah with one leg that could hop on the sandy lane
For Christmas I would like a snake with three heads that could jump everywhere it goes
For Christmas I would like a large snail that could zoom along the path
That's what I want for Christmas.

Isobel Sheppard (9)
The Tynings School, Staple Hill

Gremlins

Gremlin, gremlin look at your eyes
Wow! they look just like mince pies

Gremlin, gremlin look at you run
Just like a hot cross bun

Gremlin, gremlin look at your jump
On your head, what a huge bump

Gremlin, gremlin look at you swim
Watch out here comes a shark
He'll tear you limb from limb.

Kyle Murray (11)
Tintagel Primary School, Tintagel

Shadow And Light

By the shadow there is light
From the shadow rides a knight
He was peacefully on his horse
Not knowing what was on his course!

Thunder and lightning made a fight
From day till night
Finally at his brother's tomb
Suddenly came the knight's doom
Sadly he lay dead
Next to his brother, without a head!

Richard Flower (10)
Tintagel Primary School, Tintagel

A House In Exeter

In a house in Exeter
The doors and floorboards squeak
In a house in Exeter
They call it Willow Creek

In a house in Exeter
Spiders rule the house
In a house in Exeter
They eat lots of woodlouse

In a house in Exeter
The house looks pretty fine
In a house in Exeter
It leads down to a mine

In a house in Exeter
Paper flies about
In a house in Exeter
Up the water spout.

Connor Gee (10)
Tintagel Primary School, Tintagel

I'm A Little Candle . . .

I'm a little candle
On the candle rack
I'm a little candle
From the candle pack

I'm a little candle
With a powerful glow
I'm a little candle
In a pack on show

I'm a little candle
With a scorching heat
I'm a little candle
That you just can't beat!

I'm a little candle
From the candle pack
I'm a little candle
On the candle rack.

Rhiannon Groves (10)
Tintagel Primary School, Tintagel

Daisy Seasons

I'm a little daisy, see me grow so tall
When it comes to autumn my petals fall
I need lots of water, food and air
Don't forget to love me and give me lots of care

I'm a little daisy, I look really nice
But when it comes to winter my petals turn to ice
I need lots of sunshine and a little bit of rain
But if someone comes and picks me I'll be in pain

I'm a little daisy blowing in the breeze
When it comes to spring I speak to all the bees
I need lots of admiring and keeping very clean
If you can't do that then you're obviously mean

I'm a little daisy sitting in the sun
When it comes to summer I have lots of fun
I need lots of love for now I'm getting old
And all the grass around me has turned to moss and mould.

Hannah Miles (11)
Tintagel Primary School, Tintagel

Sweets

Cherry choppers and gobstoppers
Are my favourite sweets
Because they're so petite
Stringy strings and tingly things
Are very fizzy
They make you go dizzy!
Sweets come in different shapes and sizes
My dentist no sweets he advises

My brother's favourite
Is strawberry kerry and berry terry
My mum's favourite
Is caramel delight and raisin kite
Sweets are the best I say
So I'm going to buy some today
Chewy aliens and crispy craliens
Hip hip hip hooray!

Kimberley Howes (10)
Tintagel Primary School, Tintagel

I Wish I Were . . .

I wish I were a dog, tall and brown
I wish I were a giant walking in huge steps
I wish I were a water bottle, tiny and round
I wish I were a lion running like a cheetah
I wish I were a pencil case, red and rectangular
I wish I were an elephant trumpeting like a trumpet
I wish I were a pen, thin and long
I wish I were a sheep that bleated
I wish I were a book that was rectangle-shaped
But most of all I wish I were myself.

Conor Bradshaw (9)
The Tynings School, Staple Hill

I Wish I Were . . .

I wish I were a frog who can jump to the sky
I wish I were a power man to observe energy
I wish I were a bird who can glide for an hour
I wish I were a spider who can fly
I wish I were a powerful boy who had powers
I wish I were a boy who doesn't die
I wish I were a cartoon person on the town.

Scott Hickery (9)
The Tynings School, Staple Hill

Another World

A tiny portal inside a cave
Entered only by the very brave
Another world at the very end
Feels just like you're round the bend
Come inside, make yourself at home
You really will not be alone.

Robert Mayger (10)
The Tynings School, Staple Hill

I Wish I Were . . .

I wish I were a huge monkey swinging from tree to tree
I wish I were a cheeky cheetah zooming through the damp rainforest
I wish I were a little mouse so I could sneak silently from house to house
I wish I were an enormous lion so I could be king of the terrifying jungle
I wish I were a fat rabbit so I could hop all day long
I wish I were a bloodcurdling shark so I could swim in the glistening sea.

Kyle Poole (9)
The Tynings School, Staple Hill

I'm Leaving

I was leaving, I packed my suitcase
I was going to a different place
I saw the beast of Bodmin Moor
Walk through my mouldy door

I got into my car
I tried to drive really far
I looked out the window, I saw a man
He was holding an old tin can

My heart was burning
My head was churning
I saw my family in my mind
They were the only people I couldn't find

I felt my blood go cold
I was turning into mould
Suddenly I was dead
With nothing but a head!

Matthew Griffiths (9)
Tintagel Primary School, Tintagel

My Mum's Sweet Shop

My mum owns a sweet shop
It has marshmallows as soft as pillows
It has shoelaces and chewy cases
I love my mum's sweet shop

I love my mum's sweet shop
Because it's got all the sweets in the world
They are twisted, wiry and curled
I love my mum's sweet shop

I love my mum's sweet shop
It has chocolate, cocoa and blackberry
It has toffee, hard and crisp and chewy
I love my mum's sweet shop

I love my mum's sweet shop
Because it has all the sweets in the country
They are crispy, chewy, wiry and munchy
And mum's sweet shop is top.

Georgia Weatherstone (10)
Tintagel Primary School, Tintagel

The Seasons

Autumn breeze
Flows through the trees
Most leaves are dead
Green, gold and red!

Winter is here
Snowfalls are near
Freezing cold snow
Falls soft and slow!

Spring lambs are born
There's grown crops and corn
There's birds in their nest
And people at rest!

Summer's begun
We're gonna have fun
Let's go and play
And shout hip hooray!

Elizabeth Wright (10)
Tintagel Primary School, Tintagel

Sleepy Hollow

Sleepy Hollow is a place
Sleepy Hollow is not safe
With a headless horseman around
It seems to be down the ground

Sleepy Hollow everywhere
Sleepy Hollow, come if you dare
Come and see the dead tree
It's full of heads if you see

Johnny Depp is so cool
Make sure he doesn't turn cruel
Sleepy Hollow, more than more
Sleepy Hollow at the door

Dead people everywhere
As I said, come if you dare
Make sure you bring your
Head . . .

Holly Crone (10)
Tintagel Primary School, Tintagel

The Sea At Night

Over the sea at night
In the silver moonlight
There's something in the big blue sea
But it's as quiet as can be

I see a big green tail
But it's very pale
It might be something very scary
Or something very dainty

The night begins to get old
And getting very cold
I will see the thing shimmering in the sea
What can it be?

I see it now
I take a bow
Because it's something very beautiful
It is very cool

Out of nowhere came the mermaid
And she said,
'Come with me
Amazing sights you will see.'

We swiftly swam
I saw mermaids with very nice tans
I was beginning to get very cold
So out I swam all big and bold

I had never seen such a sight
I loved my dark moonlit night
That mermaid and me
We saw things that I had never seen.

Megan Sharman (11)
Tintagel Primary School, Tintagel

Little Fairy!

Little fairy, little fairy
Come with me, come with me
I have something for you
Oh what is it?
Oh what is it?
I will show you, if you come with me
It's a wand, a sparkly wand!
Oh thank you
Now you can do magic spells on me!
The little fairy made her magic sparkly wand
Made me into a little fairy too!

Annie Callaghan (10)
Tintagel Primary School, Tintagel

Chainsaw!

Chainsaw, chainsaw
I'll cut off your head!
Chainsaw, chainsaw
Now you're dead!
Chainsaw, chainsaw
I'll put you in Hell!
Chainsaw, chainsaw
I'll ring a funeral bell!

Chainsaw, chainsaw
I'll cut out your heart!
Chainsaw, chainsaw
Don't think you're smart!
Chainsaw, chainsaw
I'll cut off your arm
Chainsaw, chainsaw
Can do a lot of harm!

William Pearse (11)
Tintagel Primary School, Tintagel

World

Our world covered in land
Grass and meadows and quite a lot of sand
Flowers, stones and pretty seashells
Religion in churches ring out the bells

Disasters and mystery struck in places
Black or white, there are lots of races
Waves or earthquakes, there are lots of bad things
Beautiful animals, birds that sing!

Disease and illness, humans might die
Police capture the criminals they always lie
Robbery or theft, they might get away
People that beg are starving all day

Tsunami in Thailand, I feel quite sad
Dirty water and pollution, it's very bad
There's one more thing I have to say
Keep our world safe . . . now that's good day!

Ryan Moth (11)
Tintagel Primary School, Tintagel

I'm A Flower Growing Free!

I'm a flower growing free
But for some reason no one looks at me
I don't understand why
They just walk by
I try to show my beautiful face
But they just wander in a different place
I try to shine morning and night
I will show you my petals so bright

I'm a flower growing free
But for some reason no one looks at me
I have petals that are green
Maybe sometimes I am mean
It's just not fair
All they do is sit on that old chair
I try to look so pretty
But they just walk by, it's such a pity.

Ellie-Jane Desousa (11)
Tintagel Primary School, Tintagel

Winter

Winter is very cold
Like the skin of a toad
Winter is dark
And all the dogs bark

All the kids wait for Santa Claus
With the cat ruining the chairs with its claws
Santa gets all the milk and cookies all for him
The children are asleep including Tiny Tim

The children wait for
A snowman to come through the door
Have a Christmas dinner
Then try and get thinner

Go out and build a snowman
During summer get a tan
Winter brings ice
And to your parents be nice.

Ben Russell-Gray (10)
Tintagel Primary School, Tintagel

Mum!

One day, up a tree
I saw my little sister called Bea
She was chasing something around
It looked like a big, hairy, brown hound!

'Mum, Bea's stuck up a tree!'
'No, no, it can't be.'
'I'm sure of it, I don't know how.'
'Well I'm going to get her right now.'

'But Mum there's a dog up the tree.'
'You're confusing me, you said it was Bea.'
'No, Bea is chasing a dog.'
'Are you sure it's not a frog?'
'Mum!'

Xavier Craine (10)
Tintagel Primary School, Tintagel

A Pound Of Jelly Babies

A pound of jelly babies
Just for me
Gobble, chomp, slurp, gulp
Tee-hee-hee
A pound of jelly babies
Eat my fill
Gobble, crunch, slurp, gulp
I feel ill
A pound of jelly babies
Oh dear me
Gobble, chomp, slurp, gulp
Burp! Pardon me!

Jason Turner (10)
Tintagel Primary School, Tintagel

Witch, Witch

'Witch, witch where do you fly?'
'Up in the trees where the birds soar high.'
'Witch, witch, what do you eat?'
'Rotten old toes from farmers' feet.'
'Witch, witch what do you drink?'
'The old bits of food from the drain of your sink.'
'Witch, witch where do you sleep?'
'Up in the sky where the tax is cheap.'
'Witch, witch where is your home?'
'Down in the garden with the garden gnome.'

 Tyler Gowan (11)
Tintagel Primary School, Tintagel

There Was An Old Lady Called Mrs Meggs

There was an old lady called Mrs Meggs
Who decided to put up her laundry pegs
Her pants blew away
She said, 'Lead the way
While I dance around in my white legs.'

Katie Holdsworth (8)
Trinity CE Primary School, Acton Turville

Sorry Got To Go - Haiku

Sorry got to go
See you tomorrow, bye-bye
No time for Haiku!

Lilly Stephenson (8)
Trinity CE Primary School, Acton Turville

I Am Seven Now - Haiku

I am seven now
I am very old I think
Soon I will be eight.

Alice Griffin (7)
Trinity CE Primary School, Acton Turville

Just A Short Poem - Haiku

Just a short poem
My small hands are all worn out
I am so sorry.

Claudia Wallis (7)
Trinity CE Primary School, Acton Turville

Bubbles - Haiku

I have a kitten
He likes to play with his mum
And we have great fun.

Charlotte Butcher (8)
Trinity CE Primary School, Acton Turville

Daydreaming - In School

Zoom, bang, hop, whizz
I'm doing superhero biz
Guns, swords, axes, shields
All running across the field
Suddenly a monster approaches . . .
'Jack, what is 9 times 7?'
The reply, 'Dunno Miss!'

Molly Murnan (7)
Trinity CE Primary School, Acton Turville

Before School - Haiku

'I want to stay here!'
'Go to school! It's poetry.'
'Oh! I forgot that!'

Kennedy Neal (7)
Trinity CE Primary School, Acton Turville

My Slipper - Haiku

My slipper is lost
It's black and blue, very new
Now what can I do?

Gemma Clay (8)
Trinity CE Primary School, Acton Turville

Hunting - Haiku

Victor is my name
Hunting is the game to play
Which I like to do.

Oliver Millner (8)
Trinity CE Primary School, Acton Turville

The Way The Sea Goes

Morning brings the sea a twinkle of light
The waves dance like a hyperactive child
Surfers ride the waves like dolphins
The sea listens to the waves like a laughing child.

Leah Mufford (9)
Troon Primary School, Troon

Around The Country

The sea cries as it hits the seashore
Like thunder and lightning racing across the sky

The laughing flower dancing across
The wide open fields

The car moans as it stops
Like an old lady trying to cross the road

Dawn guides the stars to bed
Stones dancing in the sunlight.

Kerenza Catterall (10)
Troon Primary School, Troon

Day And Night!

The flower longs for raindrops to fall onto grassy ground
The beautiful warmth of the sun reminds the dancing flowers to open
Dawn cries for the red-breasted robins to sing in the tiring morning
The glowing sea rises, skips and dances as it flows onto the hot sand
The river flows down the dusty mountains
Night shows its beautiful skies and stars' beauty.

Elena Hoskin (10)
Troon Primary School, Troon

Every Day

The flower screeches for water
The tree cries out, 'Don't cut me down.'
The train brakes, scared to crash
The bus cries because it can't get across the road
The moon looks like sparkling diamonds.

Jacob Rail (11)
Troon Primary School, Troon

Morning Into Night

The burning sun sizzles like a glistening fireball
Dancing flowers move like graceful ballerinas
The old mouldy tree cries out, 'Please don't cut me down!'
The speedy train whistles into the evening darkness
The silvery shining moon dances to the sound of the singing owl.

Josh Trescowthick (10)
Troon Primary School, Troon

Seashore

The sea glides across the queen coral reef like a turquoise sheet of silk
When it hits the sand it dies again
A person passed on the sand, which is as hot as the sun in the sky
Then he goes to play in the sea
He plays with a dolphin then he goes to climb a cliff
He jumps off the cliff to fall into a shark's lip
He pulls a tooth off the gum
He bleeds to death and goes up high to Heaven
He goes to see the Lord Jesus.

Harris Fisher (10)
Troon Primary School, Troon

The Magic Of Morning And Night

The sun smiles fantastically bright
Evening listens to the night

The stars sparkle extremely bright
As moon wakes in the starry
Glistening night

Morning dances as it wakes
Dawn cries as it shakes.

Charlotte Wardley (11)
Troon Primary School, Troon

The Mountain's Life

The mountain's listening to the flowing river
The trees are like soldiers rushing up the mountain
The mountain screeches like a monkey who's lost its mum
The river dances down the mountain like a ballerina
The mountain enjoys all the excitement like a happy child.

Sadie Mufford (11)
Troon Primary School, Troon

Under The Sea

The glistening turquoise ocean is crashing against the harbour
The dolphins are flipping like gymnasts
The jellyfish are swimming in the Atlantic Ocean
The turtles are as fast as the waves getting to shore
The starfish are as still as a stone.

Tamara Browning (11)
Troon Primary School, Troon

Beach Glory

As the sun rises into the open sky
The birds will sing but not tell a lie

As the birds glide across the sand
The sun smiles and waves her hand

As the glistening water gushes down the mountain
Birds will bathe in the sparkling fountain

The dark blue sea skips as it overlaps the tropical sand
As raindrops fall over the land
Slimy green turtles nest in the sand.

Amy Greig (10)
Troon Primary School, Troon

Morning Glory

The dazzling dawns break
As cold, dark nights fall
The crystal clear sea glides across glinting sand
The flower awakes and shouts out a yawn
The sun tap dances with the puffy white clouds
The snow blows it powders across the world, but it also catches a cold.

James Wassell (9)
Troon Primary School, Troon

Morning Sun

The tree dribbles at the sun
The tree cries because it is being cut down
The car races through the track
A screeching car cries for oil
The double-decker bus laughs at the car.

Liam Stone (10)
Troon Primary School, Troon

Night Sky

The moon moans as the sun goes down
Night cries as it becomes morning
Stars glisten in the pitch-black sky
Cars screech at the night sky
Planes fly in and out.

Curtis Wherry (9)
Troon Primary School, Troon

Darkness Settles

The jet cries through the dark blue sky
Darkness settles as it falls
The stars flicker in the night sky
The moon glows in the night sky
The sun rises as morning awakes.

Andrew Figgins (11)
Troon Primary School, Troon

The Wind

The wind is like a sky god whistling in the clouds
The wind is like a gardener blowing up the leaves
The wind is like a wolf howling to his pack
The wind is like a thief hiding behind the trees
The wind is like a hairdryer blowing the entire world
When the wind is here it makes my hair curl.

Aaron Moon (9)
Uffculme Primary School, Uffculme

River

Water-provider
Stone-washer
Reef-hider
Pebble-mover
Leaf-catcher
Fish-carrier.

Troy Clench (10)
Uffculme Primary School, Uffculme

The River Poem

It meanders like a speedy slithering snake
Making tributaries which sparkle in the sun
Hitting the rocky, big, bold banks
Jumping fish like Jack-in-a-box
Water skimming over pebbles and stones
Sliding and slipping to the deep blue sea
Whooshing to the sandy, soft, yellow seashore.

Keiran Palfrey (10)
Uffculme Primary School, Uffculme

Jack's Poem

J ust likes playing football
A pples are my favourite
C an kick a ball
K ind to everyone

W ill stop
E ats too much
L ucky
L ikes to do teamwork
M eet friends
A pparatus are my favourites
N oisy boy.

Jack Wellman (8)
Uffculme Primary School, Uffculme

Riddle

They run
They have no legs
Flowing down to the sea

They meander
They curve and loop
Steadily getting stronger

They move
Like a cheetah or a snail
Ending at a mouth

What are they?

A: Rivers.

Lucy Cheetham (8)
Uffculme Primary School, Uffculme

The River Poem

It starts at its source
A small river going as fast as a jet
Getting wider and deeper
As it starts to meander
Curving like a slithering snake
Waterfalls like clouds of shiny water
Becoming slower now as it nears the sea
This is where the river ends.

Harry Webber (10)
Uffculme Primary School, Uffculme

River

It starts in the mountains, very small
It flows downhill, extremely fast

It runs along, in a trench
As fast as a cheetah, chasing prey

As it starts to meander like a snake
It may leave behind ox-bow lakes

Tributaries join, to make it wider and slower
They may be smaller, but they travel faster

As it nears the sea, it meanders more
Until it reaches its mouth, where it quickly flows into the sea.

Josh Cox (9)
Uffculme Primary School, Uffculme

River

Starting from underground, spring or source
Lower and wider
Gentle ripples
Meandering like a slithering snake
Other rivers join like speedy intruders
Its merging mouth meets the sea.

James Millorit (10)
Uffculme Primary School, Uffculme

River

Starting from its source
Meandering like shoelaces
Trickling down the hillside
Flowing faster north
Jumping fish like dolphins
Creeping calmly like a robber.

Cameron Jones (10)
Uffculme Primary School, Uffculme

My Daddy

My daddy smells of perfect perfume
My daddy looks like red roses
My daddy tastes sweet as a strawberry
My daddy feels like a cuddly cushion
My daddy sounds like a cuddly bear.

Lucy Gammon (7)
Uffculme Primary School, Uffculme

Pets

Kittens are cute, kittens are cuddly
Puppies are playful, puppies are cheeky
Foals are funny, foals are tall
Calves are little, calves are jumpy
Snakes are really wiggly and squiggly
Birds are flappy and clappy
Guinea pigs are as funny as can be
Hamsters are cute, hamsters are funny.

Harry Jee (8)
Uffculme Primary School, Uffculme

King Kong

K ing of his island
I t lived on a rock
N ever stops fighting
G uards a girl called Ann

K ills dinosaurs
O n the Empire State Building
N ever cares about dinosaurs
G oes to New York.

Conor Joyce (8)
Uffculme Primary School, Uffculme

River

Starting at a source, a small trickle of water
Flowing fast through the hills, like a speeding rocket
Levelling out on flat land and slowing down
Meanders bobbing crazily along
Getting wider as land appears
Sliding into the salty sea, where its journey ends.

Robert Nicholls (10)
Uffculme Primary School, Uffculme

My Name

C lever as PS2
O n the PlayStation
R hyming is good
Y oghurt quite nice.

Cory Clench (8)
Uffculme Primary School, Uffculme

The Sun

The sun is like golden glitter glistening in the sky
The sun is like someone kicking a yellow football into the sky
The sun is stuck together with pieces of lava
The sun is like golden baubles dazzling in the summer sky
The sun is like an octopus
Swaying in the breeze
The sun looks
Like jellyfish
Wobbling their tiny tentacles.

Adam Crocker (8)
Uffculme Primary School, Uffculme

My Name

T anks are my favourite vehicles
Y oghurt is yucky
R eminds me of everything
O ften stays up
N ever would jump off a cliff
E arth is where I live.

Tyrone White (8)
Uffculme Primary School, Uffculme

Fishes

F ishes swim in a dirty green fish tank
I like my fishes because bubbles come out from their mouth
S ucker fishes stick to the tank to make it clean
H e likes my fishes because they are different colours
E llie likes my sucker fish the best because it sucks things
S he loves all of my fishes even my sucker fish because they are nice.

Freya Milton (7)
Uffculme Primary School, Uffculme

Cats

C urly whiskers, floppy tail, glinting claws
A nd they scratch the carpet, scratch the chair
T hey climb trees and fall out, they play in the bush
S linking in, slinking out.

Michael Thornton (8)
Uffculme Primary School, Uffculme

Love

Love is cherry-red
Like a shimmering heart
At the end of a tropical beach

It feels like a velvet cloth
Every time you feel it you go up to Heaven

It smells like a white rose
When you put it near your nose
Like when you are a glowing star

It sounds like keys rushing through the sky
Like balloons popping, swaying round the room

It tastes like strawberries and cream
Like burgers sizzling on a grill

It reminds me of hugs and kisses
At a posh hotel and at a Hawaiian beach.

Lauren Stevens (10)
Uffculme Primary School, Uffculme

Anger

Anger looks like a pitch-black cloud
Covering over the heavenly blue sky
With strikes of black lightning thrashing out
It reminds me of Anakin Skywalker who let the anger in and lost everything he ever had
It reminds me of whenever my brother annoys me and I try to hate him as hard as I ever can
Anger smells like burning coal and wood spreading through a house on fire
Anger smells like a fiery explosion with loads of cries inside
It sounds like a thunderstorm destroying villages and cities as everyone pleads for mercy
Anger hurts with loads of pain and agony
Anger makes you feel like you hate everyone and you could rule the world.

Alexander Miles (11)
Uffculme Primary School, Uffculme

The Wind

The wind is like a giant lion's roar
The wind is a giant blow from God
The wind is like lines of ice
The wind is like transparent ice cream
The wind is like a tornado twisting around.

Matt Millard (9)
Uffculme Primary School, Uffculme

Anger

Anger is blood-red
Like a glimmering juicy cherry
Hanging from a tree

Anger sounds like a volcano
Blowing its top off at the sky
Trying to get its revenge

Anger looks like a tsunami ripping through a town
And furniture flying everywhere

Anger smells like strong apples dipped in warm chocolate
With sweet sugar spread on the top

Anger tastes like really hot mustard with hot chillies on the top
In a hot dog

Anger feels like a big solid brick
Banging against your head when you're angry

Anger reminds me of when you
See people dying on TV when they have no food.

Michael Cooney (11)
Uffculme Primary School, Uffculme

The Wind

The wind is like a wolf howling to the moon
The wind is the sound of a hairdryer whistling away
The wind is like a race car zooming around a track
The wind is like electric power running through the wire
The wind is like a mini twister
The wind is the sound of a golden whistle blowing
The wind is beautiful.

Hayley Dix (9)
Uffculme Primary School, Uffculme

The Earth

The Earth is like a huge big rubber
The Earth is like a dazzling multi-coloured end of a lolly
The Earth is as big as a huge big egg
The Earth is like a big orange
The Earth is as pretty as a coloured apple
The Earth is shiny as new, fizzy, green, sour strings.

Josh Whitehead (8)
Uffculme Primary School, Uffculme

Love

Love is hot pink
Like a mansion of melting chocolate
Covered in strawberry sauce
In the centre of a Hawaiian island

It sounds like a guitar
Rocking to the rhythm of my heart
Over the glowing sunset

It smells like a bouquet of the deepest, pinkest roses
Growing in the lushest meadows
Being picked for Valentine's Day

It looks like dolphins
Leaping over the horizon
With the silver moon reflecting over the sea

It feels like a velvety hot water bottle
Being hugged by a gentle child
As she starts to fall asleep

It tastes like finest whipped cream
Frothing in your mouth
As you bite into a sugary strawberry.

Jemma Murphy (11)
Uffculme Primary School, Uffculme

The Stars

The stars are like glitter sparkling.
The stars are like tinfoil scrumpled.
The stars are like frozen rain.
The stars are like pebbles that
have been polished.
The stars sparkle
like diamonds.

Beth Cookson (8)
Uffculme Primary School, Uffculme

The Sun

The sun is like a ball of fire
The sun is like an orange pebble
The sun is like an orange football
The sun is like a ball of lava.

Cameron Murrell (8)
Uffculme Primary School, Uffculme

Happiness

Happiness is blazing green
The colour of the summer grass
In the middle of a peaceful countryside

It sounds like little children messing around
On a hot tropical beach
In the middle of Miami
Where the palm trees cover them

Happiness tastes like a sour apple
That takes your mouth into a watery sensation
Like a fast flowing waterfall

It reminds me of friends working together
For a famous TV show
Which shows you ice skating

It looks like the bright sun glistening
Over a funfair
At the beginning of spring

Happiness feels like a complete white cloud
Where a rainbow finishes
In a faraway land.

Hannah Tucker (9)
Uffculme Primary School, Uffculme

Love

Love is blood-red
Like a glittering heart
At the end of a sunset

It feels like a silky web
Every time you feel it
You glow inside

It smells like a red rose
A sparkling class of champagne
Glowing by the stars

It sounds like a wind chime
Swaying by the clouds
Like bubbles popping in a jacuzzi

It tastes like strawberries dipped in cream
And covered with sugar with ribs sizzling on the barbecue

It reminds me of hugs and kisses
At a romantic restaurant in a Hawaiian hotel.

Lauren Burke (11)
Uffculme Primary School, Uffculme

Laughter

Laughter is mustard-yellow
Like SpongeBob Squarepant's spongy skin
As golden as a fresh cornfield

Laughter reminds me of a clown falling over
And making a fool of himself
And everybody laughing at him

Laughter looks like the nice crispy bubbles in ballet clothes
Or dancing on the Eiffel Tower

Laughter sound like a monkey laughing at the same time as a pig snorting
And all the animals making strange noises.

Colin Stockman (10)
Uffculme Primary School, Uffculme

The Stars

The stars are like cats' eyes in the dark skies
The stars are like cakes in an oven rising or shiny
The stars are like sparkling diamonds in the sky
The stars are like silver glitter
Twinkling in the night
The stars are like a bonfire lighting in the dark
The stars are like an oven baking a cake
The stars are like shiny tinfoil
The stars are like polished pebbles every time I look at
The stars it makes me feel happy.

Shannon Tinworth (8)
Uffculme Primary School, Uffculme

The Stars

The stars are like the lights of Heaven in the sky
The stars are like pin pricks on blue silk
The stars are as pretty as diamonds twinkling in the sky
The stars are like plants with glistening speckles in the sky
The stars are like scaly fish glinting in the morning sun
The stars are as gold as the sun
The stars are like winking eyes in the sky
The stars are winking in the sky up high
The stars are looking down
I like the stars way, way up in the sky.

Lily Andrews (9)
Uffculme Primary School, Uffculme

Books

Books have horror
Books have romance
Books have all sorts
But I like mystery

Books are red
Books are blue
Books have many colours
But I like dazzling blue

Books are big
Books are small
Books have variety
But I like them all

Books come in French
Books come in Spanish
Books have different languages
But I like English

I like DVDs
I like games
There are other things too
But overall my best thing is *books!*

Scott Stevens (10)
Uffculme Primary School, Uffculme

The Stars

The stars dazzle
Like sparklers into the night
Its just like a magical sight
They're like diamonds
Twinkling in the sky
They glitter like crystals
And then say goodbye
Whenever I look up a the stars
I feel all twinkly inside!

Jasmine Shaw (8)
Uffculme Primary School, Uffculme

Racing Rockets

Roaring rockets up in the air, never knew they lived up there
Zooming, booming up in the air, never knew they screamed like a bear
Screaming, squealing, flying in the air, never knew they raced up there
Flying like I never even knew.

Daniel Stevens (8)
Uffculme Primary School, Uffculme

Laughter

Laughter is a dazzling yellow
The colour of the burning summer sun
Reflecting off of the sparkling ocean

Laughter sounds like children
In a funfair
On the merry-go-round horses

Laughter looks like the cheeky smile
On a little girl's face
While eating candyfloss

Laughter smells like hot dogs
Sizzling on the grill
In the boiling Spanish heat

Laughter tastes like strawberries
Melting in my mouth
After a luscious Christmas dinner

Laughter reminds me of my first swim
In the cool school swimming pool
Out in the playground

Laughter feels like a velvet cloud
Like a marshmallow in the sky
On the border of Heaven.

Gabrielle Jones (9)
Uffculme Primary School, Uffculme

The Wind

The wind is like a big block of sea spreading across the ocean
The wind is like a camel's humps on his back
The wind is like a lion's mouth opening for a big roar
The wind is like some thunder crackling in the sky
The wind is like bushes in the woods swinging
The wind is like a heart beating and thumping while you're tired
The wind is like a tornado.

Leah Burridge (9)
Uffculme Primary School, Uffculme

The Stars

The stars are like a bowl of glitter
The stars are like a floor that's just been polished
The stars are like a diamond shining from every corner
The stars are like a shiny sparkly crystal
The stars are as glistening and sparkly as a pot of glitter.

Ashleigh Lowman (9)
Uffculme Primary School, Uffculme

The Moon

The moon is as big as the Twin Towers were
The moon is like a banana
The moon is like an enormous white egg
The moon is like a bright cat's eye at night
The moon is like a white sparkling tooth
The moon is like a golden round piece of cheese
The moon is like a yellow banana-shaped sun
The moon is like a piece of ice
The moon is like a raindrop.

Shana Clarke (8)
Uffculme Primary School, Uffculme

The Stars

The stars are like glitter sprinkling from the sky
The stars look like tiny dots floating around
The stars are as shiny as the sun on a hot day
The stars look bright and beautiful in the night's sky
The stars dazzle my eyes like crystal
The stars are as white as a tooth can be
When morning comes the stars
Disappear but they'll be back tonight.

Jessica Little (8)
Uffculme Primary School, Uffculme

Fun

Fun is bright yellow like a colourful sun rising above a circus
It sounds like a hall of laughter after a clown has told a joke
It reminds me of when I have just watched SpongeBob Squarepants
It tastes like chocolate because it tastes lovely and is fun to eat
It looks like a big clown face and its big red nose making everyone laugh
It smells like scents of fun
A bit like soap water squirting out because it's completely hilarious.

Oliver Heptinstall (10)
Uffculme Primary School, Uffculme

The Wind

The wind is like invisible snakes in the air
The wind is like a fan blowing the leaves
The wind is like the breath of Jesus
The wind is like a big hairdryer
Whenever I feel the cold wind I shiver.

Joshua Colgate (9)
Uffculme Primary School, Uffculme

Peace

Peace is the soft colours of the rainbow
Like the race of human beings
On the face of the Earth

It sounds like the calling of the enormous whale
Looking for its family
In the spectacular Pacific Ocean

Peace looks like the calm waves
Stroking the sand
Reflecting the gorgeous sun

It smells like the freshly cut grass
At the brisk of morning
Just as the birds start to sing

Peace feels like a velvet dress
Just been ironed
With the heat seeping through

It tastes like traditional baked Eve's pudding
Covered with thick cream
Too hot to eat

Peace reminds me of summer songs
With people happily dancing
To the beat.

Jade Shoulder (11)
Uffculme Primary School, Uffculme

Love

Love is a pink rose
Like a shining cherry
At the end of the beach

It feels like an angel pulling you into the sky
Like you're in Heaven dreaming away
Having a glass of champagne

It sounds like birds singing in the treetops
Like popping popcorn
It sounds like a sizzling cooker

It tastes like strawberries dipped in chocolate sauce
It tastes like candyfloss on a stick
It tastes like a big chocolate bar

It reminds me of a big, soft teddy
Like a hot bubble bath
In a German hotel.

Jessica Cottrell (10)
Uffculme Primary School, Uffculme

Love

Love is blood-red
Like a bouquet of sparkling roses
At the end of a long glimmering trail

It smells like chocolate being melted
In a boiling hot saucepan
In a cosy warm cottage

Love looks like a castle
Under a gleaming rainbow
In the land of goodwill

Love sounds like a piano
Playing romantic music
At a candlelit dinner

It tastes like fresh strawberries
With clotted cream
In the countryside of Devon

Love feels like a silky cushion
On a giant bed
On a tropical beach in Miami

It reminds me of a dream
About floating on a velvety cloud
Way up high in Heaven.

Rowan Jeffrey (9)
Uffculme Primary School, Uffculme

Love

Love has a bright orange sheen
As does the warnings it brings
Like a distant sunset on the horizon

It sounds like a DJ spinning his vinyl
Calling all the party animals in the club
Banging out the beats for all the world to hear

It looks like a bouquet of luscious flowers
Like the silver lining at the end of the tunnel
Woven using the finest silk

Love smells like the latest fragrance
Like roses in a meadow
Being picked for the one true day of love.

James Bradley (11)
Uffculme Primary School, Uffculme

Peace

Peace is a soft pink
Like a luxurious fluffy cushion
Hidden in a secret place

It sounds like a harmonious harp
Playing to relax
And calm the restless

It looks like strawberry ice cream
Six scoops with marshmallows
And scrumptious chocolate drops

It smells like the sweetest perfume
Made from perfect roses
And contained in a magenta bottle

It feels like a velvet dress
Specially made
By top class designers

It tastes like
Sugary raspberries combined with cream
On a tropical island

It reminds you of
A flowery orchard
Blooming in the summer sun.

Ellen Cheetham (10)
Uffculme Primary School, Uffculme

The Stars

The stars are like dazzling glitter
The stars look like crystals in the air
The stars are bigger than forty Big Bens
The stars are more beautiful than diamonds
The stars are like silvery dazzling eyes
The stars are winking in the sky
When I look up at the stars I feel warm inside.

Jake Clarke (9)
Uffculme Primary School, Uffculme

The Moon

The moon is as big as the Earth
The moon is like a half-bitten cheese wheel
The moon is like a football with no hexagons
The moon is like a yellow banana in the sky.

Tom Joseph Hanson (8)
Uffculme Primary School, Uffculme

Laughter

Laughter is chiming blue
Like a cave of shimmering pearls
In the middle of the scorching desert

It sounds like a sparkling glass of bubbly
Dipped in a blazing hot jacuzzi
Or a spare rib sizzling on a grill

It tastes like luscious apple pie
Dunked in whipped cream
On a Hawaiian beach

It smells like buttery popcorn
Dropped in chocolate syrup
In a luxury hotel

It feels like candyfloss
On a stick
At a carnival

It reminds me of a luxury holiday
On a tropical beach
With a blinding glass of champagne.

Tyler Clarke (11)
Uffculme Primary School, Uffculme

The Stars

The stars are like pieces of silver sparkling ice frozen in the sky
The stars are like tiny diamonds
The stars look like very small white teeth
The stars are like shapes covered in glitter
The stars glitter in the sky
The stars are like tiny eyes looking at you
Stars are like golden shapes hanging in the sky
Every time I look at the stars I feel happy and sparkling.

Hannah Meek (9)
Uffculme Primary School, Uffculme

The Stars Are Like . . .

The stars are like a speck of glitter
The stars are like sparkling litter
The stars are like a pit of fire
The stars are like bits of wire
The stars look like a tap dripping
The stars are like someone knitting
Every star I see twinkling I would make a wish.

Georgia White (8)
Uffculme Primary School, Uffculme

Laughter

Laughter is a tropical blue
Like the beaches of Hawaii
Transparent with the sun shimmering off it

It sounds like a trumpet blaring a soulful tune
On a wide open range
Echoing through a deep valley

It is the deepest smell of lavender
On a radiant green hill
Overlooking a broad meadow

It has the taste of the lushest chocolate
Melted to perfection
Coated with whipped cream

It reminds me of being out of breath
Your stomach aching
And your lungs nearly collapsing

It looks like a blazing light
Growing and growing
So bright that it will blind you

It feels like someone jumping up on a summer's day
For their fingers
To skim the branch of a towering chestnut tree.

Roshan Kumar Chopra (10)
Uffculme Primary School, Uffculme

Silence

Silence is the colour of the water
Far out at sea while the sunset
Is glimmering across the last of the
Choppy waves before dark

Silence feels like wind slowly passing though your hair
While you're standing on top of a cliff looking at a calm sea miles below

Silence sounds like waves slowly
Breaking over and the last of the sandcastles being washed away

Silence smells like the clear sea air while the sun sets

Silence reminds me of a private beach in the Mediterranean all alone
While the last of the birds fly overhead.

Jonathan Goldsworthy (11)
Uffculme Primary School, Uffculme

Joy

Joy is pink like the scent of a rose, on a summer's day
It sounds like nuns singing in the abbey
It smells like fresh hot bread from the bakery
It tastes like a J20 running down my throat
It looks like fields of golden corn that wave in the wind
It feels like cuddling my mum or dad every night
Joy reminds me of putting the ball in the back of the net.

Amy Reddaway (11)
West Coker CE (VC) Primary School, Yeovil

Happiness

Happiness is red like a happy face
It sounds like waves lapping on a beach
It smells like cake cooking
It tastes like cherry yoghurt
It looks like an orange sun
It feels like love
It reminds me of Mum and Dad.

Crystal Neville (10)
West Coker CE (VC) Primary School, Yeovil

Excitement

Excitement is yellow like a daffodil blooming in the sun
It sounds like an Italian opera
It smells like boiling pasta
It tastes like Margherita pizza
It looks like a chocolate cake on my birthday
It feels like a fluffy toy in my arms
Excitement reminds me of holidays with my mum and dad.

Daisy Copland (11)
West Coker CE (VC) Primary School, Yeovil

Grumpiness

Grumpiness is black like the darkest cave
It sounds like evil is coming
It smells like dead rats
It tastes like sour lemons
It looks like an ugly troll
It feels like a bucket of hatred
Grumpiness reminds me of bad dreams.

Bran Pick (9)
West Coker CE (VC) Primary School, Yeovil

Stress

Stress is red like the sun exploding
It sounds like a kettle boiling
It smells like a chimney burning
It tastes like a burning chilli
It looks like hot lava
It feels like getting cut
Reminds me of times when people want to fight.

Connor Rose (9)
West Coker CE (VC) Primary School, Yeovil

Friendliness

Friendliness is yellow like the hot sun
It sounds like a lot of people cheering
It smells like a chocolate fountain
It tastes like strawberries
It looks like a lava lamp
It feels like your heart beating
Friendliness reminds me of my friends.

Josh James (9)
West Coker CE (VC) Primary School, Yeovil

Shyness

Shyness is cream like a cream sofa
It sounds like people creeping around at night
It smells like strong perfume
It tastes like stringy runner beans
It looks like an empty stage
It feels like being on your own
Shyness reminds me of singing out loud.

Francesca Graziano (9)
West Coker CE (VC) Primary School, Yeovil

Jealousy

Jealousy is dark blue like a murky part of an ocean
It sounds like a horn which won't stop
It smells like smoke rising from a chimney
It tastes like spinach and casserole
It looks like a bonfire on a big event
It feels like a bumblebee stinging you
Jealousy reminds me of fire red-hot.

Molly Morris (9)
West Coker CE (VC) Primary School, Yeovil

Tiredness

Tiredness is black
Like when you close your eyes
It sounds like a lazy yawn
It smells like your lovely freshly made bed
It tastes like a cup of hot tea
It looks like you putting your child to bed
It feels like your head on a soft pillow
Tiredness reminds me of my cuddly toys.

Jennifer Taylor (9)
West Coker CE (VC) Primary School, Yeovil

Sadness

Sadness is the colour light blue
Like the sky floating away
It sounds like water carefully dripping from a tap
Sadness smells like salty water at the seaside
It tastes like sour cooking apples
Sadness looks like a deserted town, no one there
It feels like the fur of my rabbit who died last year
Sadness reminds me of my dead animals.

Chloe Partridge (10)
West Coker CE (VC) Primary School, Yeovil

Pressure

Pressure is red like blood squeezing through your heart
It sounds like water squirting out of a hose
It smells like a bloody knee
It tastes like a plate of vegetables
It looks like a grenade exploded
It feels like something about to burst
Pressure reminds me of a volcano.

Samuel Evans (9)
West Coker CE (VC) Primary School, Yeovil

Worry

Worry is dark purple like blood circulation being cut off
It sounds like a heart thumping
It smells like spinach
It tastes like Brussels sprouts
It looks like a sheet of hard homework
It feels like mushy peas.

Niki Thiella (10)
West Coker CE (VC) Primary School, Yeovil

Greece

Greece makes me feel happy
I like the way the sea moves like a snake
Slithering on the ground
The fierce crabs on the rocks
Clanging their claws together
The volcano on the other side of Greece
Kos Town
All the people walking to the supermarkets
Busy but peaceful all at the same time.

Josh Collins (10)
West Coker CE (VC) Primary School, Yeovil

Flying Makes Me Feel Happy

Flying makes me feel happy because you are high in the sky
When you fly high in the sky you can hear the wind
Whistling like a distant cry just fading away
When you fly you get tasty snacks from the food court
Sometimes you get to see the pilot in his cockpit just flying faster and faster.

Tom Gorst (10)
West Coker CE (VC) Primary School, Yeovil

The Magic Box
(Based on 'Magic Box' by Kit Wright)

I will put in my box . . .
The three dinosaur periods of the prehistoric past
And the stickiest strawberry jam ever invented
Plus a PlayStation 7 from the year 2097

I will put in my box . . .
The heaviest rhino on the planet Earth
And Jupiter out of the universe
Also I will put in my box the biggest smelly belly ever

I will put in my box . . .
The lovely smell of petrol in a petrol can
As well as the smallest tick bird in England
Plus the biggest monster truck ever made

My box is fashioned from gold and silver and bronze
And on the lid there are dinosaur teeth as sharp as a butcher's knife
With polar bear fluff inside

I will ride on a falcon high in the sky and
Land on a mountain of gold.

Ryan Davey (10)
Winkleigh Primary School, Winkleigh

The Magic Box
(Based on 'Magic Box' by Kit Wright)

I will put in my box . . .
The end to all wars and illnesses
Love and happiness of father and son
A massive chocolate fudge cake

I will put in my box . . .
A friend, someone to care for you
Clean air and water for everyone
An education for every child for free

I will put in my box . . .
The inventing of the time machine
The inventing of chocolate and money trees
People laughing and having fun

My box is fashioned from gold, bronze and silver
With purple silk and ocean ribbon
There are mountainside patterns in the gold
The key looks strange and round

I shall gallop on my horse in my box
With pink ribbons flowing through my hair
Clip clop, clip clop the horse will go
Then I jump off onto a sandy beach.

Sammy Skinner (10)
Winkleigh Primary School, Winkleigh

The Magic Box
(Based on 'Magic Box' by Kit Wright)

I will put in my box . . .
The view from a skyscraper
The lick of a pet dog
Fresh food

I will put in my box . . .
The taste of chocolate ice cream
A calf being born
The smell of strawberries

I will put in my box . . .
A home for the poor
The wish to own a farm with my brother
Clean water.

Ian King (11)
Winkleigh Primary School, Winkleigh

My Magic Box
(Based on 'Magic Box' by Kit Wright)

I shall put in my box . . .
A shimmer of a dolphin's tail
A witch, a wizard and a werewolf
The long awaited end to all poverty

I shall put in my box . . .
The whole of the wonderful universe
When a kitten first opens its eyes into the world
The birthdays of every living creature past

I shall put in my box . . .
A dragon's fire flame from its nostrils
A magic wand made of ebony
Every child's wondrous hopes and dreams for the future

My box is fashioned from
Shells and phoenix feathers
With happy memories in the corners
And a full moon on the lid

I shall fly and swim in my box
Fly through the galaxy
The open sky
And swim through the oceans wide.

Rebecca Norman (11)
Winkleigh Primary School, Winkleigh

I Saw A Carrot

I saw a carrot with a purple wing
I saw a parrot with a golden ring
I saw a girl with a punctured tyre
I saw a truck telling off a liar
I saw a teacher with a fiery furnace
I saw a house being very earnest
I saw a boy eat a worm on a log
I saw a bird walk like a dog.

Luke Western (9)
Winkleigh Primary School, Winkleigh

Magic Box Poem
(Based on 'Magic Box' by Kit Wright)

I will put in my box . . .
An ice skating rink
A house with all my mates
An indestructible house

I will put in my box . . .
Liverpool's football pitch
Some plants that can talk
A professional footballer

I will put in my box . . .
A big swimming pool with lots of slides
To be the best footballer in the galaxy
And for everyone to be rich

My box is fashioned out of gold and ice
The hinges are made out of glass of the finest quality
The box is made by evil gods
And is carved out of a gold mine

I will skate in my box
I will swim in my box
I will sleep in my box
And I will look after my box.

Robbie Risdon (10)
Winkleigh Primary School, Winkleigh

I Saw An Aeroplane

I saw an aeroplane make a guy
I saw a man flying in the sky
I saw a bird trotting through the hail
I saw a horse delivering the mail
I saw a postman lying on the ground
I saw a ball making a sound.

April Burgoyne (10)
Winkleigh Primary School, Winkleigh

My Magic Box
(Based on 'Magic Box' by Kit Wright)

I will put in my box . . .
A swish of a peacock's feather falling
A bark of a newborn silky spaniel pup
And a dusty delicate wing of a butterfly

I will put in my box . . .
The thunder of a galloping horse
A bright Spanish sunset filling the sky
And the taste of creamy sweet ice cream

I will put in my box . . .
A black shiny stripe of a growling tiger
The brightness of a golden yellow sun
And the smile of all my best friends

My box is fashioned from ice and purple silk
It glows with all the colours of the rainbow
It has wishes in the corners
And its hinges are the horns of magic unicorns

I will fly in my box
Over the wide blue Atlantic seas
I will land amongst the mountains
And sleep amongst the stars
I will surf in my box, across the bluest water
Amongst the rainbow fish of the ocean.

Abbie Scarlett (10)
Winkleigh Primary School, Winkleigh

The Magic Box!
(Based on 'Magic Box' by Kit Wright)

I will put into my box . . .
The hope to be a professional footballer
The taste of freshly made chocolate
And the sound of FIFA 06

I will put into my box . . .
The hope to keep football up
The smell of fish and chips
And the sound of scramble bikes roaring

I will put into my box . . .
The hope to have a house with all my friends
The smell of spaghetti Bolognese
And the sound of my friends laughing

My box is fashioned from
Aluminium in a bright silver
The hinges are made of clear glass
And the lock is in a dull gold and silver

I will ride in my box
I will run in my box
I will sleep in my box
And I will look in my box.

Kris Jordan (10)
Winkleigh Primary School, Winkleigh

My Magic Box
(Based on 'Magic Box' by Kit Wright)

I will put in my box . . .
A life-saving friend
A fairy godparent who grants you any wish

I will put in my box . . .
The sound of my kitten
The taste of chocolate cake
And that everybody lives
Till they're 107

I will put in my box . . .
The sound of an elephant
The taste of ice cream

My box has stars in the corners
Secrets on the lid and an elephant's footprints on the sides

I will ride an elephant in my box
I will sleep on a cliff top underneath the glowing stars.

Jessica Flitter (9)
Winkleigh Primary School, Winkleigh

My Magic Box
(Based on 'Magic Box' by Kit Wright)

I will put in my box . . .
A map of the world that shows everything
A proud, prancing, pruning parent
Exciting experiment with energy

I will put in my box . . .
A box that contains life and death
A huge hulking manor house
A power proud phoenix egg

I will put in my box . . .
Something that makes you feel loved
Umpteen animal rights
And heaps of humungous happiness

My box is fashioned of ebony, gold and titanium
With suns on the lid and moons on the back
The hinges are made of platinum

I shall play video games in my box
On the hills of life to death's door
Then run into a restful room
The colour of the moon.

Hamish Inglis (9)
Winkleigh Primary School, Winkleigh

Red

Bright gleaming rose perched in the sunset
Bright pippy strawberries ready to be picked
Pumping heart squashed near your stomach
Shining bright red lips ready to be kissed
Rosy red poppy swirling in the field
Rosy raspberries plumped on top of each other
Round and ripe apple falling on the floor
Orange and red bricks loose on the wall.

Chelsea Galloway (8)
Woolavington Village Primary School, Bridgwater

Limericks

There was a strange dog called Bath
Who did nothing but make us laugh
A man who was passing
Said, 'Excuse me for asking
But your dog appears to be daft.'

Kieran Smith (8)
Woolavington Village Primary School, Bridgwater

Friends

Friends are cool, friends are fun
Friends are for everyone
Friends are for life, you should always know
Your friends will follow you wherever you go

You can have friends that are boys or friends that are girls
You can have friends that are chocolate or strawberry swirls

Your best friend could be a cat or maybe a dog
It could be a horse or a bat or maybe a frog!

Never walk away, always stay together
Another thing you should know
Your friends are forever!

Natalie Brakes (10)
Woolavington Village Primary School, Bridgwater

Red

Prickly and shiny roses shot by the sun
Spotty, soggy strawberries with wetness of water
Kissy and fat lips; big from lipstick
Fast floating river of blood slowly going round your body
Stretchy and smooth gums with toothpaste on them
Lumpy and stumpy heart covered in blood
Stamped on and muddy poppies sad from war
Helpful and thin pencil useful to write with
Giggly and funny orang-utans swinging in the trees.

Rebecca Bugler (7)
Woolavington Village Primary School, Bridgwater

Green

Tall, wavy grass swishing in the cool breeze
Crunchy, shiny apples tasty on my wet lips
Slippery frogs hopping in the dirty mud
Four-leaved clovers growing by the mossy tree
Swishy bushes dancing by the golden fence
Wet, cold lilypads floating in the clear pond
Falling leaves landing in the cold river
Squidgy peas frozen in a busy supermarket.

Tamsyn Stone (8)
Woolavington Village Primary School, Bridgwater

Green

Wavy grass swaying up and down
Sporty frogs jumping in the garden
Squidgy peas rolling around the classroom
Watery leaves swaying from side to side
Bendy pencils dancing in the enormous hall
Rocking chairs squeaking across the floor
Crunchy apples on the bushy tree
Windy bushes flowing around the hall.

Courtney Webber (7)
Woolavington Village Primary School, Bridgwater

Red

Pippy, juicy strawberries lay in the garden
Bright red poppies blooming by the graves
Crunchy apples hanging on a tree
Prickly rose in the sunset garden
Sticky lipstick like a red raw cherry
Gleaming ruby sparkling in the night
A frosty post box made of metal.

Samantha Platt (8)
Woolavington Village Primary School, Bridgwater

Red

Crunchy apples falling off a brown tree
Smooth strawberries ready to eat
Juicy cherries with a stone inside
Tiny berries lying in a berry bush
Shiny hair gleaming in the distance
Pulsing heart beating inside my body
Round balloon flying in the air.

Jason Webster (8)
Woolavington Village Primary School, Bridgwater

Green

Crunchy apples on bushy tree
Sweet grass in the windy breeze
Cosy pillow for sleeping well
Bumpy box all hard and pointy
Hard pencils green scribbling
Beeping cars quickly advancing.

Jacob Hill (7)
Woolavington Village Primary School, Bridgwater

Our Notice Board

We're such a busy family
We have to keep a list
Pinned on the kitchen notice board
Making sure nothing's missed!

On Mondays I have swimming
On Tuesdays I have dance
On Wednesdays I have piano
And my sister thinks I'm pants!

On Thursdays I have youth club
On Fridays I have drama
On Saturdays my cousin comes to play
And her name is Alana!

On Sundays I have horse riding
My favourite club of all time
The horse I ride is called Minnie
And I wish she was all mine!

Megan Dear (11)
Woolavington Village Primary School, Bridgwater

The Alien Spacecraft

It's as triangular as a pyramid
It's faster than lightning
It's armoured like a warrior
It shines like buried treasure
Its missiles are gigantic
They're waiting . . . to invade Earth . . .
So watch out!

It's measured
500 metres
It's as red
As dripping blood
Its fire would burn
Down forests
They're waiting . . . to eat your flesh . . .
So watch out!

Sam James (8)
Woolavington Village Primary School, Bridgwater

The Haunted Mansion

The clock struck midnight
The zombies do awake
Haunting the spooky mansion
But I'm just tucked up in bed

They are just waiting . . .
To get us spooked! Drip, dripping
With green, red blood

There is nothing I can do
There is nothing I can do!
But why? But why?
Because they just haunt us
They just haunt us!

Next it is moaning the ghost
Go under the stairs
Next it is moaning
Go under the stairs.

Zoe Ashdown (9)
Woolavington Village Primary School, Bridgwater

Batista

He's as strong as a rhino
He's as tall as a giant
He's an unbeatable player and he's my favourite wrestler
Although he's just like a bulldozer
And as vicious as the Bulldog
He's still the best . . .
Batista.

Macauley Godfrey (9)
Woolavington Village Primary School, Bridgwater

Red

Sweet rose, sweet red
Sour raspberries sour and juicy
Ripe sugary strawberries ripe
Paper poppy in a field
Ruby lipstick smudging on the carpet
Wine pouring in your mouth.

Caitlin Bawdon (7)
Woolavington Village Primary School, Bridgwater

YOUNG WRITERS INFORMATION

We hope you have enjoyed reading this book - and that you will continue to enjoy it in the coming years.

If you like reading and writing poetry drop us a line, or give us a call, and we'll send you a free information pack.

Alternatively, if you would like to order further copies of this book or any of our other titles, then please give us a call.

Young Writers,
Remus House,
Coltsfoot Drive,
Peterborough
PE2 9JX

Tel: 01733 890066

Email: youngwriters@forwardpress.co.uk

Website: www.youngwriters.co.uk